The Rough Guide to

Shopping Online

There are more than two hundred
Rough Guide travel, phrasebook and music titles,
covering destinations from Amsterdam to Zimbabwe,
languages from Czech to Vietnamese,
and musics from World to Opera and Jazz

D0784726

ROUGH
GUIDES

Credits

Text editor: Paul Simpson

Contributors: Victoria Williams, Helen Rodiss, Sue Weekes

Production: Sarah H Carter, Ian Cranna, Caroline Hunt

Thanks to: Simon Kanter, Mark Ellingham, Robert Jeffery

Photographs: Tony Stone/Photonica

This book is dedicated to Jack Simpson, Alex Hunt, & Theo

Publishing Information

This second edition published October 2001 was prepared by
Haymarket Customer Publishing for Rough Guides Ltd,
62–70 Shorts Gardens, London WC2H 9AH

Distributed by the Penguin Group

Penguin Books Ltd, 80 The Strand, London, WC2R 0RL

Typeset in Adobe Clarendon and Helvetica to an **original design by**
Cathy Constable, Sarah Jane Voyce, Martin Tullett.
Printed in Spain by Graphy Cems.

CONTENTS

Part One: Basics

Introduction 6
So what is all this fuss about online shopping anyway?

Shop till you drop 9
The beginners' guide to buying a product over the Internet

Safe as houses 19
How to make your online shopping experience as safe as possible

Going, going, gone 25
How online auctions work, where you can find them and how to make sure you don't get conned

Buying from abroad 33
The tax you'll pay, the cost of shipping, and the best bargains

Things you can do online 38
How to use search engines, review sites, get bots to do your work and find out if a product's any good

Part Two: The Directory

Antiques 46
Arts 49
Babycare & maternity 55
Beauty 61
Beer 65
Bikes 67
Boats 69
Books 70
Cameras 78
Cars 82
Celebrities 86
Chocolates & sweets 88
Clothes & fashion 90
Coffee and tea 108
Collectibles 110
Comics 116
Computers 118
Computer games 126
Crafts 136
Crazes 138
Department stores 140
Drugs 142
Eco living 147
Educational 149
Films and video 152
Fishing 157
Flowers and gifts 159
Food 165
Football 181
Freebies 185
Gadgets and gizmos 188
Games 192
Gardens 194
Golf 198

Contents

Health and fitness	200	Shoes	277
Hi-fi	208	Snow sports	280
Hobbies	212	Sports	286
Home	214	Television & video	294
Jewellery and watches	228	Tickets	299
Magazines	231	Toys	303
Motorbikes	233	Travel	309
Museum shops	235	Watersports	323
Music	237	Weddings and Bar Mitzvahs	324
Net stuff	240	Weird stuff	328
Office supplies	242	White goods	332
Outdoor	244	Wine and spirits	338
Parties	248		
Pets	251	**Part Three: Reference**	
Phones	253	Glossary	347
Property	257	Index	355
Records & CDs	263	57 Things you can buy online	359

A public safety announcement

Remember that websites can go down as well as up. Although this book was produced to the tightest production schedule possible (pages flying over to Spain to be printed little more than a month before the book arrived at a bookshop near you), some of the sites, addresses and prices which are quoted here will have changed by the time you peruse this. As the book went to press, the web addresses here actually worked and the recommendations made were accurate.

Since then some websites may have closed down, others will have radically revamped their sites. We're sorry but there is nothing much we can do about it except to say that even so, with information on online shops in 63 types of product from arts to wine and spirits, with well over 1700 web addresses quoted, and with specific guidance on where you can buy anything from butterflies made out of banknotes to Caprice's autograph and the smallest car in the world, you should find this guide really very useful indeed. Anyway, let us know how you get on by e-mailing the editor at paul.simpson@haynet.com.

Part one

The secrets of successful (and safe)
shopping over the World Wide Web

THE BASICS

Save money, save time, save your blushes...

ONLINE SHOPPING

Don't believe what you read in the papers. The Internet isn't about to revolutionise the way we have sex, but it is already revolutionising the way we shop, whether we're looking for a car, ordering groceries or just buying some new fridge magnets

Is the Internet shopping revolution all hype?
Not at all. Evidence suggests that by the end of 2000 the UK had nearly 6.5 million unique users of retail sites. So, far from online shopping being in decline, it seems Britons are increasingly turning to the Net to buy stuff. And when we say 'stuff' we mean anything from cheaper electricity (***www.buy.co.uk/Personal/Index.asp***) to a 27-acre island off Panama (***www.vladi-private-islands. de/sales_islands/sites/06_gallo.html***) or a new car through *Which?* Online's (***www.carbusters.com***). And in

many cases – ie with the exception of that island – it is now quite possible to save money if you buy over the Net.

So how does online shopping work? Economically it's supposed to be a very simple model. Traditional retailers invest millions in their premises and countless sales staff in the belief, sadly not always vindicated, that you will pop in and buy something. **Freed from such financial shackles,** e-tailers, as they like to refer to themselves, only have to worry about taking your order on their website, ensuring they've got the item you want stored somewhere, and then organising its delivery.

Some of the savings from not having a bricks-and-mortar presence in the high street can be passed on to you, the buyer. This is why so many online stores offer **savings of at least 20 per cent** over street prices. The added bonus – as Tesco has discovered with its online

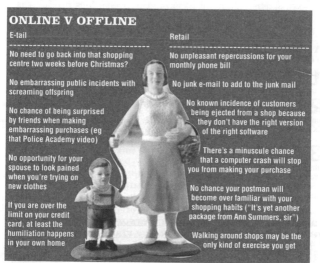

ONLINE V OFFLINE

E-tail	Retail
No need to go back into that shopping centre two weeks before Christmas?	No unpleasant repercussions for your monthly phone bill
No embarrassing public incidents with screaming offspring	No junk e-mail to add to the junk mail
No chance of being surprised by friends when making embarrassing purchases (eg that Police Academy video)	No known incidence of customers being ejected from a shop because they don't have the right version of the right software
No opportunity for your spouse to look pained when you're trying on new clothes	There's a minuscule chance that a computer crash will stop you from making your purchase
If you are over the limit on your credit card, at least the humiliation happens in your own home	No chance your postman will become over familiar with your shopping habits ("It's yet another package from Ann Summers, sir")
	Walking around shops may be the only kind of exercise you get

grocery service – is that people buying online spend more.

There is, of course, a catch to all this. For a start, many online businesses soon realised that there was rather more to the mundane business of delivering a product than met the eye. Online shops also discovered that, although they were making savings on logistics and staffing, they needed to invest between 60 per cent and 83 per cent of their earnings in marketing themselves, a level of spending which would prove ruinous in the long term. There is also evidence that online shoppers are even less loyal than regular shoppers although, once again, no one can say if this will still be true in five years' time.

14 million Brits now access the Internet from home

So is the online shopping revolution stuffed? No, because even the most pessimistic forecasters predict that five per cent of our shopping will be done via the Net by the end of this decade. About **14 million Brits now access the Net from home**; between June 2000 and February 2001, UK time online shot up by 94 per cent; and by 2005 it is estimated the UK online travel market alone will be worth in excess of £2.7 billion.

Sadly for those who prefer to see the Net through the eyes of the *Sunday Sport* ("Click here to **buy a World War II bomber** – found on the moon!") it is actually very hard to buy ballistic missiles, human kidneys or illegal drugs online. It is, alas, all too easy to buy the greatest hits of Brotherhood of Man. And that ultimately is what online shopping is all about: giving you **freedom of choice**, something capitalism was supposed to guarantee but, in an increasingly monopolistic age, has found it too often uneconomic to do so.

A FEW TIPS FOR YOU...

1 Use two search engines.

2 Configure your search engine(s) to look at only UK sites or UK sites first.

3 If you're searching for 'Tommy Hilfiger', some sites search better with a '+' sign between the names. Others won't.

4 It's worth keying the item you want into your search engine's shopping area. As well as key auctions.

Welcome to a world
where you can...

SHOP TILL YOU DROP

Online shopping needn't be technically
arduous, financially hazardous or even
unduly time-consuming as long as you
abide by a few simple principles. This chapter
is designed to explain the ins and outs, dos
and don'ts, ifs and buts, etc, for beginners

How to buy over the Internet

Let's assume, for the sake of argument, that you want to
buy a copy of Leonard Nimoy's seminal album *Highly
Illogical*, a must-have for every connoisseur of truly bad
singing. Composed, in unequal parts, of songs sung in
character as the first science officer of the USS Enterprise
and his own versions of such standards as *If I Had A
Hammer*, these recordings explain why his post-Enter-
prise career as a cabaret artiste was so shortlived.

There are two ways to proceed. You can key 'Leonard
Nimoy' into the shopping part of a general search engine
like Yahoo and see what comes up, or you can go straight
to a specific site like Amazon which you suspect may
stock the goods you're after. The advantage of going to a

specific site is that you might feel much safer dealing with a company known to you, or recommended by a friend, or by one of the multitude of Internet magazines, or indeed by a convenient little guide like this.

Log on to your online shop

For the purposes of illustration, log on to your favourite browser and key ***www.amazon.co.uk*** into the address bar. In the time it takes to say "Live long and prosper" you should get a page which says, **'amazon.co.uk'**. Like most such pages, Amazon's bombards you with a bewildering array of apparent bargains designed to tempt the online shopper who wants to buy something but isn't sure what. Be single-minded and go to the box next to the search button (top middle) and key in **'Leonard Nimoy'**. You know you want a CD, not one of his vulcanised volumes of memoirs, so change the **'All Products'** strap to **'Popular music'** to save time, and click on **'Go'**.

You are then presented with a choice of two items, one of which is the real thing. The other is an inferior version with the 'bonus' of even more embarrassing performances by William Shatner, notably an extraordinary rendition of

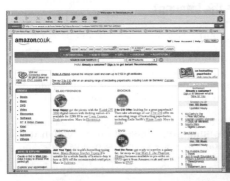

If you're new to this online shopping lark, you could do worse than find yourself at Amazon's homepage, which is easier to use than many

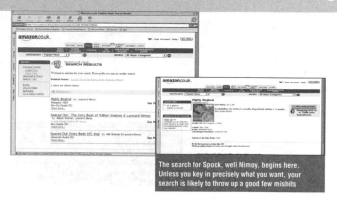

The search for Spock, well Nimoy, begins here.
Unless you key in precisely what you want, your
search is likely to throw up a good few mishits

Lucy in the Sky with Diamonds. The price, £11.99, does
not include post and packing (that comes later). Delivery
could take a couple of weeks if the item is not in stock;
amazingly, for such an obscure artefact of popular culture, Amazon expects to dispatch *Highly Illogical* within
24 hours so it should arrive within two days.

Often a product will be accompanied by a customer's
review but you should bear in mind that these may well
be written by true devotees, people with an axe to grind
or people for whom penning reviews on such sites is their
nearest brush with fame.

So now you've found what you want...

Sometimes you can inspect the product in closer detail
(by seeing a track listing or a larger photo of the
cover). If you're buying a book, you will usually get a
paragraph-long synopsis. To buy Nimoy's finest hour,
click on the **'Add to Shopping Basket'** button which will
say you have one item in your cart, costing £11.99, and
gives you a chance to order more than one copy.

Click on **'Proceed to checkout'** and you will then be

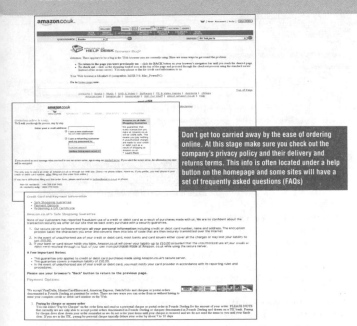

Don't get too carried away by the ease of ordering online. At this stage make sure you check out the company's privacy policy and their delivery and returns terms. This info is often located under a help button on the homepage and some sites will have a set of frequently asked questions (FAQs)

asked whether you're a new customer or not. If you are, clicking on the right button takes you to a form which asks for the usual details (name, address, e-mail, etc).

It's at this point that new online shoppers may have a few qualms about handing over this information, wondering just what else this personal data might be used for. Most reputable online stores have a button at the foot of the page marked something like **'Privacy Policy'**. If you click on this you should find a statement which will explain what information they need, why, what they use it for, how they protect this data, and whether this information will be given to anyone else. (For more detailed info on these issues see chapter 3.) But if a site does not have such a policy then you should only buy an item if it really is not available anywhere else.

What happens if things go wrong?

While you're checking out the online store it's probably worth examining their policies on returns, refunds and delivery. Some, like Amazon, have a **'no quibble'** guarantee which states that if you are unhappy for any reason and can be bothered to wrap up the goods that you've bought and send them back, they'll refund the purchase price. These policies may be buried beneath a **'Help'** button situated on the homepage but too often a casual browse will fail to reveal any obvious policy on these mundane but vital issues, in which case e-mail or phone the company concerned for the lowdown.

After filling in all the correct fields you will be invited to enter a password and re-enter it. Best practice is to use a unique word which has personal significance so your memory won't need jogging, throw in a couple of numbers if you can be bothered, and use this all the time.

Having read the privacy policy (and chapter 5 of this guide) you should feel confident enough to enter your credit or debit card details and click **'Continue'**. Most online stores let you key in your details on what is known as a **secure server**. With the almost daily reports of hackers pillaging the Pentagon's database, you may be wondering if 'secure server' is an oxymoron. Suffice to say these services wrap an extra layer of code around your confidential details to protect them (for more on this see chapter 3).

You can pay by cheque, but Amazon says this delays orders by seven to 10 days. Alternatively you can just enter the last five digits of your card number and

Only buy from a site with no privacy policy if you can't go anywhere else

the expiry date, on the site, and phone up to give the rest of your number. Some companies have experimented with a separate pin number so financial details do not have to be given out over the Net.

Let's assume you go for the full online shopping experience and hit that **'Continue'** button. You are then invited to confirm your address and delivery method. Many online shoppers like to have stuff delivered to work rather than find a card telling them they have a parcel at a sorting office which can't be found without the purchase of a local A-Z, but it depends on how much trust you place in your company's postroom.

You're only a few clicks away now

If you order more than one item you will be offered the choice to have them all delivered at once (cheaper, but can you wait that long?) or have them delivered individually (more expensive but faster and you help the postman's campaign to save his back). Another click and you get to confirm your debit or credit card number and then you are presented with the electronic

Just time for a last-minute count-up – hoping that you haven't busted your budget – before setting the whole process in motion

'invoice' which tells you how much you have to pay for post and packing. (Some sites deliver for free but you usually find 'free delivery' is reflected in the purchase price.)

You are now just a click away from doing something which will mean pounds and pence disappear from your account. Time to take stock and decide if you are that keen on Nimoy. If you are and click on **'Place your order'** a 'mean that most sincerely' thank you page will pop up.

You may want to print out a copy of what you have ordered. Some online stores (and Amazon does this) e-mail confirmation of your order and tell you when they've got around to sticking the item(s) in the mail. Within two weeks, you should hear that soon-to-be-familiar scraping noise as the postman tries to squeeze the cardboard-wrapped CD through your spatially challenged mailbox.

If not, most reputable online sellers have some kind of button (usually marked **'Your account'**) which you can click on to check what's happening to your order. On some sites, however, 'Your account' buttons simply tell you, on inspection, that your order is in progress.

Buying on the Internet really is (almost) that easy and, despite all the scare stories, only a tiny percentage of online shoppers find that, having disclosed their financial information to a respectable online store, their bank accounts are mysteriously depleted of large sums which are subsequently traced to international drug syndicates.

Sometimes it's not as easy as it looks...

So why is Internet shopping only 'almost' that simple? Partly because many online stores have very different user interfaces. The late, unlamented **Boo.com** (not to be confused with its latter day incarnation, the 'new' Boo) had the kind of user interface which gave visitors a headache and feelings of deep technological inferiority. Even mainstream sites demand you download a certain software package to make the most of their virtual shelves.

First-time shoppers can get lost in the process. While buying a CD from Amazon is pretty straightforward, buying your week's groceries can take up to an hour the first time and that's if your computer doesn't crash. Even on well-tried sites like Amazon, if you click **'back'** to look at the preceding page, sometimes a page pops up with the intriguing headline **'Browser bug?'** Usually it's easy to get back on track but nervous buyers might get lost.

FORGET THE HYPE... CHECK OUT THE STATS

Don't believe all you read in the press. Online shopping is still growing despite the 'dot bomb' hype. Research by IMRG, the interactive media in retail group, indicates e-retailing grew 162 per cent between April 2000 and April 2001. Which sounds even more impressive next to the paltry 5.6 per cent growth of general retail sales.

For the 12 months to March 2001 the total UK e-retail market was reckoned to be worth £1.8bn. Doesn't sound like the end is nigh, does it?

...especially the delivery part

Then there's the delivery, which is where online shopping too often goes wrong. Last Christmas the press was full of sob stories about online shoppers who didn't get what they'd ordered when they'd been promised they would. Indeed, the US government went so far as to fine seven US e-tailers for late delivery and several irate customers even took out a class action suit against Toys R Us for spoiling their Christmas.

When Mick Jagger famously belted out "you can't always get what you want", he almost certainly wasn't thinking of online shopping, but that sentiment is certainly applicable.

Even apparently reputable e-tailers have been known to send the wrong CD in a box with a fat 'postage due' sticker planted erroneously on it. And yet surveys continue to show that seven out of every 10 online shoppers are satisfied with the service they get, the most conclusive result since Whiskas first consulted cats.

The right product, the right price

For simplicity's sake, the purchase of Leonard Nimoy's CD was followed through just one site. In reality, once you'd found Amazon had the product and the price (£11.99) you might conceivably be tempted to see if you could find it cheaper elsewhere. So let's type in **www.yahoo.com** and click on the word **'Shopping'** that's just below the slit where you normally type whatever you're trying to find.

Up comes a natty little page snappily captioned **'Welcome, Guest'** and, in the search box just below, you type in those mesmerising words **leonard+nimoy** and, lo and behold, you discover that there are some 228 products associated with the pointy-eared personage, available from 16 stores.

One of them is another collection of Nimoy's greatest hits which may only cost $15-16 (less than £11). Upon further inspection you see you can buy it from a company called **cd world**, and they even deliver to the UK. However you are stymied in all your attempts to see how much post and packing will cost, so you give up.

This experience has not been totally in vain, however. New though you are, you have realised that although online shopping is usually an intensely exhilarating experience, it can also be as frustrating as those January sales where you spend hours flicking through racks of CDs marked down to £5.99 only to discover that they have cut the price of every **Talking Heads** album apart from the one you haven't got.

And finally, a few words of advice...

Be organised. If you just surf hopefully in the belief that you'll stumble onto the right present for dad's birthday, you could drown in cyberspace. Generally the more specific you are about what you want to buy, the faster, and more pleasurable, shopping online will be.

Set a budget. Virtual shopping still uses real money but somehow it doesn't feel as financially painful when you just click a button on your computer screen. Sticking to a budget is particularly vital if you are buying through an online auction (see chapter 4).

Consider using your credit card. If you do, your consumer rights will be protected, as Visa points out in its round-up of handy hints (***www.visa.com/nt/ecomm/ consumer/main.html#tips***), although obviously it could work out being more expensive if you don't instantly pay off the £250 you lavished on that rarist of books, *Turkey Remains And How To Inter Them With Numerous Scarce Recipes From The Note-Books Of F Scott Fitzgerald*.

Don't rush. Online shopping still takes time, especially if you're looking for something rare, so check delivery times and don't leave it to the last possible minute.

Trust your instincts. If you don't feel comfortable buying, back off. According to The Internet Fraud Watch (***www.fraud.org/internet/intset.htm***), high-pressure sales tactics are often a sign that there is something fishy going on.

You may find these sites of help:

http://uk.kelkoo.com helps you compare prices before you buy.

www.bizrate.com rates companies in the online shopping business, comparing different sites' price/delivery details on the same product.

www.consumerworld.org is big and brash and American but handy for product reviews and consumer news

www.imrg.org Interactive retailers' trade body but useful for consumers.

www.which.net/ now has its own e-tailer accreditation scheme.

www.zdnet.com/pcmag/features/e-comm_sites/sb2.htm "Shop safely in unknown corners" is this site's boast and it almost lives up to that promise.

**How to shop online
and not feel paranoid**

SAFE AS HOUSES

" 'd like to go shopping online but..." The
"but" in that sentence invariably refers to
a fear that shopping over the Internet is
likely to expose you to all sorts of frauds,
scams and cybercrimes, many of which you
may not even be aware of. With online bank
aooounts appearing to be about as private
as the post-PE lesson shower in your
schooldays, and daily headlines about
a global epidemic of cyberfraud, shopping
over the Internet seems fraught with
unacceptable risk. In truth, there's no
conclusive proof that online shoppers are
more likely to be the victim of fraud than
those who do their shopping offline

If it's so safe why do I read so many scare stories?

The Federal Trade Commission, the US government body which keeps an eye on this, says: "There's a general public concern about transmitting credit card numbers over the Internet which is not well-founded. All in all, it's much riskier to give your credit card to a waiter or waitress than it is to send it over the Internet." Many reports of online credit fraud actually relate to breaches of security in offline databases. That said, there is a risk, but you can reduce your chances of becoming a victim.

What are firewalls?

At its simplest, a firewall is a cyberforce which protects corporate IT networks from external communications systems such as the Internet. Often the firewall will be a physical computer with a couple of network interface cards: it will check every packet of data going between the internal and external networks and reject those it is programmed to consider inappropriate. You need to be aware of this if you're buying from work, because some **corporate firewalls can actually prevent your order** from being processed without you realising.

If a site has 'UK' in its address, can I assume that it is a British company?

No. Which is why you're better off checking their physical location (or 'snail mail' address) to be sure.

Any other general advice?

Beware of sites/e-mail offers with too many exclamation marks and capital letters for NO APPARENT REASON, which promise "secrets of success", have ludicrous testimonials from customers defined only as 'Mrs S, Canada' and start their pitch with the protest-too-much headline: "This is not a scam!" Also, guard your **shopping baskets**. Some sites stick stuff in them when you click for more info while some won't let you pull items at the last minute.

Some sites now greet you by name if you have ordered from them before. If you do place an order, and you share your terminal or use a public one, be sure to **log out** of that site after you have completed the transaction. Otherwise the next user of that terminal could mistakenly order items with your credit card details (though at least the items will be sent to you).

Security guards

www.ftc.gov/bcp/conline/pubs/online/sitesee/index.html is the Janet-and-John guide to surfing for the ultimate newbie from those nice folks in the US government.
www.oft.gov.uk/html/shopping/index.html is the British version of the above, dealing with online shopping.
www.whichnet/shopping/guide.html is the unhysterical *Which?* guide to the pitfalls of online shopping.
www.scambusters.com does exactly what it says on the web address but be warned, it may make you paranoid.
http://privacy.net may leave you even more paranoid.
www.web-police.org is Interpol's electronic arm, which comes complete with a comedy western sheriff's badge, a string of Java error messages and may crash your machine.

It's a dirty job but someone's gotta do it – the International Web Police, dedicated to protecting the Internet community since 1986

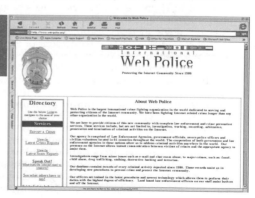

You can take precautions...

1 **When you visit a site, check how secure it is**. Sites which are encrypted may have an address which begins **'https'** (the extra 's' indicates the site is using a bit of technical know-how called Secure Sockets Layer to encode your data).

If you're using either Internet Explorer or Netscape Communicator, a secure site should have a little golden padlock at the bottom of your screen. (But remember that this lock may only appear when you enter the part of the site where you actually buy something.) In Netscape version 4.6 onwards, there is a security button on the toolbar next to **'Print'** which, if you click on it, will tell you whether the site you're on uses encryption.

If you're still uncertain, check their web address with a service like **_www.enonymous.com_** which will tell you, for instance, if the online store you're visiting will give out your data to other companies.

2 **Don't use a simple password** when registering on a site. Dates of birth, mothers' maiden names, etc, can easily be guessed. Try something more obscure (like mixing letters and numbers) which you can still easily remember. If you're still worried, use complex passwords and store them in a software program like Password Keeper (**_www.gregorybraun.com/PassKeep.html_**) which will cost you the sterling equivalent of $20. Or you could surf the Web anonymously with free trial software from **_www.anonymizer.com_**.

3 **Don't buy anything you hear about in junk e-mail**. According to those awfully vigilant people at Internet ScamBusters (**_www.scambusters.com_**), your chances of getting anything at all from such a source are less than 45 per cent and your chances of actually getting what you ordered are a statistically unimpressive one in 20. Also, take care if a seller is using a free e-mail service. While most people using these services are as honest as the 21st of June is long, these services make it easier for a seller to hide their real identity.

4 **Use a credit card**. It limits your liability if you're ripped off. Barclaycard, for example, guarantees you against any fraudulent use of your card providing you haven't done anything daft like send your card number and expiry date to everyone in your e-mail address book.

5 **Look out for cyber-wallets** and other systems designed to make buying online safe. Securicor's Safedoor (***www.safedoor.co.uk***) system, for instance, actually buys the goods for you as an intermediary.

6 **Don't buy anything from a website with no physical location** or a physical address that begins and ends with a PO Box number. Similarly, if a person you're buying from at auction won't reveal their real name, address and phone number, go elsewhere. The EU's distance-selling regulations that are now in force state that if you're paying in advance you have to be told the identity of the supplier and their address before concluding the contract to buy.

New ways of paying for online shopping are emerging which mean you don't have to key in your credit card details. Securicor's Safedoor actually buys the goods for you

The basics

IF THINGS GO WRONG...

Complain to the e-tailer with the usual info. Most will have a 'help' button with a contact address and their returns policy.

If you're still not happy, you can do one of the following: call your local Trading Standards department; see if the e-tailer belongs to a trade association (and if it runs an arbitration scheme); sue; complain to the Office of Fair Trading, the Advertising Standards Authority, your MP or, if desperate, Watchdog. For issues with an overseas e-tailer go to www.oft.gov.uk/html/shopping/index.html

There's also the free consumer watchdog service of the Inter-active Media in Retail Group on www.imrg.org. Set up to raise awareness of online shopping it has its own code of practice.

If you don't get delivery in 30 days and haven't agreed to another date, you should be able to get your money back.

7 **Buy branded names from known sources**. One estimate suggests that between 10 and 20 per cent of luxury goods sites are selling fakes. Sticking with sites linked to accreditation schemes, like Trust UK and *Which?* Web Trader, could spare your blushes.

8 **Save copies of every e-mail** and document, complete with reference numbers, related to your purchase. It might just help if you're ripped off.

9 **Check every little detail**. Bargain headline prices may be offset by ludicrous shipping costs, especially if you want the item delivered yesterday. On the plus side, some e-tailers will have goodwill policies which mean they'll refund your shipping fees if you're not happy for any reason.

10 **Be careful with any personal information**. We're probably all just about smart enough not to stick a Post-it with our passwords onto our keyboard, but don't give out any other info about yourself (addresses etc) unless on a secure site.

11 **Remember: if you do decide to buy from an individual**, your rights of redress will probably not be as good as buying from a company.

12 **Know your software**. Both Internet Explorer and Netscape Navigator have devices which can help you to shop more safely. For example, in the way most Internet users have their browsers set up, their name and e-mail address are available to every website they happen to visit.

Auctions are for everybody,
not just Hugh Sculley or Lovejoy

GOING
GOING, GONE

uctions are no longer the preserve of art
collectors or dealers in dodgy motors.
The current glut of auction sites allows
folk all over the world to recycle their stuff.
That is not to say that online auctions are
problem-free but the more way-out rumours
about desperate people selling their kidneys
for transplant or buying nuclear weapons
from the former USSR are unfounded

Know the ground rules

Even if someone were trying to offload their internal
organs to the highest bidder, reputable auction sites are
pretty strict about what they will accept as a lot. They are
subject to the same laws as any offline retailer about what
they can sell, although individuals who sell through the
sites are not governed by consumer laws, which can lead
to problems for the buyer (see *How Not To Get Conned*,
p29). But sellers who try to break the rules will find their

auction accounts terminated and very possibly replaced by an intimate tête-à-tête with the local constabulary.

That's not to say that you won't still find some bizarre and compelling items. If you missed your chance in 1981, you can now pick up a Charles & Diana Commemorative Wedding Coin for a very reasonable price. Others may decide they must have a 1914 edition of *Golf Monthly*. Where caution is required is the urge to possess any number of strange items that will end up collecting dust until you finally get around to auctioning them yourself.

How auctions work

Most online auction sites, whether they offer general or specialist merchandise, work the same way. On general sites, like eBid (**www.ebid.co.uk**) or QXL (**www.qxl.com**) the offerings are broken down first into rough categories such as computer hardware, household goods, or toys and games, with further sub-categories appearing as you progress through the site. There are usually featured auctions on the homepage, as well as on the main page for each category, but these are not necessarily the best bargains on the site – the sellers probably paid for their lots in order to get some extra publicity.

Auction sites are free to buyers. They make their money by charging sellers small fees to list an item, and another fee if a sale is successful. On specialist auction sites it helps to know exactly what you are looking for, or to be very careful in assessing what's on offer.

A computer package may seem like an extraordinary deal, but look closely and you may find that it comes minus small details, like a monitor. This may not worry you, but if you were looking for a ready-to-plug-in PC, it's not the deal for you.

If you are just surfing auction sites to see if anything appeals to you, in most cases you don't need to register. But once you decide to buy or sell, you will have to register to show that you are a real person and can be contacted if there's a subsequent dispute.

Private sellers usually have to provide more information on themselves than the buyers do, including credit card details. And after a series of online shouting matches, as well as disputes over deals that didn't

Not content with 'standard' online auctions, QXL has now upped the stakes by introducing live virtual auctions and real-time bidding

go through or goods that never turned up, some sites now insist that you provide an e-mail address that is registered either at your home or place of work (a Hotmail address that can be run from a cybercafé is much too worryingly anonymous).

The art of selling

Once you have decided which site will benefit from the contents of your attic, you need to list each item as a lot on the site. The first things you will be asked for are fairly obvious – a title for your lot, a brief, accurate but attention-grabbing description, and a starting price.

After that it can get a little more complicated. You will have the option to upload a picture of your item, and to put a reserve amount on your lot. So if your rollerblades cost you £60 and a broken wrist, and you don't want to sell them for less than half of what you paid, a good trick is to make the starting price very low to attract attention, but then place a reserve price of £30 on them.

Some sites discourage reserve prices, which they say make a sale less likely. This is true, but their concern is really more for their sale fees than for your profit. Other decisions to make include: the duration of the auction, who pays for shipping (almost always the buyer), and what forms of payment you will accept. It is also vital to let potential buyers know a little bit about yourself in order to allay fears that you might be a criminal.

If someone wins your auction and is now looking forward to breaking bones of their own, you are legally obliged to sell the rollerblades to them. The auction site will forward you details of who has won the bidding and it is up to you to arrange payment and delivery.

The art of buying

Before you do anything, remind yourself that any bid you place is a binding contract and if you win the lot, you cannot change your mind – so don't bid for anything just for a laugh or that stuffed badger could be yours.

Make all the checks you want (see 'How Not To Get Conned' opposite) and if everything looks good, the best and most efficient way to proceed is to decide the most you are prepared to pay, and then ask the site to bid on your behalf up to that amount. If no one bids above you, and the reserve has been met, the blades are yours, hopefully below your top price. If someone outbids your maximum, the site will notify you to see if you want to bid again. This is when auction fever can set in. Don't fall into the "oh, it's only another tenner" trap. Go and make a cup of tea. Then rush back, throw caution to the wind and bid like crazy until they're yours. You know you're going to, at least once.

Don't make a bid just for a laugh or that stuffed badger could be yours

Once you have fought off the other contenders, the seller will contact you to let you know the final price of the rollerblades, including their shipping cost. Think about this extra expense before you make your final bid.

HOW NOT TO GET CONNED

According to the National Fraud Information Center *(www.fraud.com)*, 78 per cent of Internet fraud in 2000 was on auction sites. This is no surprise. Personal auctions are like car boot sales with the added thrill of not knowing if the goods will even turn up. Placing a lot for sale or bidding, is in theory a binding contract but in practice it's unlikely to be worth the effort and cost to enforce it. The big sites have tightened up security, but you can reduce the risks.

Start small. It's not the end of the world if you lose a fiver on something that turns out to be dodgy.

Try to buy only from rated sellers. You can check out other buyers' experiences with sellers in the feedback section of the site. See if the seller is a regular on the site's message boards and is open about what they're selling.

Buying from the auction site or a registered company using the site as a sales tool is a lot safer than buying from an individual. Most consumer protection laws don't deal with private sales, so disputes could be hard to settle.

If you do buy from an individual, get an address and other identifying information before sending money.

If buying from a company or auction site, check details of returns, warranties and service if the product is faulty. Ask that higher priced items are insured in transit.

Beware: some sellers get friends ('shills') to bid on items to raise the price. Rushing back to bid on an item (unless the auction is closing) will only reveal how keen you are.

Pay by the safest way you can. If possible pay by credit card, then you can dispute the charges if the goods are misrepresented or never arrive. Some auction sites offer online wallet payment facilities such as PayHound *(www.payhound.com)* which act as an intermediary.

Tell the auction site if you come across dodgy dealings, as it can (and will) investigate on your behalf.

Remember the golden rule of auctions – if it sounds too good to be true, it probably is.

General auctions Something for everyone

Aucland
www.aucland.co.uk

Originating from France you might expect a rather more stylish interface but then we are talking auction sites here and Aucland's front end is perfectly serviceable. The site features a handy walkthrough for first-time users and you can view all the items for sale that have pictures in its gallery. Aucland has also done deals with third parties for job-lots of kit such as Albion Business Computers which is offering a range of secondhand IT equipment.

Auction Town
www.auctiontown.co.uk

If you can forgive them the cutesy categories (Computer Crescent, Transport Terrace) there are bargains to be nabbed here. Check out Miscellaneous Mews for everything from tubes of Bostik to a pair of natural wood dolphins. Basic listings are free to sellers (or you pay 50p or £1 for a bold and featured listing, respectively) and the site also provides good instructions for novices.

Bluecycle
www.bluecycle.com

Backed by the insurance giant CGU this is where to come for items seized by the police and never claimed or left after the insurers paid out. Head for the Salvage section for incredible bargains on some truly bizarre lots.

eBay
www.ebay.com

The first (and still one of the biggest) auction sites with items ranging from Elvis's Cadillac to retired Beanies when we dropped by. The homepage looks hectic but it's well set out with lots of info about each lot and lively message boards. It's free to buyers but for sellers there is a complex fee structure. On each sale there's a listing fee based on your starting price of between 15p and £1.25 – though listing items like houses or businesses is a higher fixed tariff – plus a final value fee based on a percentage of the sale price. There's also a fee to put a reserve price on your item – though this is refundable if it sells.

Ebid
www.ebid.co.uk

Not a bad site for novices to launch themselves in the auction world since the homepage doesn't overwhelm you with hordes of categories and choice. Not as many lots up for grabs as the big boys but they still ranged from Madonna concert tickets to books on hypnosis when we dropped by. They charge a handling fee for any lot that reaches its reserve price, plus a closing charge based on your final sale price.

FSAuctions
www.fsauction.co.uk

Cheery, all-flashing homepage which certainly hasn't
heard of the minimalist
movement. Still, online auctions in general aren't about
taste and style and
Freeserve's offering excels in
most other aspects: it provides the buyer with plenty of
detail about the lot, there are
user ratings available and
you can link to other lots
from the same seller if you
feel an affinity with their cast-
offs. A real pluspoint is that

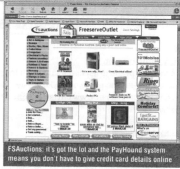

FSAuctions: it's got the lot and the PayHound system
means you don't have to give credit card details online

you can pay using the PayHound cash wallet system so don't have to give
credit card details online.

QXL
www.qxl.com

QXL has taken things one step further by introducing live virtual auctions and
real-time bidding. The live auctions are usually themed (in areas such as
computing, telecoms, DVDs) and among the bargains that had been scooped
when we visited were three nights in Paris for £71 and a toning belt (an apparently ubiquitous item on auction sites) for £32. QXL still runs standard, non
real-time auctions and it also has a £1 No Reserve Shop where we could have
bid for Alan Titchmarsh's garden design software for £1 (but suddenly came
to our senses). There's no insertion fee, but QXL charges success fees.

Shoptour
www.shoptour.co.uk/framed/shoptour_auctions.html

Not so much an auction site as a powerful search engine which allows you to
search for an item across a wide range of auctions. We searched for Madonna
tickets (hot property at the time of writing) and it found 2,089 instances of
them being on sale. But even the Queen of Pop was eclipsed by Pokémon,
which returned a staggering 29,473 related items on sale.

Yahoo Auctions
http://uk.auctions.yahoo.com/uk

The mighty portal is big on auctions and there's always plenty to browse
through here. It's free to list lots on this site though they do insist on holding
any seller's credit card details for security purposes. Buyers are only allowed
to bid on a few items at a time until they have some positive feedback from a
seller. The better their rating, the more lots they can bid on.

Specialist auctions Something in particular

Art

www.sothebys.com

Not the kind of site to get click-happy with the mouse – it could cost you thousands. And find plenty more Old Masters at www.bonhams.com while the handy LotFinder at www.christies.com is good if you're searching for a specific painter's work.

Business Equipment

www.morgan-auctions.co.uk

Outstanding site for nearly new and refurbished office equipment, which lets you key in your maximum and automatically puts the bids in for you. See also www.businessauctions.com which lists a variety of auction sites offering office clearance goods and refurbished computers.

Collectibles

www.antiques.co.uk

Quality collectible antiques from Art Nouveau metalwork to a clay Victorian armadillo on wheels (sadly it had gone). Plenty of precious lots that would keep the *Antiques Roadshow* team in superlatives for years.

Computers

http://auctions.cnet.com/

Great US bargains but some lots may have export problems and specs are not necessarily suitable for the UK. See also www.computers4sale.co.uk, a UK site for private sellers to offload anything connected with computing.

Sports Memorabilia

www.sports-memorabilia.co.uk

Part of QXL and although the range of goods isn't huge, you can pick up some classics, such as Finlay Calder's British Lion's captain's blazer.

Stamps

www.sandafayre.com

A stamp collector's paradise. Online bids are put against postal bids, and all lots come with a no-quibble guarantee, which is nice.

How to make sure
it's worth your while

BUYING
FROM ABROAD

It seems so simple. An international site has the camcorder you want at a price that turns local retailers pale. Tap in your credit card details, await delivery and you're quids in, right? Well, not always. Those huge savings can be wiped out by irritating extras like shipping, import duty and VAT, so for the real cost lowdown, read on…

Things to remember

Some goods, particularly in the electronic and computing markets, may not be available for shipping overseas. Many US-based companies restrict which goods can be exported to protect their international markets. So you could find a website with exactly the 3COM Palm Pilot you're after, and at a mind-boggling price, only to be told at checkout that it can't be shipped overseas.

You should also check if the manufacturer will honour warranties if the goods have been shipped overseas, or offers technical support for international users. Many do not. This isn't such a problem if you want Calvin Klein underwear, but if it's anything electrical or electronic, do some research before you click 'buy'. If you're looking for a video product – be it a camcorder or DVD player – remember that many countries use formats incompatible with UK television sets. We use PAL video, so check that anything you buy can be converted to that format.

Make sure it's worth it

Once you find the right thing to buy, shipping can often be worked out online before you finalise the order, but be prepared to provide credit card details and start the buying process before you find out how much delivery will be. Less savvy sites may have to e-mail you separately. Either way, be sure to check costs thoroughly, as a FedEx delivery can add a shocking amount to the price.

Once shipping costs are clear, and you still think you've got a bargain, you then face the tricky business of import duty and VAT on goods entering the UK. You don't

EXAMPLES OF CUSTOMS DUTY RATES (%)

AUDIO-VISUAL		GARMENTS	
Compact discs	3.5	Women's and girls'	12.8
Car radio/cassette/CD players	14	Men's & boys'	12.8
Cassettes *(recorded)*	2.6	Baby	10.5
DVD player	14	JEWELLERY	
DVD discs	3.5	Of precious metals	2.5
Colour televisions	14	*(inc. jewellery with pearls*	
Video cameras & camcorders	4.9	*or semi-precious stones)*	
Video games	2.2	Imitation jewellery	4
Video tape recorders *(domestic)*	14	Microwave ovens	5
Bicycles *(including children's)*	15	Mobile phones	1.6
Computers *(Including peripherals)*	FREE	PHOTOGRAPHIC	
Fax machines	FREE	Still cameras	4.2
FOOTWEAR		Digital still cameras	FREE
Ski boots & board boots	17	Skincare products *(inc. make-up)*	FREE
With uppers of leather	8	Spectacles and sunglasses	2.9
FURNITURE		Tools	2.7
Metal, wood & plastic	FREE	TOYS	
GAMES & SPORT		Construction sets *(wood)*	4.5
Golf clubs and tennis rackets	2.7	Construction sets *(plastic)*	4.7
Skis	3.7	Other	4

This is only an example of duty rates on some items. The full list can be found at the Customs and Excise website (*www.hmce.gov.uk*). Further advice can be obtained by calling 0845 0109000

have to pay tax on most imports of less than £18 in value, but tobacco, alcohol and perfume are liable from the first penny.

All international parcels must have a standard label on them declaring the contents so Customs and Excise can assess the duty and level of VAT to apply. If this label is missing, incomplete or unclear, they will open the parcel to inspect the contents. Some websites tried putting misleading information on packages to foil the tax man but the authorities are cracking down on this so don't rely on it as a ruse to lower costs. If the parcel is opened and it's discovered that the contents are illegal in the UK – in the unlikely event you're importing, say, a nunchuka – the goods will be confiscated and you will be prosecuted.

As with most tax matters, the amount of duty and VAT payable on personal imports is not one simple calculation applied to all goods. Taxes are charged at differing rates depending on the type of product imported and its place of manufacture. We've compiled a duty table for items you're more likely to find while shopping online, but this is only a fraction of the complete Customs Tariff, which reads like advanced calculus.

If you are unsure what category your purchase falls under (and you probably will be), ring your local Customs and Excise Advice Centre or try **www.hmce.gov.uk** for online

WORK OUT THE TAX

1. Look up the item's duty rate % and VAT %.

----

2. Multiply the Purchase Price Abroad (PPA) by the duty rate %. This is the amount of duty to be paid (AMOUNT A).

----

3. Add AMOUNT A to the PPA and multiply the result by the VAT %. This is the amount of VAT to be paid (AMOUNT B).

----

4. Add AMOUNTS A & B together and that will be how much tax you have to pay on your order.

EXAMPLE:

You've ordered some CDs from abroad. The cost, including postage and packing, was £100. So, you find out that the duty rate is 3.5% and that VAT is 17.5%. Multiplying the cost of the CDs by the duty rate gives you £3.50. Add this to the original £100 and you get £103.50. Multiply that by the VAT rate, which is 17.5%, and that all comes to £18.11. So £121.61 is what you'll pay for your CDs in all, of which £21.61 will be your total Customs and Excise charge.

guidance. Rather unfairly, the charges you pay for shipping are counted as part of the purchase price, so don't forget to factor this in too.

Paying the tax man

If your order is sent by post, the Post Office will collect duty and VAT on behalf of Customs and Excise, or store the goods if Customs needs to make further inquiries. Usually, the Post Office will collect charges on delivery (a label will be slapped on the package at the Customs Postal Depot, showing the charge as well as any Post Office fee), and it adds a small charge for doing this – Royal Mail charges £1.20, Parcelforce charges £5.25 for standard deliveries and £10.25 for express. Sometimes collection of these charges can be a bit random but don't count on a dozy postman to save your pennies. If there's any query, they'll send you a form to complete and return to them before your parcel can be delivered.

If your order is sent by an international courier, they will pay any taxes due and invoice you for reimbursement. Federal Express (**www.fedex.com/gb/**) and DHL (**www.dhl.co.uk**) do not charge for this service, but you may have to pay a £10 Customs administration charge for dealing with a courier.

A bit of online detective work can lead to some stunning buys

But don't let all this bureaucracy, tax and abstruse mathematical calculation put you off. There are loads of items worth seeking out on foreign sites, such as camera equipment, fax machines and some furniture, which are low-rated (or even free) for duty, leaving only VAT and shipping that you need to worry about.

A bit of online detective work can lead to some stunning bargains. For example, an Olympus C3000 zoom digital camera, quoted at £549 (inc VAT) on a leading British website, was only $597.99 on US-based The Camera Club

You don't need to travel to Gracelands for Elvis memorabilia when you have Shop Elvis. But, as with all shops abroad, just check that delivery charges make any purchases viable

(**www.thecameraclub.com**). When you convert that, add VAT and shipping (about $40), you're looking at a total price of about £450 – still a saving of around £100.

Savings can also be made on less expensive items such as CDs, books or clothing if you buy in bulk. A best-selling CD might cost $13.28 (about £9.09) on **CdNow.com** compared to £11.99 on **Amazon.co.uk**, but you'd have to buy at least 11 titles before shipping and taxes were overtaken by savings. Similarly high-quality cotton men's T-shirts from Lands' End are £12.50 each on **www.landsend.co.uk**. but only $12.00 (about £8.22) on **www.landsend.com**. But after taxes and shipping you're only saving around £1 per shirt even if you buy a dozen.

Some foreign websites offer items that are just not available in the UK. This could be anything from Elvis memorabilia (**www.elvis.com/shopelvis/**) to authentic Italian deli food (**www.gourmet2000.it**). There's piles of stuff out there that will never reach your high street, but it can come to your front door. Above all, online shopping should be fun. If that Okuma Titus TG50 fishing reel ($199.99 from **www.gofishin.com**) looks like it could bring a bureaucratic headache rather than an awesome saving, think again. But after a bit of surfing and a few price comparisons, you should be able to catch an international bargain to brag about for months to come.

**How the Web
helps you shop**

USING THE INTERNET

Okay, you've been to your local PC World and put a snazzy beige box on your credit card. You've listened to your modem gurgling, clicked on the browser and you can see something which the manual describes as a homepage. And the rest, as they say, is a mystery. Don't click on the 'Help!' button until you've read this

Searching the Web

A search engine is exactly that. A means of searching the Net for whatever it is that you want. Just type in key words and click on **'Search'** or **'Go'**. Hundreds of links of some relevance to your chosen topic should appear. But type in Madonna and you may find yourself reading reams of religious sermons instead of quirky facts about the Queen of Pop.

The grandaddy of all search engines has got to be ***www.yahoo.com***. Its straightforward design gives you the choice of browsing through the categories listed, such as **'travel'**, or just typing in your chosen topic. Yahoo can search sites in a specific country or the whole Web.

A wealth of young pretenders have emerged to challenge Yahoo with new technology and new ways of linking you to your request. For example, ***www. google.com*** delivers results based on those sites which have been linked to the most from other sites. So Google should lead you to the most useful, if you accept that the most useful are also the most popular. If you want quantity rather than quality, ***www.altavista.com*** claims to hold the largest index available, with 350 million web pages.

From the best of the rest, ***www.alltheweb.com*** is a parallel search tool, exploring a range of other engines to find results, ***www.dogpile.com*** gets good word-of-mouth recommendations whereas ***www.askjeeves.com*** could be called the idiot's guide to the Net as you can type in the exact question you want answered. Though Jeeves can focus on the 'ifs' and "buts' rather than the real question.

Making sense of directories

If you lack the patience to browse the thousands of pages that most search engines list, directories provide a narrower field of enquiry. They group together URLs of like mind so if you want to know about skiing, a directory will offer a list of sites all relating to the ski world.

> Some directories review sites so you can sift the best out from the worst

The best UK specific directories include ***www.yahoo.co.uk***, ***www.looksmart.co.uk*** and ***www.ukplus.co.uk***. Click on a specific category and browse through the list of related URLs. Many, such as UK Plus, review each site so you can sift the best out from the worst. There are directories defined by age (***www.seniorsearch.com/ssuk/home directory.htm*** for fifty-somethings) or where you live (***www.250000.com*** lists sites by geographical location).

If you want a one-click process, some sites act as online equivalents of *Yellow Pages*. If you're moving house or moving country, ***www.yell.com*** contains property and travel guides with resort guides, insurance quotes, removal men etc, while ***www.scoot.co.uk*** can find products from furniture to your local Chinese takeaway.

Shopping bots

With many couples' Saturday ritual being to hit the high street at 11am, have the men lose interest at around lunchtime and both head home at around 2pm with not a purchase in sight, offline shopping has ceased to be a pleasure and become something that causes 57 per cent of arguments between couples in the UK. Shopping from your computer could ease the tension if you know how (and where) to look. And help is at hand.

Shopping directories are the online equivalent to shopping malls. Most, like ***www.just35.com***, ***www.shopsafe.co.uk*** and ***www.shopandwin.co.uk***, offer a list of popular shopping categories alongside reviews and ratings. Many are taking directories that one step further by creating **shopping bots**. Most sites advertise themselves as cutting high-street prices so you should get some kind of bargain, but a shopping bot searches cyberspace to find the best deals for you. This sounds too good to be true – and in some cases it is – but many good bots will do exactly what it says on the box.

All you do is tell them what you're looking for, they take a few seconds to scan the globe and return with a list of the best bargains. One of the best bots is

www.kelkoo.com with a database of 25,000 online stores. Categories include music, film, wines, electrical appliances and computing, and you can make your search as simple or complex as you like. For obvious reasons they'll only look at companies that deliver to the UK. **http://uk.shopsmart.com** and **www.mytaxi.co.uk** are other solid sites to follow. Price comparisons are limited to CDs, videos, games and books, but the vast selection can save you up to 30 per cent on high-street prices, paying as little as £3 for a Harry Potter book.

If you're after a specific bargain, simply type **'price comparison'** and then key whatever you're looking for into your search engine. Most search engines come up with something, but try **http://wine-searcher.com** for the boozy bargains, **www.bookbrain.co.uk** for literature and **www.computerprices.co.uk** for computers.

Some shopping bots only search the vendors who they have deals with so you won't always get the ultimate deal. An easy way to check this is to do a simple search for quite a common item and see how many different stores are listed. If it's limited to only a couple you may find a better deal elsewhere. Some companies such as **www.pricescan.com** and **www.mysimon.com** make a point of actually saying that they don't accept money from vendors.

If you're still not convinced, both **www.botspot.com** and **www.smartbots.com** offer guides to the best around. In the future, bots will constantly e-mail you with new bargains. Some of them might even be relevant to you. Either way, you need never face a Harrods sale again.

Group buying power

If you've got enough friends, group buying is another way to save. Sites such as **www.letsbuyit.com** and **www.mercata.com** work on the premise that the more people who buy an item, the cheaper it becomes. It's a bit more complicated than that, but not much – just make sure you look out for the Best Price marking. Even if you persuade your whole family to join in, you'll never knock the price so low you get a digital camera for £10. They usually state a **cut-off price point** which may be **40 per cent off** the normal price. Letsbuy offers the chance to bid at the current price or only on the best possible price. You can also tip off a friend about the latest great deals.

www.letsbuyit.co.uk   **LetsBuyIt**

www.buyasone.com   **Mob Shop**

Getting the best reviews

The Internet is teeming with review sites for everything from film and music to computer and household goods. There are even sites reviewing other websites so you can find the best site from which to start your online search.

Of the more general review sites, ***www.epinions.com***, ***www.ciao.com*** and ***www.consumerguide.com*** are probably the best. Each covers popular online buys like CDs and computer equipment, as well as more unusual stuff like cigars, sleeping bags and shampoo. You can submit your own reviews or read those from independent buyers. Product Review also offers buying guides and shopping tips, and Consumer Guide offers a concise history of each item and a guide to what the technical nonsense in the handbooks means. Useful if you still can't manage to set your video timer.

Don't be put off by the countless computer reviews that you'll find during your searches. There's a review site on the Net to

A growing band of consumers impart their views on products and services at www.ciao.com – and get money in return for them

cover every product and topic imaginable. Book reviews are posted on the sites of some e-tailers like BOL, Waterstones and WHSmith. Or you could peruse. The ***www. booksonline.co.uk*** site from the *Daily Telegraph* allows you to

Review sites give you what no retailer can: an objective opinion

search by author, title or genre. *The Times*, the *Independent* and the *Guardian* also run online review sections and links to independent sellers. With ***www.blether.com*** you can discuss the book you've just read and say whether you loved or hated it.

For an alternative to the perhaps over-familiar movie reviews of Barry Norman, you can always try ***www. popcorn.co.uk*** which covers reviews of every movie currently showing in the UK, and lets you submit your own. ***www.odeon.com*** follows a similar premise with the added bonus that you can buy online.

If you want computer reviews but simply can't face looking at every Tom, Dick and Harry's entry, one of the best is ***www.zdnet.com***. Covering PCs, peripherals and digital technology, ZD collects reviews from different sources and offers simple overviews, full reviews and test scores for a good all-round picture of the product before you buy.

Internet review sites are infinite in number, especially if you're looking for something like a car or a computer. But even if you're after something more specialised, the Internet can help. If you're just getting into scuba diving but aren't sure what to use, ***www.scubadiving.com*** will help you decide if the Aqua Lung Impulse 2 or the Zeagle Flex is the best snorkel for you.

Review sites give you what you'll never get from the mumbling sales assistants who can barely recall the name of the products they're selling: an objective, informed opinion. A site like ***www.audioreview.com*** offers you the opinions of the public and experts. At ***www.usbuy.com*** they'll help you decide what deal best suits you, rather than what suits them. If you're after a mobile phone you just answer a set of questions, from which they'll determine what kind of phone to get, if any. They will then link you to reputable retailers who stock the product you need.

www.reviewfinder.com   **Review Finder**

And now for the bad news...

Online shopping hasn't enjoyed the best public image since it burst on to the scene. In 1999 – the year that really should have heralded a festive bonanza for online shoppers and e-tailers – seven online shops ended up agreeing to pay $1.5m in penalties for various failures to deliver the goods during the season of supposed goodwill.

Since then online service has vastly improved but various studies have shown that the biggest problem wasn't anything to do with delivery or fraud, it was that the sites themselves didn't work. About one in four purchases, according to one of the growing tribe of Internet consultants, were halted by technical hitches. That figure has since fallen to eight per cent.

Many customers, confused by sites which offered too much choice and too little guidance, left cyberspace's electronic aisles littered with abandoned shopping carts. But again, most shops have now simplified their sites. Indeed, Amazon's approach to online shopping, usually cited as among the Web's easiest to use, is now being used by Toys "R" Us.

And, wonder of wonders, e-tailers are now replying to shoppers' e-mails faster (in an average of 12 hours, not 48). So even the bad news is getting better.

Part Two

How to buy everything online
from azaleas to zithers

THE DIRECTORY

Antiques

The world's youngest mass medium is the fastest growing marketplace for civilisation's oldest treasures. Even your ragged old teddy bear can get in on the act

Abercrombie Antiques
www.abercrombie.fsnet.co.uk

Specialists in antique glassware, jewellery and toys, along with collectible stamps and postcards, this Powys-based site has plenty to offer besides its online catalogue. There are details of antiques sales and fairs in mid-Wales, training courses for amateurs and professionals, and house-clearance services for mid-Wales and nearby.

Antiques.co.uk
www.antiques.co.uk

This speedy and beautifully laid-out site promises antiques which have been vetted and guaranteed by a team of experts for sale and delivery all over the world. You can build up your own portfolio wish-list, arrange to view an item (the business is London-based) or just go ahead and buy it, all online. Pay by credit card, cheque or wire transfer from your bank, and delivery charges are calculated at the time of buying. A very professional and impressive site.

Antiques Trade Gazette
www.atg-online.com

Nothing for sale, but unless you employ the services of Hugh Scully himself, you're unlikely to find a better information resource for the antique world. This trade site offers a range of services, including an events calendar, catalogues, a directory of antique centres and websites, and an online price guide. You do need to register to use this service, but it's simple and free. You'll also find a limited classifieds section listing everything from antique jewellery to property.

Antiques UK
www.antiques-uk.co.uk

This antiques portal offers links to many regional stores and auction houses, from specialist dealers to salvage warehouses. There's an excellent classified section where you can post a message if you're looking for a particular item and any dealer with a matching piece can get in touch through the site.

Antiques World
www.antiquesworld.co.uk
A succinct yet comprehensive directory of antique events and organisations in your area, as well as recommended publications and its own library of features. A useful resource for both beginners and old hands.

Arts And Crafts Furniture
www.artsandcraftsantiques.co.uk
An online catalogue of restored late-19th and early-20th century furniture from the Art and Crafts movement. The store is based in Manchester, but there are good photos on an otherwise basic site, so you can get an idea of the beauty of some of the pieces. You can e-mail for details or phone for a viewing.

Christer Schulz Antiques
www.schultz-antiques.com
This site is the easy-to-use catalogue of a south-east England-based dealer who specialises in high-quality English and northern European antiques, ranging from Georgian secretaires to Victorian chandeliers. Christer Schulz will accept enquiries online, and the site has contact details for his various retail outlets. There are also links to various other antiques information sites.

The Howard Gallery
www.thehowardgallery, article7.co.uk
This well-stocked dealer is a specialist in 17th- and 18th-century furniture, but also has a limited range of clocks and porcelain. The site is simply designed with good photos of available pieces, each of which you can enquire about online. The gallery promises to call you back within a few days.

Invaluable
www.thesaurus.co.uk
Nothing on sale at this site but a useful collection of news articles, information on upcoming auctions and fairs, plus tips for enthusiasts. There's a comprehensive search facility through auction catalogues and dealers' lists, plus contact details for dealers all over the world and – a great idea this – a section on stolen property and protecting your valuables. A great starting point for amateurs.

Not a site that requires you to fish around for a credit card, but for auction newbies Invaluable is, well, invaluable

Antiques

Lassco

www.lassco.co.uk

Lassco is an architectural antiques salvage company that offers a glorious selection of fixtures and fittings saved from old buildings. Apart from the more traditional baths, radiators and recycled flooring, interesting items on offer when we visited included old telephone kiosks and huge brass doors from closed bank branches.

Mir Russki

www.russiansilver.co.uk

Got an urge to collect Fabergé? Mir Russki can help you drop serious cash on exquisite silver and enamelled pieces made in Imperial Russia. If you have £895 to spend on a matchbox cover you can contact the company online, although they recommend any purchase is made over the phone.

Old Bear

www.oldbear.co.uk

Antique teddy bears are big business, so take a look at this site to see if your ragged childhood friend is worth a bob or two. Collectors can get their fill of Steiff teddies and stuffed animals, along with other manufacturers' items and teddy-related memorabilia. There's an online form to complete if you are seriously interested in any teddies for sale.

Richard Gardner Antiques

www.richardgardnerantiques.co.uk

Cautiously billed as 'possibly the largest single antique dealer website in the world', this classy operation displays an enormous selection of truly lovely pieces of quality furniture and decorative items. The Miscellaneous section includes lots of fun items, ranging from mechanical birdcages to 17th-century leather trunks from Russia.

World Collectors Net

www.worldcollectorsnet.com

Despite a limited selection of items to buy, this quaint-looking site is an excellent general directory. The Shopping Arcade offers links to a host of shops from County Durham to San Francisco, while the Collections Featured section and online magazine offer the usual guides and general information to help you both get started and to progress.

AMERICAN ANTIQUES

Old things from the New World are increasingly popular, particularly craft items. Antique Quilts (www.antiquequilts.com) is one of the best sites for quilts; it also stocks other genuine Americana such as Bennington pottery. There is plenty to browse, or you can buy the catalogue for $10. Other good transatlantic antique sites include:

Essex River Antiques
www.essexriverantiques.com

Leigh Keno American Antiques
www.leighkeno.com

Time Travellers
www.tias.com

Antique Fest
www.antiquefest.com

Dawn Hill Antiques
www.dawnhillantiques.com

Arts

The Net is the biggest art market in the world, letting you buy everything from a signed Roy Lichtenstein print to vintage Polish posters. You can even commission paintings from your own photographs

General For those with an artistic temperament

Allwall

www.allwall.com

Formerly Art.com, Allwall offers an impressive selection of posters and fine art. Simply pick a category – there's everything from cuisine to world culture – shop according to your favourite artist or, if you're a novice when it comes to art, the top 100 selection should steer you in the right direction, in terms of popularity at least. As a US site shipping is pricey, starting from $20, but such a vast selection with the added bonus of framing makes it worth a look.

Art Crimes

www.graffiti.org

It's graffiti, Jim, but not as we know it. None of that 'Kilroy woz 'ere' stuff here – just an introduction to a network of artists who indulge in the world's biggest (and most debased) participation art, some of whom will do graffiti to order. All that and a catalogue of magazines with great names like *Molotov Cocktail*. This site is definitely worth a bookmark.

Art for Sale

www.artforsale.co.uk

Although you can only enquire about the works featured on this tastefully designed store, London-based Art for Sale serves as a useful introduction to new artists and media. You can browse through an A to Z catalogue featuring such names as Patrick Caulfield, Tracy Emin and Paul Maze, or simply select a medium and price range to view a selected section. Prices start from £150 up to around £9,000. Enquiries can be made directly through the site.

Arts

Art Is A Tart
www.art-is-a-tart.com
Limited edition paintings by contemporary artists, bronze resin sculptures and greetings cards (delivered free) are all on sale at a site which never quite lives up to the chutzpah in its title. The ordering system was temperamental but you're given enough clear cues to find your way around easily.

Art Planet
www.artplanet.com
There are enough links here to condemn the art fan to a lifetime in cyberspace. Want to find out what contemporary Lithuanian artists are up to? Follow the links to www.culture.lt/ArtDB and your curiosity will be satisfied. The only criticism is that there's just too much here and some links are not that relevant.

Brit Art
www.britart.com
Fantastically funky site celebrating British artistic merits. Although held fast in the modern vein, the huge selection still manages to encompass a wider range of styles from the abstract to figurative and landscapes. With prices ranging from hundreds to thousands, it may be worth taking advantage of the facility to make an offer on a work, rather than just paying up for it or passing it by.

Christie's
www.christies.com
If you have $82.5m burning a hole in your pocket or purse, this is the place to buy that Van Gogh. But not everything on this famous auction house's site costs that much: you can buy a Warhol print for less than $9,000. Failing that, a subscription to the company's *Christie's* magazine will set you back a measly £40. A word of warning: once you've visited this site, you will want to keep coming back, if only to hang around a very classy part of cyberspace.

Eyestorm
www.eyestorm.com
Flashy site which offers contemporary art and art photography from A (Marina Abramovic) to W (James Welling) and enables the technologically challenged to enter a 'quick, simple' version. If you use credit card ordering (there's a handling charge of $1) your item will be delivered free, usually within two working days of the order being processed. The breadth of artists on display is impressive, but the work on show may not always be their finest.

New British Artists
www.newbritishartists.co.uk
Reasonably priced selection of work from British artists you may not have heard of, complete with potted biographies of each prodigy and an e-mail ordering service. There's also a good money-back guarantee if the work of art you get doesn't look quite as tasty as it did on the computer screen.

Red Dot

www.reddot.co.uk

This site's exhibition of the month typically features a select number of artists with prices starting at about £125. Pictures can be returned if you contact the gallery within three days and pay for delivery. If you're a new buyer, you should find the excellent back-up info (advice, terms and conditions etc) helpful. You can't yet buy online but you can reserve a painting by e-mail.

Sotheby's

www.sothebys.com

It may be just the colour scheme but this feels more formal than Christie's. You can register to bid online and, as with Christie's, there's no shortage of stuff to bid for. Those of you who find yourselves, almost against your will, glued to Loyd Grossman's *Through The Keyhole* may find the catalogues intriguing, especially the one devoted to the estate of the late Jacqueline Kennedy Onassis. After all, £56 is a small price to pay for such prurience.

 One Lord and the Thin White Duke

David Bowie

www.bowieart.com

After close inspection of just one of the works displayed here, all but the most hardcore Bowie fan would probably decide there are cheaper ways of getting his autograph. The site is uncluttered by any information such as its returns policy and how they ship the stuff to you. When e-mailed, the site responded that it delivers within 14 days of a credit card order and will refund or exchange any item if you are not happy. These policies weren't posted on the site, the e-mail explained, because BowieArt is not a big company. Really.

Jack Lord

http://sites.inka.de/sites/edruta/jlmaler.htm

In the 1950s Jack Lord, aka Steve McGarrett of *Hawaii Five-O*, tried to make a living as a painter. On this site you can find a collection of his work in the style of masters such as Van Gogh and Gaugin. The drawings suggest there was genuine talent before he became famous as the world's most conspicuous consumer of hair lacquer. You can't buy Lord's work online, but you can buy that of another US TV cop Buddy Ebsen, who played Barnaby Jones, from www.buddyebsencreations.com/gallery/fine1.html – but please don't.

Andy Warhol

www.warholstore.com

Andy's official online art mart contains the less-than-reassuring statement to customers outside the US: "We will attempt to honor all international orders." Pity, because there's a huge range of stuff here, much of it at good discounts.

Galleries Fine art, butterflies and flowers

20th Century Fine Art Gallery
www.geocities.com/SoHo/Den/6243/index.html
The title is slightly misleading, omitting as it does the key word 'Russian', but this is a lovely, almost naïve, site which simply showcases some wonderful paintings from (among others) the Leningrad school and simply asks you to e-mail the gallery if you are interested in buying any of the work on display.

Animation Art
www.animationartgallery.com
There aren't many works of art which Joe Public can afford, but just $400 at this online gallery will buy you an original piece of colour animation art from *The Simpsons*. The site – which showcases cartoons and animation from Dr Seuss through to Disney and Matt Groening – is slightly chaotic, but secure.

Flowers East
www.flowerseast.co.uk
East End warehouse gallery which has been showcasing the best of British art for over 30 years. You can buy special-offer prints by e-mail or view original works from such artists as Eduardo Paolozzi, whose sculpture *Newton After Blake* was quoted at £14,000. All in all, a seductive, low-key site where you want to linger. It's also worth following the links to Flowers Central and West.

Keens Secure Art Galleries
www.keen-art.com
If Tom and Barbara Good had branched out into the art world this is probably what the results would have looked like. Surbiton-based Shirley and Michael Keen bring you a homely yet professional art site selling a diverse selection, including contemporary, floral, marine and wildlife art. There's an A-Z list of artists, a gallery, news and artist biographies. Prices are good, so you won't need to resort to keeping livestock in your home just to pay for a print.

Les Pabillons
www.galerie-dcor.com
There's no easy way to say this: this is a French gallery which sells butterflies made out of banknotes. And for roughly four £10 notes, one of these financial butterflies can be yours. This could be the next big thing. Or it could just be the daftest thing to do with banknotes apart from setting fire to them.

Students Gallery
http://ws.safestreet.co.uk/StudentsGallery
Though based in London, Student Gallery acts as a showcase and vendor for the works of young artists across Britain. A range of media is displayed, from

photography and digital images to simple sketches and contemporary paintings. Don't assume the work of a student means student prices (or is payable in Pot Noodles). You could pay anywhere up to £3,000, but if you're looking for something less controversial than Tracy Emin's discarded sheets, it's worth it – and it may prove to be an investment in the long run.

Tate Gallery

www.tate.org.uk

The Tate's site sells mostly posters, prints, books, cards and slides of works on display, but jewellery, clothing, ceramics and computer accessories can also be found, plus giftware and products inspired by current exhibitions.

Posters & prints — Wall to wall

Artland

www.artland.co.uk

Lots of great offers – buy a print over £9.99 and get another one free; if you buy a print here and find it cheaper elsewhere within a week, they'll refund twice the difference – but Artland excels in other areas too. It's well organised – select a category to view a huge range of prints by great artists and student favourites (Klimt, Dali, Homer Simpson etc) – and prices are excellent (most are under £20, with free delivery).

Art Republic

www.artrepublic.com

Impeccably designed, superbly presented, incredibly easy to search, commendably unpretentious – it's impossible to overstate what a refreshing change ArtRepublic is from the average online shopping emporium. All this comes with a fine selection of posters and prints which you can search by artist, biographies and explanations of artistic terms.

Contemporary Posters

www.contemporaryposters.com

Like the (Russian) Fine Arts Gallery, this site's name is missing a key word – 'Polish'. That caveat aside, there are some very cool posters here, including the classic Solidarity poster from 1980. Sadly, you can only view this site to music that sounds like it's from the soundtrack of one of those animated Czech films that used to fill the cracks in the BBC2 schedule.

GORILLAS ON CANVAS

Koko is the first (and so far only) gorilla to host an online chat session (no Sylvester Stallone jokes please). With his friend Michael, he is also one of two gorillas to sell his own paintings on the Net.

Gorillas like to paint? US psychology professor Roger Fouts says, "It's in their nature. They like to use crayons, pencils and finger paints. Of course, they also like to eat them."

You can see the art that they produce before hunger takes hold at www.koko.org/kokomart/art.html (prices start at $25).
It's all in a good cause too: saving the species.

EasyArt
www.easyart.com
It can take a while to download the art available in a specific category (eg seascapes and landscapes) but everything else about this site lives up its name. Registering is simple and minimal, delivery is within five working days and free on framed prints. Someday all websites will be this easy-to-use.

GBPosters
www.gbposters.co.uk
If you suffer from a fear of originality, this is the poster store for you: only the obvious selections for the obvious subjects (the Beatles, Digimon, Austin Powers). If you want movie posters, you'll find a much bigger collection at www.blarg.net/~dr_z/Movie/Posters_LJK.html – the mysterious Dr Z's site. Yes, it is worth keying all that in, although the site could be better organised.

NAS Gallery
www.ndirect.co.uk/~nas
Want something different? How about an oil-on-canvas reproduction of that Constable picture your auntie always had on her wall? If you want something livelier, this site offers more modern artists too. You can even commission your own painting from a photo. Sounds tacky? There's a money-back guarantee if you're not satisfied. You can order online but you still have to send a cheque.

Poster Shop
www.postershop.co.uk
A particularly stylish site considering Britney Spears and a host of other pop starlets feature strongly. There's a vast selection of fine art prints, original works and pop culture posters, but prices are generally higher than elsewhere.

Rare Posters
www.rareposters.com
A stonking collection of exhibition and museum posters, with more Roy Lichtensteins than even the Lichtenstein family might want. This nifty and unpretentious site could lighten your wallet by as little as $12 or as much as $1,250 if you were tempted by a signed, limited edition Lichtenstein print.

Visoni Poster Art
www.visoni.com/index1.html
Good, if small, stock of classic posters, mostly from the tourism industry, with frequent special offers (like 10 per cent off if you buy more than five posters).

World Gallery
www.worldgallery.co.uk
They may only be selling prints, but World Gallery takes its work very seriously. Once you've selected a print from their expansive range (including everything from abstract to feline art), you can also choose suitable frames and mounts.

Babycare & maternity

Call on the Internet to feed baby's brain in the womb, ease the sting of childbirth (very slightly) and cure Junior's nappy rash. Oh, and find some decent clothes for mum

How to cope without getting out of your pram

Babies "R" Us
www.babiesrus.co.uk

The baby Toys "R" Us offers nappies and gadgets as well as more heavy-duty items like prams and high chairs. Its own-branded nappies are cheaper than Boots' own but it's not worth buying single packets because the postage and packing cancel out the savings. Bulk-buying with friends could be the answer.

Babycare Direct
www.babycare-direct.co.uk

Winner of the 1999 Shops on the Net Awards, this clearly laid-out site offers a wide range of products, from the basics to prams and car seats. There are also some attractive discounts, and a good shopping trolley that gives you a running total including post & packing (£3.95, free on orders over £200). The main gripe is that the customer service number isn't easy to get through to if you want to doublecheck something. Deliveries are within five working days.

Babycentre
www.babycentre.co.uk

You'll feel in safe hands at this professional and comprehensive site. It no longer sells anything, but instead offers advice and info for prospective parents – calendars, calculators and quizzes – plus useful buying guides by experts on a range of relevant products (from pregnancy testing kits to car seats for toddlers). There are also helpful bulletin boards with questions from the site's users and debates on such hot topics as disposable nappies.

It's hard to imagine bringing up baby without Boots and the online operation is on hand to take some of the strain

Boots

www.wellbeing.com

Despite hiding itself behind the Wellbeing banner, Boots' online shopping is still going strong. The basics – toys, clothes, equipment – are all there, with a much bigger range than in even the biggest Boots stores – there were 15 cots and cot beds when we visited. Functional rather than flashy is the watchword here – though the pictures are clear – but you can't fault the site for speed or ease of use.

The mother and baby section is broken down into crystal clear categories ranging from New Mum to Nappies and Potties. Standard two-day delivery costs £2.50, you can track your order, and a freepost returns label makes it simple to send stuff back.

Cribs2Go

www.cribs2go.com

This American site doesn't deliver outside the US but will ship to a US freight forwarder to get your purchase across the water – and that can still be worth it on items such as sports strollers (those trendy three-wheel buggies) that are massively more expensive over here. But don't be tempted by the child safety items, which are a lot more expensive than you'll find at home. A professional service that e-mails its answers to your queries promptly.

Diaper Goop

www.innopharm.com

Here's a top product for those parents whose babies tend to get nappy rash. This US site sells a highly recommended cream for treating sore botties. If you can stand the name (it really is called Diaper Goop), this stuff really seems to work. It costs about £5 for a 60g pot – the company charges $3 to deliver single jars to the UK – and it arrives promptly in two to three days.

Genius Babies

www.geniusbabies.com

Hilarious American site that offers all sorts of products designed to hothouse your own little prodigy. The Embryonics section includes a range of goods that 'encourage' a brainy foetus, like the *Mozart Womb Songs* CD. And what concerned parent could be without a *Baby Shakespeare* video? Joking aside, this is a great site with lots of witty ideas for presents. Due to "tremendous loss and fraud" they've had to halt shipping outside the US but e-mail your order and send them a US money order and they'll be happy to do business.

Green Baby

www.greenbabyco.com

As the name suggests, environmental concerns lie close to the heart of this
site but while the word 'organic' does feature in a major way, it's not all about
reusable nappies and organic babygros. You can also pick up a cutting-edge
three-wheeled stroller along with your Olive Oil Soap Flakes (great for washing
the family silks too, apparently). They aim to deliver within 72 hours of dispatch
(cost £3.50), but ask you to give them seven days to be on the safe side.

Katie's Playpen

www.katiesplaypen.co.uk

This Kent site offers a good selection of goods from mobiles to bedding, and
some decent discounts on the larger items, but they don't make life easy for
you. You have to e-mail them for prices on many products, which makes you
wonder what they're keeping quiet. Nor do they offer a shopping cart or any
information on delivery charges (again you have to e-mail them), but these
were promised for autumn 2001 as part of a site upgrade. Hopefully this will
also mean the end of the annoying split screen, which is fiddly to use.

Mothercare

www.mothercare.com

It was no great surprise when many branches of Mothercare closed down
a year or so ago, as the service and range in many shops were often
woefully lacking. Their website, on the other hand, has got more things right
than wrong, with a pretty comprehensive range of products and a useful
comparison facility to help you make your mind up. The own-brand stuff
offers a good budget option, and prices include delivery within five days.

Planet Baby & Child

www.planetbaby.co.uk

A very professional site that offers a welcome break from the overly busy
designs of many mother-and-baby pages, though the required horizontal
scrolling is irritating. You'll find lots of good ideas for equipment, toys and
nursery products here, including unusual stuff such as the Tooth Timer, a toy
to encourage tots to brush their teeth. It's helpfully divided into sections with
headings such as 'It's my room' and 'The great outdoors'. Next-day delivery
is promised for just £3.50 (free on orders over £50) and the site makes a point
of stating that all its toys comply with European safety regulations.

Premiere Baby Direct

www.babygoods.co.uk

You'll find some useful nursery equipment here that you might not have seen
anywhere else, such as a raised baby bath that attaches handily to an adult
bath, and an unusual sunshade to prevent your slumbering baby from being
roasted alive in the car seat. The ordering system is a pain in that you have
to do it by fax or phone, but it's worth it for what's on offer. The site won't

commit itself to a delivery time, saying that it should take 10-14 days but might take as long as 28. Packaging, however, is just £2.95 per item (free on orders over £60). If you're greeted by a lurid yellow page about the car seat, scroll down the page and you'll see a small text hyperlink to the Premiere Baby Direct store which, confusingly, has the same URL.

Teeny Tots

www.teeny-tots.com
Eager for you to feel at ease when shopping for the little ones, the Teeny Tots homepage highlights links to ordering, delivery and privacy information before you even enter the store. Once inside you'll find items for playtime, bedtime, bathtime and all-terrain stroller time, with prices to suit every pocket. Delivery within five days is free for orders over £150, otherwise it's a standard £3.50.

The Total Baby Shop

www.thetotalbabyshop.com
Some brilliant bargains can be found at this excellent Internet-only business, both on equipment and organic baby food, which is worth buying in bulk at around 10p a jar less than in the supermarket. The Baby Bjorn slings are also much cheaper than in the shops. There's a nice range of reasonably priced clothes too: a whole newborn kit, with several changes of clothes, costs just £30. Deliveries take two to five working days and cost £2.99.

 **The fashion parade starts here**

Baby Clothes Direct

www.babyclothesdirect.co.uk
A basic site specialising in clothes for babies up to 18 months old. There isn't a huge variety of clothes and styles, but what they do have is good value. You'll find decent quality packs of two sleepsuits, for example, for well under £10. Postage and packing is £3.50 and deliveries take three working days.

Bonny Beginnings

www.bonnybeginnings.com
This pretty site sells equally appealing children's clothes and christening wear. Each item can be bought in a variety of sizes, with prices starting under £10, but this site is particularly good if you're looking for that something special for your baby's big day – traditional christening gowns, robes and accessories start at around £50. Ordering is easy but delivery can take up to a fortnight.

Mischief Kids

www.mischiefkids.co.uk
What concerned parent could be without a Donna Karan romper suit for their bambino? This well-organised site has a warm, personally written approach

which helps take the sting out of the designer prices – £75 for a Moschino pink zebra T-shirt for an 18-month-old! Still, if you're happy to pay, there's a great range here; delivery is by first-class post.

Sunday Best
www.sundaybest.co.uk

A British baby clothes site pitched at Americans seems odd until you see what it's selling. The christening outfits have names like The Fauntleroy, The Country Squire and The Bronte, which give you a clue about what to expect – lots of velvet and lace, and more frills and froth than you could shake a rattle at. UK delivery costs £5 and takes two days if the item is in stock.

Trotters
www.trotters.co.uk

Trotters caters for kids up to 11. It sells more than clothes, but merits a mention for its selection of baby essentials. These range from polos to sweatshirts to cardigans – there are even baby rugby shirts for your fledgling Jason Robinson. Delivery is £3.95, free for orders over £60, and can take up to 14 days.

Vertbaudet
www.vertbaudet.co.uk

Oddly you have to order a printed catalogue first, but once you've got that in your hand you're away. Baby clothing ranges from newborn essentials through chic christening outfits to down-to-earth play wear. Prices are good for the quality and styling, and the baby basics are seriously good value. Delivery is £2.45 per order but can take up to 14 days as everything's shipped from France.

> **BABY TALK**
>
> Pick any part of the UK and Baby Directory at www.babydirectory.co.uk will give you an alphabetical listing of baby-based information to make life easier. Hospitals, baby massage, toy shops... it covers the lot.
>
> ---
>
> It also has an encyclopaedia of pregnancy, and a Baby Directory Bookshop with classics like Eric Carle's *The Very Hungry Caterpillar*.

Gifts Finally! Personalised sick cloths

Baby bloomers
www.babyblooms.com

Everything has been handmade on this Alabaman site, which specialises in ultra-twee memorabilia such as baby bracelets and personalised first curl boxes. Your baby can even have its very own personalised sick cloths, which may actually come in useful if you linger too long here. But if this is your (hand-embroidered) bag, shipping rates to the UK are pretty low at $5 an order. You might have to wait for three weeks for delivery because of the handmade nature of each item.

 **When there's a bun in the oven**

Active Birth Centre
www.activebirthcentre.com
Giving birth needn't be all about misery and enemas. This straightforward site gives advice (on why massaging your wriggler is a good thing, for example) and sells everything from bras and birth balls (for optimal foetal positioning) to oil to be massaged into the perineum – supposed to prevent it from tearing during labour. Delivery (ho ho) is £2.95: items come within seven days.

Blooming Marvellous
www.bloomingmarvellous.co.uk
This site has a great selection of fashionable maternity and lovely baby clothes. It's also good for presents for new parents or pregnant friends – the gently chiming Mayan heart necklace, for example, to be worn by the mum-to-be to soothe the unborn baby. Deliveries within two to ten days, cost £3.95.

Bumps Maternity
www.bumpsmaternity.com
Bumps specialises in maternity clothes for pregnant women not satisfied with sack dresses. Sizing guides are on hand and prices are good, generally within the same range as pre-pregnancy clothes, but the images are too small to get an adequate picture. Insured delivery costs £4 and takes five days.

Formes
www.formes.com
Maternity fashion with bags of French chic: everything from jeans to jackets, pedal pushers to pullovers – though the figure-hugging design of much of the collection may not be to everyone's taste. Nice touches include a sizing guide, but online ordering is still on its way and more info on the products would help.

Jojo Maman Bébé
www.jojomamanbebe.co.uk
Easy-to-use site offering a good quality range. The maternity section offers some useful business clothes and pretty nursing tops to help with discreet breastfeeding. You'll find lots of attractive kids' clothes too, plus useful gadgets and basic equipment. Deliveries cost £3.50 and take five working days.

Precious Cargo
www.preciouscargo.co.uk
Not the hippest collection of maternity clothes, but some good outfits for special occasions such as weddings. A useful feature is that you can order clothes in different fabrics and get samples sent to you beforehand. Deliveries take up to ten working days and cost £2.50 for orders to £75 (£3.50 over that).

Beauty

Mirror, mirror, on the wall, which is the loveliest site of all…? While the newer, trendier brand names seem surprisingly shy of selling online, good grooming is there for those who know it's chic to click…

 It's the details that make the difference

Allcures
www.allcures.com
Beautifully designed, totally navigable and unfeasibly fast, this dream site is where to come for bulk orders of toothpaste, cleanser and bubble bath. All the household names are here, plus specials such as Roger & Gallet bath products; the house cosmetics line is the ever-reliable Bourjois. Orders take one to four days. Priority delivery is £5.99, standard is £3.49 (free over £35).

Body Reform
www.bodyreform.co.uk
Body Reform offers an own-brand range of natural beauty products. The site is slow to load, the products are not cheap (£4.99 for 250ml of muscle-soak bath oil) and the packaging resembles the freebies in hotel rooms. However, shopping is simple once you get going and delivery is 79p per item.

Boots
www.wellbeing.com
Don't expect the entire Boots range, and there are none of those 'buy one get one free' offers that make Boots such a hit, but prices match those in store, and you can use your Advantage card online. Delivery starts at £2.50.

Hand Made Soap
www.handmadesoap.co.uk
Choose from a catalogue of fruity, flowery and even chocolate smelling soaps, all made from natural ingredients and priced around £3.50. If you're looking for something more than colour co-ordination in your skincare routine, the soap guide will tell you which soap is best suited to your individual skin type.

King of Shaves

www.shave.com

Fed up with sticking toilet paper to your face or nasty doses of shaving rash? King of Shaves sells products to make this necessary experience a bit more pleasurable. The site is easy to search and gets straight to the point – do you want that in a balm or a gel, and maybe a facial scrub to go with it? Prices are cheaper online, plus there's a women's section and you can get free samples.

Look Fantastic

www.lookfantastic.com

This is the place to buy those expensive hair products your hairdresser tries to sell you. Get reductions (at least 15 per cent) on Aveda, Kerastase and Tigi by taking out free membership, but delivery (£2 plus 50p per item by first class post) is not cheap.

PERFECT FINISH

It's all very well clinging on to the hope that, somehow, spending £100 a month on cosmetics will make you look like Demi rather than Dudley Moore, but there is a certain knack to applying four layers of make-up.

Several companies who don't yet tout their wares online are happy to give tips on how to slap it on. Check out these links to move one step closer to glossy hair, smooth skin and perfect nails.

Maybelline
www.maybelline.co.uk

Pantene
www.pantene.com

Tea Tree
www.teatree.co.uk

Lush

www.lush.co.uk

If you're a fan of exceptionally smelly products with silly names like Pea Green soap and Draught of Immortality moisturiser, you'll love Lush. Delivery (£2.95 – free for orders over £25) takes a sluggish 14 days but the FAQ section is highly entertaining.

Manpak

www.manpak.com

Reputable brands at high-street prices on a plain black homepage. No huge savings, but delivery is free and the personalised subscription service is mega-convenient – they re-send your order when you feel the need. Two-day delivery costs £3.50.

MenLab

www.menlab.co.uk

That's men who spend their time in the pub, or so the image of Oliver Reed next to a hangover tonic suggests. Products include everything from bath tea to eye gel, but you won't find Nivea here – more WU, Ahava and Acca Kappa, which can be just as pricey. Shipping isn't cheap either but ordering is simple and there's a no-quibble returns policy.

Molton Brown

www.moltonbrown.com

Glamorous products, but the confusing navigation is all over the place. With no sub-categories, you have to scroll through images of everything they

sell in no particular order, Sea Moss Stress Relieving Soak next to Hand Wash.
Alternative categories include Chinese Remedies and Travel Companions
alongside the usual cosmetics and bathing products. Bewildering.

Superdrug

www.superdrug.co.uk
Bright and cheerful as you would expect from Superdrug, this is a great store
for beauty essentials. It's easy to search, prices match those in store, and you
can take advantage of special offers. Two-day delivery costs a standard £2.50.

 **Save a bundle on big-name beauty**

Beautique

www.beautique.co.uk
This glossy site offers a limited selection of products, but it's perfect if you've
already bought the foundation professionals use but aren't actually sure what
to do with it. Make-up artists to the stars and beauty editors are behind the
recommended products, and you can e-mail the experts for handy hints.

Class Cosmetics

www.classcosmetics.com
Cheap (very) and cheerful, Class Cosmetics' stock varies from week to week
but Elizabeth Arden, Lancôme, L'Oreal, Max Factor and Revlon are its main
names, and it's strong on lipsticks and nail polishes. Goods are a third of
high-street prices and delivery, in three to four working days, is a snip at a £1.

Direct Cosmetics

www.directcosmetics.com
Many goods, from hair care to accessories (including items from long-dead
lines such as Charles of the Ritz) are less than half-price. Searching is simple
and brands include Boots and Superdrug alongside Calvin Klein and Clarins.
However, standard delivery at £3.95 seems steep if you're not bulk buying.

Island Trading

www.island-trading.com
Stylewise this resembles a tacky US magazine, but many of the big cosmetic
and perfume brands are discounted, including Estée Lauder, Almay, Revlon,
Clinique and Bobbi Brown. Savings range from £1 to £25; shipping is free too.

Magic Makeup

www.magicmakeup.co.uk
Select a category and scroll through an ample selection of brands, complete
with images and descriptions, at less than half-price. Agree to spend £5 and
you can choose any number of delights from the bargain bin. Delivery is free.

Fragrance — The sweet smell of the Web

Augustus Oils

www.augustus-oils.ltd.uk/

Augustus sells essential oils, aromatherapy oils and floral waters – by the drum. It supplies mainly to the trade, but will sell 500g (1lb) orders to customers who make their own scented soaps and candles. Buy with friends and share.

Fragrance Net

www.fragrancenet.com

Virtually every difficult-to-find fragrance lingers on these pages. Creed, Annick Goutal and Jean Couturier, Coriandre fans – are all represented. Search by product or scroll down the alphabetical list. Soaps and body washes are also available. Although a US site, it ships to the UK: the shipping calculator will work out from the start whether it's worthwhile browsing the rest of the site.

Fragrance Store

www.fragrance-shop.co.uk

This simple site specialises in Scottish scents but offers good discounts on popular brands. You can pick up CK Be, with postage and packaging, for less than £20. Ordering is simple, with both online and offline options.

Garden Pharmacy

www.garden.co.uk

Another Annick Goutal stockist, this site has lots of big-name fragrances at reasonable prices. It also has a neat line in Tisserand aromatherapy products, and, oh joy, stocks the increasingly hard-to-get Kneipp Bath Botanics. Shipping takes three days and costs from £2.95.

A trip into the Garden could prove fruitful if you'd given up all hope of replenishing your stock of Kneipp Bath Botanics

Opal

www.opal-london.com

Short and sweet, Opal has a particular passion for loofahs, and for stuff smelling of tangerines, watermelons and limes. The buying process is cute, concise and cheap, with prices ranging from £1 for travel soap to £3 for body lotions.

Beer

"Time gentlemen, please!" That's
not a shout you ever hear in
cyberspace where it's never too
late to order a sour red beer, set
up your own brewery or settle
down for a night 'on the tiles'

Beerparadise

www.beerparadise.ltd.uk

The ultimate site for beer snobs although if you want to order the manifold
ales on display you go to a linked site, www.beerritz.co.uk (see below).

Beer Ritz

www.beerritz.co.uk

Simply select a country and browse the fine selection on offer. Depending on
how exotic your selection, prices for a crate of 24 generally range between
£30 and £50 with a £1.50 delivery charge. The site could be improved with
descriptions of the beer, but this probably won't matter to most.

Belgian Beers

www.belgianshop.com

With Stella Artois a frequent last, desperate guess in the perennial 'name five
famous Belgians' pub quiz question, this site should do a reasonable trade.
With eight sour red, 17 Trappist and 20 white beers, it's well stocked too,
which makes it doubly sad that the ordering feature is so temperamental.

Drinkshop

www.thedrinkshop.com/main.php3

You won't just find beer at the Internet's largest off licence (or so it claims), but
wines, spirits, hampers and ice sculptures. You'll find most of the household
names here but it's not quite as impressive when it comes to more esoteric
brews. Delivery (by courier) is charged by weight (£6.99 for a case of 24).

Home Brew Shop

www.homebrewshop.co.uk

Will home-brewing be the latest 1970s craze to make a comeback? Probably
not, but home-brew devotees may want to visit this site which offers kits from
beginners to advanced. There are also special offers on a few beers.

Real Beer Box: the names alone could keep you entertained for hours...

Real Beer Box

www.realbeerbox.com

Don't be put off by the homepage. Simply select a brewer – familiar names include Badger, Batemans and Tisbury Brewery – and head for your favourite tipple, or browse the huge selection on offer. Alternatively you could create a mixed crate of beers with the most unusual names: On The Tiles, Jockstrap and Skullsplitter are all possible inclusions. Prices vary somewhere between £17 and £25 for a crate of 12 bottles, with delivery an extra £3.

Scotland's Craft Brewers Co-operative

www.lugton.co.uk

Ideologically sound collective which will deliver its range of traditional "Hand Crafted" beers anywhere in the UK within 72 hours of receiving the order. Don't be put off by the fact that most of their brews have tartan-waving names like Loch Lomond and Bannockburn. For sheer commercial cynicism, selling eBeer – "the new beer of the Internet" – takes some beating.

Tavern on Tap

www.tavern-on-tap.com

A bit of a beer connoisseur? This site should be your first port of call. It offers hundreds of beers from Britain's smaller brewers, whose weird and wonderful names include Frog Island and Moles Brewery. Background history on each brewer is available, alongside descriptions of the ales themselves. Shipping is included in the price, generally £25 for a case of 12, but delivery time varies.

You can also order your favourite tipple online from the following breweries:

www.blacksheep.co.uk	Blacksheep
www.caledonian-brewery.co.uk/home/home.shtml	Caledonian
www.charleswells.co.uk	Charleswells
www.felinfoel-brewery.co.uk	Felinfoel
www.bdksol.co.uk/hesket	Hesket Newmarket (2.25-gallon minimum)
www.tanglefoot.co.uk	Tanglefoot

Bikes

Cut a swathe through
incomprehensible jargon,
keep tabs on what your heart
rate's up to, and find out how
often a cyclist gets almost
as wet as a drowned rat.
The power of the Internet!

Bicycle Net

www.bicyclenet.co.uk
This site is "proud to belong to the *Which?* Web Trader" code of practice.
Sadly, the code does not insist that you design a stylish homepage. But stick
with it because this is quite a decent site. There's a glossary for beginners
and tips on what model you need according to your inside leg measurement.
Delivery charges are calculated for you at the start of the checkout process
(normally £6.50 will ensure your bike arrives within four working days). Unlike
many sites, Bicycle Net only retails online and is happy to be compared to
high-street prices. The stock ranges from kids' bikes to BMX to folding bikes.

Bikepark

www.bikepark.co.uk
While not as sophisticated as some e-stores, this site looks and reads as if it
has been put together by genuine enthusiasts. The personal approach even
extends to the links, which point you to other 'fan' pages. The shop sells
a fair range of bikes, plus accessories and clothing. Another *Which?* Web
Trader, Bikepark also offers free delivery on all bikes within the UK and
there's a nice section for beginners which declares, among other things,
that the keen cyclist will get thoroughly soaked 12 times a year. "We
know because we've counted," say founders Julian Wall and Phil Cavell.

Cycle Centre Online

www.cyclestore.co.uk
This site comes with more security guarantees than Fort Knox. Down the left
you'll find a long list of topics and brand names from bottom brackets (an
essential item which start at £15) to Vredestein bikes. Delivery is £5 on orders
up to £50 within the UK and there's a good range of bikes to choose from, so
don't be put off by the picture of the lycra-clad 'team' on the homepage.

CycleXpress
www.cyclexpress.co.uk

It only stocks three brands of bikes (Diamond Back, Fisher and GT) so the range is limited, but there are plenty of categories and accessories here. The downsides are the fact that you have to choose products by brand and not style, and the product descriptions are too brief. The major plus point is the upgrade advice service, which helps you improve your bike bit by bit.

Halfords
www.halfords.com

Compared to its in-store range, Halfords' car-oriented online shop is a big disappointment. There are just ten bikes for sale – for kids up to the age of seven at that – plus helmets, accessories and a very limited selection of gifts for all ages. Information is minimal. Is this really the best they can do?

RBM Sports
www.rbmsports.com

This spartan site sells only component parts for performance bikes. There are just eight categories – the intriguingly named 'cycling computers' turn out to be heart-rate monitors and the like – and no information is provided beyond a picture and a price (although a phone number and e-mail address are listed). It's a US site and while they do deliver to the UK, you won't find out the shipping charges until you've ordered. For serious cyclists only.

ON YER BIKE

The biking world is one of the worst offenders for unintelligible jargon. While looking through any bike magazine or website you can easily get lost in custom bro built pedal spindles and LX5 Bolt cranks or 44/32/22 removable spider and four arm cranks.

Few people can cope with a mass of cantilever beam problems or older MTB triple drive trains. Some manufacturers might follow Cove Bikes, who let you choose between a stiffy, G-Spot or quickie. On second thought, let's not be too hasty about custom bro built pedal spindles...

www.covebike.com

Single Track Bikes
www.singletrack.co.uk

This comprehensive site comes complete with custom-bike calculator, interest-free credit, order-tracking and a chat room called the Graffiti Room. Another *Which?* Web Trader, it offers a great range of stock – videos, games, magazines, clothing and shoes as well as bikes and parts – and delivery (£1.50 on orders up to £50) is normally within 48 hours by first-class post.

Ultimate Bikes
www.ultimatebikes.co.uk

The logo of a crumpled bike may not look promising – actually it's one of those recumbent jobs in which they specialise – but this site promises access to 8,000 components for all kinds of bikes, with discounts of up to 20 per cent. Shop by product category, then click on an image for more information. Delivery is two to three days if in stock but you can't work out your delivery costs until right before you order.

Boats

Build your own or
buy your own and
earn the right to
say: "Hello sailor!"

Boat Hunter
www.boathunter.com
Online yacht brokers with listings of boats from all over the world. E-mail the
details of the boat you are looking for, or just browse the site and imagine
yourself sailing away on the deck of an $80,000 sloop. The site will check title
and registration documents, and ensure money changes hands smoothly.

Marine Online
www.marineonline.co.uk
There's enough kit here to build a boat from scratch. Galley equipment and
deck fittings line up next to items like plastic glasses in case Hurricane Charlie
upsets your gin and tonic. Delivery charges vary according to weight. Offshore
racing and a commendably punchy news sections have recently been added.

Southwater Marine
www.southwater.com
Sleek site for new and secondhand powerboats to add that touch of James
Bond to your seaside break. Book a viewing appointment or offer your boat
for sale. Finance packages and insurance are also available.

Virginia Currer Marine
www.vcmarine.co.uk
This is the place to come if you've always fancied river life. Narrow boats,
Dutch barges and even restaurant boats are available, some complete with
residential moorings. There are photos and deck plans for most listings and
you can e-mail for further details or to appoint the site as your sales broker.

Yacht People
www.yachtpeople.com
Okay, so you can't actually buy a yacht, but the chandlery pages of this large
sailing site have pretty much everything else you might need for some serious
messing about in boats, right down to bilge pumps and outboard motors.
There are special offers on larger items such as inflatable dinghies or an
ORC Offshore Life Raft. Shipping costs depend on the weight of your order.

Books

They're the most popular item to be bought over the Net, so it's odd how many sites have badly designed homepages or don't allow you to order online. Here are some of the best and weirdest

General The big names and the biggest stocks

Amazon
www.amazon.co.uk
Amazon is the most famous name in online shopping, having branched out into music, films and computer games (and software). It's worth searching both the UK and the US (www.amazon.com) sites because the American one has an easy-to-track-down bargain basement where, if you don't mind waiting, you could save a lot of money. The search mechanism is quick and simple, although you sometimes get different results depending on which page you access it from. The user reviews are often worth reading, and Amazon is generally very good at letting you know what's happened to your order.

BOL (Books On Line)
www.uk.bol.com
As the world's largest book publisher, it was only a matter of time before Bertelsmann started selling books online. The site has a hefty stock of titles, including some pretty obscure stuff. However, it's not always easy to make an informed choice. For example, if you buy Ross Macdonald's third Lew Archer omnibus from Amazon, it tells you which novels are included; Bol doesn't. www.barnesandnoble.com is part of the same network.

Bookshop
www.bookshop.co.uk
With a catalogue of 1.4 million books, this division of the WHSmith empire claims to be Europe's largest online bookstore. Happily it allows you to make both specific searches by author or title, or simply select a category and browse. Admittedly you could be forever selecting sub-categories, but with discounts of up to 50 per cent on offer, it's worth persevering.

Bookzone

www.bookzone.com

Bookzone is an online publishing community of 3,500 professionals who provide design, tools and site-hosting for the industry. The site also acts as a gateway to publishers who will sell direct to you, but often only if you're in North America, which could prove frustrating if you dream of owning that book of Princess Diana's celestial love, as told to a Norwegian medium.

Borders

www.borders.com

A useful US site for fans of more obscure American authors who aren't always represented on the bigger sites. Shipping costs are clearly identified. Borders is also worth bookmarking for the discounts (typically 10 per cent, but 30 per cent on CDs – already cheaper in the US than here).

Country Bookstore

www.countrybookstore.co.uk

Decorated with soft shades of blue and green, this site has a sedative effect if you've been surfing too long. But it's good to see an independent bookshop competing on the Web, and with more than a million titles on offer, competing is the word. You can even buy via your WAP phone.

The Good Book Guide

www.titlefinder.com

This is the site of the independent Good Book Guide, whose mission is to guide you through the 10,000-plus books published each month. Apart from a database of 1.2 million titles (browse by author, title or key word), it offers features, profiles, recommendations by authors and reader reviews. It also has special offers (typically 20 per cent off bestsellers) and its own specialist business books division (www.gbgbusiness.com).

Iron Kettle Books

www.ironkettle.com

Iron Kettle started off selling remaindered books to American schools. It now delivers to individuals and outside the US, and often sells its small but interesting stock for a third of the listed price. Among the bargains in its spring sale were a dictionary of cricket and a book on the obscure British aviation pioneer Percy Pilcher.

Books

Stacks of choice is central to
what Ottakar's offers. And the
discounts are pretty decent too

Ottakar's

www.ottakars.co.uk
The real star of this site is the search engine, which works swiftly to reinforce
the point that this independent bookstore has access to a comprehensive
stock of titles. There are also links to Outland, Ottakar's own sci-fi and fantasy
site, a daily quiz, and its own columnist, Yossarian. Good discounts too.

Waterstones

www.waterstones.co.uk
This site has a more erudite, upmarket ambience than either BOL or
Amazon, and has a lot to recommend it. It's well-stocked with a slick, easy-
to-use search engine and will try to find titles for you. It offers discounts
(including half-price, signed, first editions of recent titles by famous authors)
and free postage and packing within the UK.

WHSmith

www.whsmith.co.uk
WHSmith boasts that its site offers every British book still in print, a claim
this reviewer was unable to disprove after several hours of effort. If you're
searching for a particular author or book, it's worth narrowing down your field
as much as possible. A role model to other high-street brands.

Also worth a mention if you're into that sort of thing:

www.alphabetstreet.infront.co.uk for a decent alternative to Amazon etc.
www.comedybooks.com books by or about professional rib-ticklers.
www.highlanderweb.co.uk/book/shop for all about the Auld Country.
www.neosoft.com/~bmiller/fiery1.htm for those who like fiery foods.
www.netcomuk.co.uk/~james_j/Front_page.htm for books about cars.
www.redhousebooks.com for Beat Generation and other 1960s movements.
www.stanleyfish.com for books about trains; e-mail ordering only.
www.thechildrensbookcase.com for children's books.

E-books Reading at the click of a button

Books you can usually download from the Internet for a small fee and either read on screen (fine for shorter work, like poems) or print out.

Ebooks For You
www.ebooksforyou.com
Don't let the corny title or the relatively small selection of e-books on this US site put you off. Among the titles are Evel Knievel's memoirs (yes, you guessed it, *Evel*Ways*) and a smattering of classics, from H G Wells' *War of the Worlds* to Stephen Crane's *Red Badge of Courage*. Typical prices are $5-8.

E-Book Mall
www.ebookmall.com
The title won't inspire anyone, but E-Book Mall is well-organised, offers the big boys' sections and search modes (it claims more than 10,000 titles in four formats), and its prices are around $6. Literary classics feature strongly.

E-pulp
www.e-pulp.com
Great title and suitably hard-boiled design raise expectations for this store of new mystery and sci-fi writing. Sadly the authors don't quite live up to them.

FictionWise
www.fictionwise.com
Aiming to provide the most comprehensive selection of fiction on the Internet, this easy-to-navigate site offers high quality reading and some top authors. It's strongest on short stories and science fiction (Isaac Asimov for less than 50¢), but it also republishes out-of-print works and recently added non-fiction.

Leta Nolan Childers
http://members.aol.com/Bstseller1/Index.html
Leta Nolan Childers is not a lost Nolan sister but the world's bestselling e-book author for 1999 and 2000. Her output ranges from private detective stories starring Cat Callahan (who's a woman, not a cat) to tales of Gaelic family life. Look out for low-flying whimsy.

Universal Download
www.udownload.com
Most e-book sites are limited and populated by authors you've never heard of. Not this one. It allows the user to peruse T S Eliot's *The Wasteland*, inspect the Treaty of Versailles or download *War and Peace*. A thoroughly impressive selection of electronic texts with a friendly, ersatz Yahoo-style homepage.

A WORD IN YOUR EAR

Buying used books online? Remember to check:

1 Shipping costs and policies. They're not always easy to find

2 The condition of the book. Good sites offer ratings or tell you if it's worn or damaged

3 The book you're buying. When you're scrolling down your umpteenth text page, it's easy to misread the short description of the book you think you're looking for and get an unpleasant shock when it arrives

4 The policy on returns. Understandably, sellers of used books don't offer the kind of 'no quibble guarantee' you'll get from the bigger bookstores. If you can't see a policy, then ring or e-mail them before you part with any money

5 If the site is secure. A disturbing number of smaller US stores seem to expect you to key in your credit card details on unencrypted sites. If in doubt, ask

Specialist — Seriously clued up

Films

www.readthemovie.com

You would think this Amazon-associate site would help you find the book which inspired the movie. Well, you'd be almost right, except that films like *Chopper Chicks in Zombietown* (starring Billy Bob Thornton) obviously didn't require any literary inspiration, although they're still listed here. This site also sells audiobooks, soundtracks, videos, DVDs and laserdiscs of popular movies (plus a few TV series), all at discount prices. If you wanted to know how *A Bug's Life* inspired enough titles to outnumber an ant colony, this is the place for you.

Medicine

www.donfer.co.uk/d-commerce

Doctors, vets and hypochondriacs can now order online from Donald Ferrler – an Edinburgh medical bookshop which sells tomes on (among others) psychology, anaesthestics and surgery. Delivery within 24 hours for £2.50, or free for orders over £25.

Politics

www.politicos.co.uk

With anything from the latest political blockbuster to memorabilia, this site has almost everything the political buff could desire. Items on offer range from *Inspired & Outspoken: The Collected Speeches of Ann Widdecombe* (with the Bill Clinton joke book by the same author) to the simply surreal Blair and Hague salt and pepper pots (a limited edition set, just £29.95). Ordering is secure, although it can take time.

School

www.jubileebooks.co.uk

The bright cartoon-inspired site design of Jubilee Books serves well to emphasise its commitment to children and education. Although principally a book vendor for schools, bulk orders aren't necessary, allowing parents to also take advantage of the expertise available here. Divided into ages and then again into school terms, there are books for literacy, mathematics, PE or the arts. Information about each book – including how and why it was selected – is included. Prices are generally discounted and if you are buying on behalf of your school, orders can be made online but payments can be invoiced for added convenience. A brilliant resource.

Sport

www.soccer-books.co.uk

A specialist site with no frills, this site is particularly valuable for its extensive stock of football videos, including a huge portfolio of coaching videos and a biography of Eusebio. There's also a small selection of books about non-football sports, and music (if that's the right word) CDs about football. With a 10 per cent discount for orders over £60, this is aimed at the serious fan.

Talking Books

www.talkingbooks.org

Simple, no-fuss site selling audio books in a variety of formats – tapes, CDs and downloads included. Although authors such as James Ellroy, Robert Ludlum and good old Agatha Christie are included, the expansive catalogue is annoyingly divided by publisher, rather than something more accessible to the average literary enthusiast (genre, for example). If you do find what you're looking for, prices are good, with ordering proving easier than initial searches.

Travel

www.mapsworldwide.co.uk

This *Which?* approved site just screams bargain from its homepage – 20 per cent off Ordnance Survey maps! A pocket-sized guide to Sardinia for £7.50!! Or 10 per cent off a CD ROM which computes the most economical route

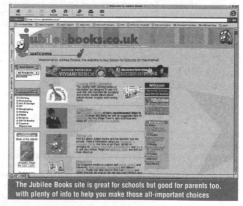

The Jubilee Books site is great for schools but good for parents too, with plenty of info to help you make those all-important choices

between any two streets in Britain!!! A must for armchair travellers.

These sites might also be worth considering:
www.deiltak.com for first editions, biographies, US first editions, non-fiction.
www.shentonbooks.demon.co.uk for clocks, watches, barometers, etc.
www.clique.co.uk/jopplety for science fiction, children's books.
www.simonfinch.com for rare books, especially early printed books.
www.esotericism.co.uk as the name suggests, this stocks esoteric stuff
from neoplatonism and gnosticism to alchemy, mysticism and paganism.
www.andromedabooks.co.uk for antiquarian and out-of-print
astronomy books.
www.compman.co.uk for computer manuals.
www.chaters.co.uk for all the motoring manuals and vids you could want.

 ## Out of print but not out of mind

A Book For All Reasons
www.abfar.co.uk
A distinctly middlebrow list of fiction (Georgette Heyer to Nevil Shute) lets
down a site best known for its extensive stock of tomes on military history.
E-mail the shop about availability etc.

Advanced Book Exchange
www.abebooks.com
The Advanced Book Exchange describes itself as the world's largest network
of independent booksellers, and its homepage is a homage to Amazon. You
can search its list of 20 million titles and find some pretty obscure stuff, such
as the European diary of a wealthy young American called John F Kennedy. A
good place to start if you want old, out-of-print books, even if they're in
paperback.

Bibliofind
www.bibliofind.com
Another site which spans an impressive network of booksellers – it claims to
have an impressive 10 million titles in its archive – and offers online peace of
mind by using a secure server for ordering.

Biblion
www.biblion.co.uk
'The home of British antiquarian and remarkable books' is an online network
of 1,000 dealers which is intended as much for the book trade as for the
general punter. Still, there can be few other places on the Web where you
could find the 1885 reports on insects injurious to hop plants, corn crops and
fruit crops in Great Britain. Whether you can complete your purchase of such

highly elusive material online depends largely on the dealer you are referred to.

Maps And Prints
www.mapsandprints.com/manuscripts.cfm
Interested in some rather older used books? Why not splash out $200 on a medieval manuscript of a *Book of Hours*? A rather limited stock of old manuscripts sits alongside a more impressive array of maps, globes and such. This site uses a secure server and is upfront about shipping costs.

Mr Mac
www.rmcd.demon.co.uk
Mr Mac is an ABE member so you can order books by credit card through that link. A fair range of books is listed by author and you can e-mail requests to Ranald McDonald – who's based, disappointingly, in Southampton.

Zardoz Books
www.zardozbooks.co.uk
Boasting such a wacky name you might expect to find a psychedelic site with equally far-out fiction, but Zardoz plays it straight, preferring to draw you to its status as Europe's largest selection of out-of-print and collectible books. It specialises in pulp novels, comics and paperbacks. Select a genre to view simple lists of the hundreds of titles on offer. Browsing isn't really an option, with no synopsis for titles, only publishing information. Good if you're looking for something specific though. Delivery is £3.

It wasn't possible to order books online from the following as this book went to press but they're still worth a look...

www.bookshelfuk.com With an e-mail search facility for out-of-print books, this site seems rather too proud of its 'famous soft toys'.

www.easternbooks.co.uk As its name suggests, it stocks lots of used books about Eastern Europe, the Middle East and the Orient.

www.edicionesgrial.com This Anglo-Spanish site contains a limited edition facsimile of the *Quest For the Holy Grail* with a reproduction of the original binding for £1,495 plus shipping. Ignore the QuickTime plug-in prompt.

www.hrkahnbooks.com This is a Canadian shop which specialises in old books on travel. Stock and prices vary from £15,400 for eight volumes and an atlas of the voyages of Captain Cook down to a more modest £345 for an account of three years in the Sandwich Islands.

Cameras

Whether you want to take better holiday snaps or be the new David Bailey, the Net is full of bargains if you know where to look. You can also find cameras which are even older than Mr Bailey himself

Best Stuff
www.beststuff.co.uk
If the range of choices seems overwhelming, consider heading to Best Stuff. In each category of electrical goods it features only one product, 'the best', along with a brief explanation of why it has earned the title. Whether it actually is the best is far from guaranteed. A quick check of leading camera sites suggests that this site's idea of 'the best' isn't on offer anywhere else…

Camera Collectors
www.camera-collectors.com
The vintage and collectible cameras on sale here include specialist models from the likes of Rollei, Linhot and Leica. James Bond wannabes can even snap up a miniature Minox CFI for $600. Delivery to the UK is available but – and it's a very big but – it costs a flat $23.50. With the average camera price on this site somewhere between $25 and $50, that almost doubles the cost. But if you want something out of the ordinary, you may just have to stump up.

Cameras Direct
www.camerasdirect.co.uk
A big selection of bargains makes this a site that you really should visit. Though you have to register to access the Today Only special offers, savings of up to 70 per cent off big-brand RRPs are available, and you can expect to save at least £20-70 on a best-selling model. Three-day delivery costs £4.99, but if you're off on holiday tomorrow you can get your camera delivered to your door within 24 hours for £9.99. Film is a particularly good buy, with RRP prices slashed by more than 50 per cent. If you're buying a three-pack, that £4.99 delivery charge is more than worthwhile. The site is easy-to-use, features 360-degree rotating images of most products, and advertises free technical assistance – a rarity for a cut-price web store. One word of warning though: changes to your selection can't be made once you've clicked through to the checkout.

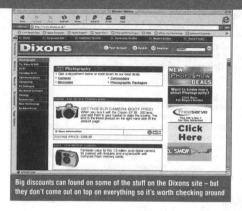

Big discounts can found on some of the stuff on the Dixons site – but they don't come out on top on everything so it's worth checking around

Comet

www.comet.co.uk

Among the PCs, dishwashers and mobile phones, you'll find camcorders and cameras. Well, you'll find a few… Comet doesn't have the biggest camera selection in the world but the site does offer useful buying tips. There are full and friendly explanations of features such as DX Coding, and advice on what to consider when making your choice. The ability to search within a price range is a good idea, let down somewhat by the lack of products to compare.

The Digital Kingdom

www.thedigitalkingdom.com

Eight big-name brands of digital camera are on offer on this US site. If you're looking to buy at the more expensive end of the market, you could be in for some very big savings indeed. You have to register and create an account before you buy, but you would do well to make yourself a cup of tea first, as you will be told repeatedly that you have not filled in all the required fields, even when it's quite clear that you have. But it's worth persevering – on a $1,000 camera, you could easily save more than $500.

Dixons

www.dixons.co.uk

The photography section of Dixons' e-store is not huge – but some great savings can be made. Choose from around ten products in each category (digital, APS, compact etc), with close-up photos and basic specs. If you're not sure exactly what you want, go elsewhere for reviews and info and head here only when you have a product name, number and RRP. But there are no cut-price guarantees: you'll find some big-brand cameras available here for a lot less than at rival online stores, but some for quite a bit more. Watch out for special deals on certain models too, such as free film for 12 months. Once you've registered, ordering is straightforward, but note that Dixons will only deliver to the address of the credit card holder, and postage and packing are added at the checkout. Delivery is within three working days.

1st Cameras

www.firstcameras.co.uk

1st Cameras is a dedicated supplier of Fujifilm and Fujifilm cameras, which does tend to colour its online recommendations. Product descriptions are detailed, and there are also a few background pieces ('Why go digital?', 'Why Fujifilm?' etc) There's even a message board, where you can post your views on the Fujifilm range. (When we checked, the only contribution was from the moderator.) Shipping costs are according to Royal Mail rates and delivery takes between one and five days, but exercise caution when buying: the advertised prices do not include VAT, which is added at the checkout.

CAMERA OBSCURA

Andrews Cameras (*www. andrewscameras.co.uk*) offers rather different cameras: collectible ones.

Prices vary from less than you'd pay for a new high street camera to £2250 for a Zeiss 180mm fz 8 Olympia Sonner and grip for Contarex 3_D.

If that's Greek to you, head somewhere more mainstream, but hard-core devotees should linger here a while even if they do find the site's rather crude design a bit frustrating. A treat for all nostalgia freaks

iGadget

www.igadget.com

This US site has a pretty big selection of cut-price cameras – you can make savings on big-brand names from $20 to more than $200. This makes it well worth a look, especially if you're after the latest digital model. The site does offer delivery to the UK and most products are dispatched within 24 hours, but you have to e-mail the company first to get a quote for the shipping charges.

Miller Brothers Electrical and Gas Appliance Superstore

www.millerbros.co.uk

This is a no-frills site with a reasonable selection of cameras and accessories for delivery anywhere within the UK mainland. You won't save a lot here – on average around £20 – and there's a £10 per order delivery charge. But still, that's £10 less than you'd pay if you walked to your high-street camera dealer and paid full whack. Before you buy, just make sure you check that Cameras Direct or Dixons don't have the same model for less.

Quality Direct

www.qed-uk.com

The cheap, bold, unattractive homepage gives the impression of an online industrial estate. Quality Direct isn't flash, but it does offer free delivery with-

US prices being, by and large, rather less than those in the UK, even with weighty shipping charges you could still make savings ordering from here

in four working days and reductions of up to 40 per cent on high-street prices. You'll find a huge range of cameras on offer, often at much cheaper prices than those offered by some of its more upmarket competitors, and more detailed product descriptions. But if it's a best-selling brand you're after, you'd be best advised to shop around before you think of heading here.

Tempo
www.tempo.co.uk
The products at this relatively new high-street discount operation are laid out by brand (all the big ones) or by category, but the selection of what it quaintly calls 'photographic' and digital cameras is fairly small. It's worth checking, but with delivery at a flat charge of £4.99 and savings averaging around £5 off the RRP, you're not likely to get that great a deal. But if you do find something you like, you can choose a delivery date that suits you – a consideration for the customer that other e-businesses would do well to emulate.

Yahoo Shopping – Photography
http://shopping.yahoo.com/electronics/photography
There is a huge selection of brands on offer in this online market of several e-stores but beware: most are US-based and may not deliver to the UK. However, the site is a fantastic resource, with vast amounts of background information and facts. You will find very thorough camera specs, lots of detail on image quality and model features, and even a Consumer Consensus. If you find something you like, the odds are that you probably will be able to order it for UK delivery if you spend a bit of time checking through the stores.

Cars

If you're keen to get a new set of wheels and are more worried about saving money than test driving, give the showroom salesmanship a miss and check these sites out

European | Buy cheap, buy abroad

Auto Europ
www.autoeurop.co.uk
Auto Europ is a pretty basic site, but it does quote offers it can currently promise – like £10,000 for a Ford Focus with extras, VAT, delivery and 12 months' road tax included. Simply e-mail the enquiry form with your request.

Carbusters
www.carbusters.com
Who you gonna call? *Which?* thinks you'll phone them. With deals like a VW Golf V5 five-door for £16,675 on the road (fee inclusive) they may be right.

Discount Imports
www.discountimports.co.uk
The Ferrari red backdrop sets the scene for this sporty offering from abroad. The simple design remains difficult to navigate with no clear indication at first of the service that they actually offer. As it turns out you can search for cars and make the usual online request for information. Prices include shipping fees, UK transportation, VAT and the fee the company charges for its search.

Go Brussels
www.gobrussels.com
Go Brussels will contact dealers in Belgium about the make of car you're interested in buying. You e-mail your request and once you've made your choice you travel to Brussels, are taken to the dealer and drive away in your new European-priced car. There are no typical price quotes for comparison.

Makes

Brand names that sell online

Ford

www.ford.co.uk

Stylishly designed (if a tad flash at times), and Ford has done a good job of creating a clean and simple four-step journey for the online buying process: build your car, find your car, order your car and buy your car. Simple and it appears to work although, sadly, our budget didn't stretch to going the whole hog and buying a top-of-the range Ford Puma in the interests of research. Maybe next year.

Renault

www.renault.co.uk

With Renault To Go you can make an online 24-hour reservation to buy nearly-new Renault cars. Select an area for local dealers, pick the make, model, engine size, preferred fuel, and even cancel the car colours you won't be seen dead driving. Every car is less than 18 months old and comes complete with history and mileage guaranteed by Renault.

Vauxhall

www.vauxhall.co.uk

Vauxhall proudly states that it was the first car manufacturer in the world to offer all of its models in all colours and specifications (plus accessories) for sale on the Internet. Its pioneering prowess shows in the site, which provides an excellent guide to the whole online car buying process with offers of help, advice and FAQs all over the shop. The Vauxhall Internet Price (VIP), usually compares favourably with the standard RRP because of the streamlined buying process but it's also always worth checking out the customer offer boxes that pop up on the site.

DO DO THAT JOU JOU

www.joujou.co.uk

Cars are like fashion: everyone buys the latest styles and eventually it becomes passé. Looking to stand out from the crowd, Jou Jou is the world's smallest car and is only available online.

It resembles a glorified golf cart, and the colour choice of lemon, sky blue, mint and Alpine rose leaves something to be desired, but no one will ever criticise you for being old hat.

Simply fill in the order form to reserve your model, confirm it and pay your deposit, paying the remainder when they deliver. Priced at a paltry £11,200 for the Turbo.

Parts

Where to go when they're not all in working order

Find A Part

www.find-a-part.com

Find A Part does exactly that, though you'll need to know the ins and outs of your car for them to be able to help – and for engine parts you'd better know everything there is to know about your gearbox. If you can cope with this, click away and wait for them to return with help.

Cars

World Parts
www.world-parts.com
World Parts can save you the time and energy it takes to find a garage with the parts to suit your particular vehicle. Select the make, model and country you live in and they'll list the garages you need to contact.

 Just one careful lady owner

AutoBytel
www.autobytel.co.uk
The bustling homepage can be intimidating if you're new to all this Internet stuff but the Research section should help to put your mind at rest. From here

Ours, all ours One motor, bought and paid for...

Buy a car online? But what about the joyous art of forecourt tyre-kicking or the thrill of inhaling that new car aroma? Well, there's nothing to stop you doing that, just go online to buy afterwards where you could enjoy potentially huge savings like our Internet car shopper did – he managed to secure £2,200 off a brand-new Fiat Punto 1.2 ELX from *www.trade-sales.co.uk*. Other good sites to try are *www.motorpoint.co.uk* and *www.jamjar.com*. Anybody would be nervous about buying a new car online but the important point to bear in mind is that only the first part, searching, choosing, specifying and paying a deposit (£100 paid by credit card in this case) need be done online. After that you can, if you wish, communicate with the dealer offline by telephone (and you can pay your deposit over the phone, if you prefer).

There are a number of issues to be aware of buying online though, the first of which is to make sure the car is UK specification. Many car supermarkets import (and there's nothing wrong with that), but check the car matches UK spec or this will affect the resale value. Also make sure you understand the warranty. Most supermarkets offer their own warranties, which can be competitive, but extended warranties from the car manufacturer might be cheaper.

Sometimes the car can be pre-registered to the dealer so you appear as the car's second owner, which isn't necessarily a problem but for resale purposes it's better if you're the first owner. What you can't necessarily bank on finding online is a strong part-exchange for your car and zero per cent finance – but then you can't have everything. Finally, beware online dealers trying to build in extras like delivery and inspection costs.

Overall our shopper reported a good online buying experience and he'd do it again. And bearing in mind new-car depreciation, the savings you make when you buy can certainly help even out the loss when you sell it or trade in.

you can compare up to three cars, focus on one particular model to judge if it's the one for you, read expert reviews and find out what your current trade-in may be worth. But you still have to then make your request and wait for the dealer to contact you.

Autotrader

www.autotrader.co.uk
No online sales but the comprehensive and frequently changing database of new and used vehicles is worth a mention. Select a category and make your search as advanced as you like, bearing in mind how far you're willing to travel. On each occasion they managed to come up with brief details of the make, model and price, and where to go from there. After making your selection you are automatically linked to insurance and finance sites.

Car Shop

www.carshop.co.uk
Simple name for a simple system. The Buy & Go section sticks out but I didn't expect it to be as easy as it is. Search for the make and model of the car you wish to buy, view specs and images of the cars on offer, choose one and put down your deposit on your credit card. The most complicated bit is deciding whether you want insurance, part-exchange or financing. Special offers include a Volkswagen Polo for £6,000. Easy as one, two, three.

Exchange & Mart

www.exchangeandmart.co.uk
You may not be able buy online but the Mart is still at the pinnacle of used car directories. Make your search as simple or complex as you choose, even down to whether you want central locking and an in-car CD player. A price guide ensures you're not being ripped off, and there are insurance quotes and car reviews. From here do the usual and ring for that car.

One Swoop

www.oneswoop.com
This brilliant site offers discounted vehicles and express shopping. Search by your chosen make, model or price range and you'll find a long list of options. Take your pick and then just e-mail your order. Each list includes their price compared to standard UK prices, and many offers include discounts of up to £4,000. Keen to keep you informed they advise you to print out every stage of the process for your own records and state exactly how long delivery will take, ranging from anywhere between two and 22 weeks.

What Car?

www.whatcar.co.uk/
Like *Exchange & Mart* site, the *What Car?* site includes a good price guide for used cars. There's also a sophisticated search engine, and you get the chance to sell your old car for less than a fiver.

Celebrities

Whether you're after an autograph, birth certificate, vintage movie poster or an Elvis fridge magnet, the Internet is your friend

Art Rock Online
www.artrock.com
Online utopia for rock and pop fans, selling posters, T-shirts and other items from a huge range of musicians and bands. Lots of unusual items, such as an original backstage pass for The Mothers of Invention ($100), or a photo of the Rolling Stones signed by each member ($2,000). They ship internationally for between $20 and $43 on top of your order. If you subscribe to their newsletter, you'll be notified when they get any interesting new arrivals.

Arundel Autograph Gallery
www.autographs.co.uk
This site offers signed photos and letters from public figures, including movie stars, sportsmen and politicians. Everyone from Caprice to Winston Churchill is here, and there's even a letter signed by Diana Spencer just before she married Prince Charles. There's no secure ordering, despite an online form, but you can e-mail for more information or to subscribe to a newsletter.

Celebrity Birth Certificates
www.online-homesales.co.uk
Actresses who fudge their ages beware. This site sells copies of genuine birth certificates from UK-born film, television, sport and public life celebrities. An unframed copy will cost you £25, a framed one £49, with discounts if you want to buy a set like all four Beatles. Marriage certificates are also available.

Elvis! Elvis! Elvis!
www.elvisproducts.com
The King gets plenty of memorabilia sites all of his own, but this is one of the better ones, despite having little in the way of original items. The kitsch value of the fridge magnets and guitar-shaped music boxes speaks for itself, but there are also DVDs and videos of the King's movies and live performances up for grabs. Shipping is via airmail and will depend on the weight of your order.

Memorabilia

www.azalmax.demon.co.uk

This site sells high-quality posters, cards, magazines, tickets and, in the case of The Beautiful South, beer mats. If your life is not complete without a 1996 Prodigy calendar, you can put that right for just £2. You can reserve an item by e-mail, but they request cheques or bankers draft for orders, which are sent out on receipt, so not a last-minute option.

Novelty Togs

www.noveltytogs.com

Jazz up a staid wardrobe with some classy items like Bart Simpson socks or Cartman slippers. There's Simpsons, South Park and Mr Men merchandise, plus a range of socks featuring characters like Winnie the Pooh and Tweetie Pie for adults and kids. Delivery is free within the UK.

Recollections

www.recollections.co.uk

Lots of autographed concert programmes and ticket stubs, along with a variety of memorabilia, much of it at very good prices – a 1983 Culture Club tour programme autographed by Boy George will set you back £15. All items have a seven-day money-back guarantee.

S&P Parker's Movie Market

http://parkermovies.com

Vintage film posters rub shoulders with photos of up-and-coming Hollywood stars on this well-designed site. A number of items lack pictures to browse, but on the whole the ordering process is fast and straightforward with the very considerable stock list arranged in alphabetical order. You have to get quite a way through the ordering process before it tells you that delivery is £1.50 within the UK, but otherwise an excellent site.

Starstore

www.starstore.com

More than 13,000 items of movie and TV memorabilia, searchable by name, show or even catchphrase. Postage costs 20 per cent of the order (maximum £5) unless you're ordering something like a life-size cardboard cutout of Buffy the Vampire Slayer, in which case they'll e-mail you with the full shipping costs.

Decorate your walls for less with the very fine selection of film posters on offer at Parker's Movie Market

Chocolates & sweets

Bars, fudge and humbugs! Is this the
Internet or the House of Commons?

Candy U Love

www.shoppingblock.co.uk/cgi-bin/candyulove.storefront

This bright and cheerful store is the perfect site to buy all your favourite
childhood sweeties from and avoid embarrassing yourself in the pick 'n' mix
aisle of Woolworths. Everyone's favourites – white mice, jazzies, snowies and
pink shrimps – are included, priced around £8 a kilogram bag. Free delivery.

Chambers Candy Store

www.chamberscandy.co.uk

This quaint site offers such traditional sweets as Elizabethan comfits in tiny
tins and unusual items like dusted chocolate-covered blueberry raisins in
Fabergé-style eggs. With delivery charges not listed until you've keyed in your
credit card details, it's best to contact the company before you buy.

Choc Express

www.chocexpress.com

Browsing according to personality may not always be that successful (boiled
sweets for the cool teenager?) but it's fun. Useful info includes the number of
chocolates in a box rather than just the weight, making it easier to determine
value for money. Pricey, but delivery is free and there's a vast selection on offer.

Chocolate Store

www.chocolatestore.com

To shop here you just need to decide whether you prefer Swiss, Belgian or
English truffles and chocolate. With pictures of most products and a brief
description of each, you at least know what you get for your £18 and 500g of
chocolate. It would be nice to know shipping costs before you order, however.

Cooks of Swanton

www.cooksofswanton.com

Not the most imaginative of sites, but a safe option for luxury handmade
chocolate delicacies. Descriptions and images to tantalise your taste buds are

limited, but the no-nonsense – though high – pricing (£9.49 for 125g, £14 for 250g) makes ordering simple. Postage and packaging is included.

Cromwells Chocolates
www.cromwellschocolates.co.uk
You won't be dazzled by the selection of fine English chocolates sold here, but it only takes a few clicks to buy a box. Each contains chocolate creams, truffles and pralines, with prices from £5.95 to £24.95. File under 'adequate'.

Fudge Kitchen
www.fudge-kitchen.co.uk
Who couldn't be tempted by rocky road, Belgian chocolate swirl, lemon meringue or Christmas cake fudge, and that's just the tip of a huge list of traditional and speciality flavours on offer at this fabulous site. Select a suitable gift box or create your own, generally priced at £10 for four slices. Images and descriptions of each flavour are available, with a free slab of your choice if you join owner Jim's mailing list.

Montezumas
www.montezumas.net
If you're particular about what you put inside your body but don't want to miss out on the food of the gods that is chocolate, Montezumas sells organic and vegan-friendly chocolate delights. Choose from a vast selection – from your everyday bars to occasion gifts. The more adventurous, and frankly those worried that organic and vegan spells dull and tasteless, can opt for the specialist selection with more interesting choices than your average Dairy Milk. Try lemon and apple, cinnamon, nutmeg or even chilli. Prices are good, with shipping at £4.

Roly's Handmade Chocolates
www.handmade-chocolates.com
If you imagined a rather rotund man selling an amateur selection of wares, on inspection what you will find is a well-thought-out and mouth-watering selection of handmade chocolates and truffles. Where many sites fall down by assuming you'll buy anything as long as it's chocolate, Roly is happy to reveal exactly what's in the box. Prices are good, £9 for an ample box of truffles, but you do need to download the order form and then use snail mail to complete your order. Not particularly high-tech but worth the bother. Online ordering is promised to be arriving soon

---

CYBER CANDY

If you're tired of your average Mars bar, Snickers or Dairy Milk, and are looking for something that little bit different and that little bit sweeter, Cyber Candy (www.cybercandy.co.uk) sells a huge range of sweets and candy usually only found in America and Australia.

America's favourites, Hershey bars, Reeses Pieces and Baby Ruths, are all included alongside items for the more adventurous such as Australia's Ovalteenies (which are tablets of Ovaltine) and Musk-flavoured Lifesavers. Each sweetie is under £1 with first or second-class postage on top.

Clothes & fashion

Desperate for a new pair of wellies?
A Crombie outfit to up the cred level
with the lads on your manor?
A sequinned basque? Size up the
Web – it's tailor made for top threads

 General **Where to go for advice, Oz gear and big glamour**

The Australian Clothing Company
www.ozclothingco.com
Heavy-duty oiled cotton coats and jackets as well as hats and boots for those
anticipating very rough weather or spending a lot of time out in the open. The
kit is as worn by Aussie stockmen for years and should last you a lifetime. No
'click to buy' but a rather time-consuming online order form. Delivery can be
quite expensive.

Ready 2 Shop
www.shopped-out.com
Nothing to buy but loads of fun to be had at this site which features the inside
fashion scoop for cities such as Manchester and Madrid. Going store by
store, the latest fashion items are mentioned, leaving you in no doubt as to
what will be worn by the trend-setters of each town. Save time, money and a
few fashion disasters.

Sixteen 47
www.sixteen47.com
A stylish and fun range of clothes for women over size 16, created by Dawn
French and Helen Teague. The clothes would probably look better if they were
modelled on people rather than mannequins, but this is an attractive and
easy-to-use site. This is just a small selection of what is available at the offline
shop, and full online ordering wasn't yet up and running when we visited, but
fill in the detailed enquiry form and the company will contact you.

Accessories
Bags, shoes and belts for all

Billy Bag
www.billybag.com
Admittedly you can't buy yourself a Billy online but you can do everything but – seek out your nearest store, view the latest collection and if you just can't wait for your next trip to John Lewis, you can ring to order. Remember, don't leave home without your Billy.

Pink Ice
www.pink-ice.com
Pink name, pink site and pink accessories. Ignore the limited range – what they have is straight from the catwalk at more affordable prices. Some of the more unusual items include body jewellery add-ons to make your pierced navel even more ravishing, with prices from £12 to £60 depending on the metal and design. Designer bags for around £50 include the Billy Bag and Kimi beaded bags, and if you're bored with your old pastel pashmina, try an embroidered one for £200.

Sunglasses 2000
www.sunglasses2000.com
Based in the US, this is the ultimate sunglasses warehouse. Designer ranges include Gucci, Ray Ban, Fendi and Nike, at more affordable prices – generally between $50 and $100. Each brand holds 40 to 50 different designs, with clear images, a choice of colours and precise measurements so you can find the perfect fit. Shipping to the UK is an extra $15, taking up to 14 days. Even so, prices are cheaper than this side of the Atlantic.

The Red Hand
www.theredhand.com
Easy-to-navigate site selling original accessories from hot young designers, including jewellery, bags and wraps. Particularly clever is the PVC bucket-shape handbag with matching spade-shape purse. A vintage accessories section is promised soon. Prices are inclusive of shipping although delivery time isn't specified.

TIES
Airport lounge favourite Tie Rack (www.tie-rack.com) offers a comprehensive site full of silk, printed, fun and classic ties. Click on the initial image to see your chosen tie matched with a shirt to provide a complete look. Prices start from £12. For similar priced alternatives try the following sites.

Fox & Chave (www.foxandchave.co.uk): limited selection of woven and printed ties. Annoyingly there is no direct link to the order form so get a pen and paper ready before you begin.

Sax Design (www.saxdesign.com): decide what you want your tie to say about you – high flyer, fashion victim, or smooth operator – and browse the ties on offer. Discounts available if you buy in bulk!

Catalogues The original mail-order concept, updated

Bluebelle
www.bluebelle.co.uk
If revealing eveningwear is your thing, you could find something you like on this womenswear site, with swimwear and leisurewear also on offer. Prices are reasonable, although styling the models as nightclub pole dancers does not exactly raise the site's class factor. Delivery is calculated when you check out; your slinky/kinky number should reach you within seven days.

Boden
www.boden.co.uk
Online version of the hugely successful catalogue selling upmarket family clothes. The range spans sturdy trousers for busy fathers to pretty velvet cardigans for women looking for a little glamour. The Mini Boden section has kids' styles you'll find irresistible. Prices online are 10 per cent cheaper than through the catalogue. There are various delivery choices starting at £3, and if you live in London you can even request a same-day courier service for £10.

Brora
www.brora.co.uk
There's nothing like the feel of cashmere and this site will tempt you to feel it just a little more often. There are gorgeous and colourful cashmere designs

Only for the super-fit or those with bodies that resemble your 12-year-old, um, brother, 'cos you're gonna be wearing it tight and short

for men, women and kids (who, quite frankly, don't deserve it) and although the prices are about average, there are some bargains to be had in the Sale section. Delivery starts at £6 and is free on orders over £300.

Cotton Traders

www.cotton-traders.co.uk

If you live in your rugby shirt, you'll know this name. Specialists in super-tough sporty shirts, CT also stocks a range of other quality cotton gear like chinos, fleece jackets and shorts at excellent prices. Online specials too.

Freemans

www.freemans.com

The trusted catalogue has had a style overhaul in recent years and now features wearable and affordable ranges from labels like Whistles and Betty Jackson. The menswear section has clothes ranging from Pierre Cardin to Red or Dead, and the whole site is beautifully laid out and a joy to use. Delivery and returns are free and take two to three days.

James Meade

www.jamesmeade.com

High quality, conservative classic clothes from a company owned by an ex-Coldstream Guardsman. There's an alteration service on trouser and skirt lengths and they will even monogram and recuff and collar your shirts for you. Should you feel the need.

Kays

www.kaysnet.com

You're unlikely to set the world on fire with these clothes, but the selection is good and the prices are keen. Kays still offers the option to spread your payments over 20 weeks to make budgeting easier. The site is easy to use with an informative welcome section for new shoppers and if you get your order in before 10am it will be delivered free within 48 hours.

Lands' End

www.landsend.co.uk

UK website for the US clothing catalogue giant. You're unlikely to see Madonna wearing Lands' End as it sticks firmly to the middle of the road in terms of design, but if you're looking for long-lasting cotton T-shirts and wrinkle-resistant chinos, you'll find them here. The stock is all good value for money, with regular sales and special offers. Delivery is speedy and efficient, and costs £3.50 no matter what the size of your order.

La Redoute

www.redoute.co.uk

Even catalogue shopping is more chic in France. Given the design and quality of the clothes, this site is excellent value for money. Women, men, and kids can all get a fix of French style, and if you don't like what you've chosen, send it back Freepost for a full refund. Post and packing costs £2.45 on all orders and your clothes should reach you within five days.

Long Tall Sally

www.longtallsally.co.uk

Wide range of stylish clothes for women over 5ft 8in from leather skirts to a formal worksuit. There's also a swimwear section for the long-bodied and maternity wear for high-held bumps. The Special Occasion wear could be a bit more special, however. Orders are usually dispatched within 24 hours, and there's a charge of £2 if you spend less than £30, or £3 for larger orders.

Lounge Lizard

www.eclipse.co.uk/pens/lizard/

This site shows details of the Lounge Lizard clothing range from Australia and it's vehemently anti-fit. If it's baggy you're looking for, you'll get it here, although some of the drawings are less flattering than they could be. There's no online ordering yet, just a form to print out and fax through, but prices are competitive and there's a good choice of colours and styles.

Racing Green

www.racinggreen.co.uk

A good, clear version of the men's and women's casual clothing catalogue, this features high-quality products, good clearance offers (available only online) and a Fast Find service to avoid downloading items that you're not interested in. The site is linked to the warehouse system so you will know immediately if an item you want is currently out of stock, and there is privilege shopping for registered regular customers. Delivery is only £1.95 and orders over £100 are carriage free.

Sweaty Betty

www.sweatybetty.com

Dance and sport inspired streetwear aimed to appeal to hard-bodied young things. There's a limited range on the website, but the snow-wear range is on its way. Make Lycra your friend with greatly desirable crop tops, halter tops and mesh dresses, all shown off to perfection on this hugely impressive animated site – though that also tends to really slow things down, so not a site to visit when in a hurry. The shopping service was not fully launched when we looked, but they promise speedy service and a fully secure shopping experience.

Usisi

www.usisidirect.com

Brightly coloured, 100 per cent cotton clothing direct from South Africa. Adult clothing includes generously sized sweatshirts and polo shirts with often lurid animal and vegetable designs (we liked the zebra), which means you're not likely to wear these on a safari. Take a look at the blue pinstriped T-shirts for something less hectic. In the children's range we loved the padded jacket printed with safari animals. Prices are very reasonable, given the originality of the garments and the fact that prices include delivery.

 How to keep them hip and happy from 0-16

Baby Planet
www.babyplanet.co.uk
Kids of up to six years old are catered for by this tie-dye emporium selling brightly coloured, fully washable, hippy hooded sweatshirts, romper suits and T-shirts in 100 per cent cotton. Your mother-in-law will be outraged – a good enough reason to buy one in itself. They were updating the site on our visit so expect new features soon and hopefully these will include a secure server.

Children's Warehouse
www.childrens-warehouse.com
Once you've found Caroline Bunting's neat, west London-based site you'll find yourself returning again and again. Her clothes are well designed and

Arcadia games Principles – and others – online

The high street wouldn't be the same without Arcadia names such as Top Shop, Dorothy Perkins and Principles, and now they're embracing the Net. Each store has its own site but all follow a similar set-up. Style-wise each is vibrant, colourful and easy to follow. Arcadia has adopted the whole package with multiple ways to shop including casual browsing and quick shopping, online magazines with news, reviews and competitions, and specialist sections, including maternity wear, petite and larger sizes. Descriptions and images could be better, but there are washing guidelines, fitting room help and packed sale sections. Most of all, the comprehensive site does make you want to buy online.

www.burtonmenswear.co.uk
www.dorothyperkins.co.uk
www.evans.ltd.uk
www.hawkshead.com
www.principles.co.uk
www.topman.co.uk
www.tops.co.uk
www.wadesmith.co.uk

great quality; there's every item you could want, in sizes from babies to 12-year olds, and from cuddly fleeces to cute pyjamas; and they're just hip enough to silence your little darlings' pleas for Karan and Hilfiger (for 10 minutes). Delivery costs £3, returns are free and prices not outrageous.

Gatefish
www.gatefish.com
Fleeces, sweatshirt and T-shirts for kids over three years old with the emphasis on practicality. All items are easily washable and hardwearing: some even have reflective motifs to help make your kids more visible. There's also a section of very cute fancy dress. Prices are higher than average, but the quality probably makes up for that. Delivery is calculated on site.

Flowerpot Clothing
www.flowerpotclothing.com
Sweet embroidered and appliquéd Aran sweaters, fleeces and sweatshirts from this small company in Loughborough. Prices are good (£19 for the pure wool Arans), given the craft that goes into each one, and the site is a cinch to surf. They also stock women's versions of some of the products, for those who like to match their kids. Scary.

Giant Peach
www.giantpeach.co.uk
Truly adorable kidswear ranging from the traditional to the very funky indeed for little people up to the age of eight. Packed with good ideas like laminated paint smocks for messy young artists, plus a range of gifts and nursery accessories. Some of the illustrations are too small – a zoom facility would help. Orders within the UK are shipped free.

Patricia Smith
www.psdesigns.demon.co.uk
Cornish clothing company making and selling traditional children's garb for well-brought up little people. Lots of smocked party dresses in cotton, and there's even a sailor suit if you really want to torture your son, although there are more up-to-date fleece sweatshirts as well. Despite the care

that has gone into designing this site, there is no shopping basket, so you have to print out a form to order. Delivery costs £3 and can take 28 days.

Poppy

www.poppy-children.co.uk

Bright and pretty crease-resistant cotton dresses, with jackets and hats to match, for little girls who want to impress. The printed fabrics are designed by local artists so you won't find the fabric being used elsewhere. The prices are not cheap but the quality is good, and there's little in the high street to match the designs. Deliveries should take no more than five days and charges start at £2.99. Coming soon is a range of room and nursery decor.

School Uniforms Online

www.schooluniformsonline.co.uk

Standard school uniform items like duffel coats and polo shirts are available on this straightforward site at much lower prices than on the high street, plus you don't have to depress the kids by taking them to the school outfitter while they're still on summer holidays. They also stock a range of Scout and Guide uniforms, and dance clothes. Five-day delivery costs £2.95 on all UK orders.

Spirit of Nature

www.spiritofnature.co.uk

Organic, unbleached and mostly undyed clothing for those babies with advanced environmental concerns. Cuteness has not been sacrificed in the pursuit of purity and where dyes have been used they are non-toxic and formaldehyde-free. Accessories include organic bedding and toys and even environmentally-friendly disposable diapers if reusable is too unbearable.

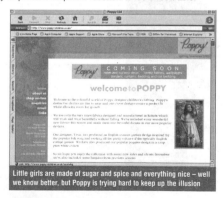

Little girls are made of sugar and spice and everything nice – well we know better, but Poppy is trying hard to keep up the illusion

Designer | If it's Versace, sweetie, it's here

Brown Bag Clothing
www.bbclothing.co.uk

Armani, Moschino and Versace are among the designers with ranges on this chi-chi clothes site for men and women. They promise to have the latest styles at discount prices, not just last year's over-stocks, and certainly some of the special-offer clothes were on sale at almost 60 per cent off the RRP. You can search by designer or by the item of clothing you're looking for and there's a 14-day no-quibble refund on all orders.

Brown's Focus
www.brownsfashion.com

As a haven for the rich and famous, you'd expect more from the Brown's website. Locating account information on the homepage is easy, but how you add items to your account in the first place is one for members of Mensa. Exasperatingly, Brown's has designed its site as if it were a book. Click on the third box, not even the first, to scroll, slowly, through the 34 pages of designer clothes and accessories. Don't try to skip pages either in the hope of finding that Swarovski bracelet quicker: a teddy bear between silver earrings and a squirrel knit jumper pretty much sums up the organisation on this site. For fans of the name and those with a gold card, only.

Designer Discount
www.designerdiscount.co.uk

Don't be put off by the tacky opening page which has a movie star peering at you (Mel Gibson when we visited). Once inside, you can search this professionally organised site by designer, or alternatively simply browse the thumbnail images of the catalogue – which, like most designer discount sites, is restricted to the sportswear ranges. If you don't usually go in for such glamour names as Versace, Valentino or YSL, the discounts could change your mind – the £40 and £50 reductions on many items reduce designer clothes to high-street prices.

EASY SHOP

Easy Shop is exactly as the name suggests with the choice of searching by brand or the lingerie item you're in need of.

Brands include Sloggi for the men, Gossard for the women and a host of top designer ranges for anyone – Moschino, Dolce & Gabbana, and French Connection.

The faster option is to select the item category, answer four simple questions, size, occasion, style and price range, and they'll come up with a selection to meet your demands.

The step-by-step ordering process avoids confusion and although prices vary from label to label, many items are discounted.

www.easyshop.co.uk

Net-a-Porter

www.net-a-porter.com

Sharp, sleek and sophisticated, and that just covers the site itself. Search by product or your favourite designer, flavours of the month include Matthew Williamson, Paul & Joe, Jemima Khan, and fetishists will drool over the Jimmy Choo shoes. Porter is a certain winner as it doesn't assume designer names will sell themselves. Descriptions and images are good, particularly as they focus on the little details, and although prices are at the top end of the scale, there are sale items in each category. Availability by size and same-day delivery for those living in London should also impress the elite crowd.

UK Designer Shop

www.ukdesignershop.com

A limited range (Pierre Cardin seems to feature very heavily amid some very high-street names), this site is only worth the time and effort of browsing if you're a man who can't say no to designer names, but also can't really afford to say yes. Up to 50 per cent off and two-for-one deals say it all.

Yoox

www.yoox.com

Yoox proves that organised doesn't necessarily equate to dull and boring. The bright and funky design matches the designer clothing on offer – Helmut Lang, D&G, Fendi and Prada to name a few. Search by designer or the item you're looking for, but with 149 pages of Miu Miu items alone, we suggest you make your search as specific as possible. On the other hand the site is great to search with zoom and varying angle options, and ideas for how to get a specific look. Prices are good but may vary slightly from day to day with prices fixed in Euros.

A must-shop.

Zercon

www.zercon.com

This site offers unisex clothes, so you needn't bother searching both the men's and women's sections as only the sizes differ in most cases. Dull and grey, the visuals are a good reflection of the clothes and only the brand labels stand out. Top names include Dolce & Gabbana, Ralph Lauren and Tommy Hilfiger.

Great, detailed illustrations and stock information turns a shopping spree at Net-a-Porter into a positive pleasure

3D is the key
The secret to that perfect fit

Until online stores find a way of simulating the changing room experience, their returns staff are likely to be as busy as a Benetton jumper folder on a sale day. Clothes remain one of the diciest online purchases when it comes to choosing the correct size, style and colour. Our own purchases have proven that but, take it from us, it gets easier.

Fat Face (*www.fatface.co.uk*), for instance, has built up a thriving online and mail order service because people can trust the quality of their clothes and once you're familiar with their styling and cuts, your shopping success rate is likely to increase each time you buy there.

But if you believe the high-tech futurists out there, we can look forward to a time when a 3D rendition of ourselves steps into a virtual dressing room and tries on the latest little black number. The Compucloz Corporation in the US owns the rights to software which allows users to use computers to select and try on garments from a digital wardrobe. It claims to "reshape a model figure and renders an image reflecting a client's specific curves, bulges and height in selected garments" (at least it's honest then). Compucloz's aim is to become the "dressing room for the digerati", and you can download a demonstration of its online makeovers at *www.compucloz.com*.

Avatarme (*www.avatarme.com*), meanwhile, the company that aims to have 25 per cent of US households scanned and turned into 3D models within six years, may see the immediate application of their technology in the computer games field, but the online dressing potential is there for all to see. It claims its 3D booths (as in those seen at the Dome) will be popping up everywhere soon. So if you're fed up of wasting your Saturday in the Gap dressing room queue, find a booth near you.

High Street
Affordable, dependable and fun

Benetton & Sisley
www.theex.it
Unlike a number of their high-street competitors, Benetton and Sisley have a convincing online venture. Links to The Exit are available on both store's own sites, otherwise head straight for the address above. The site itself looks and works like many others, search by brand or product type to view men's and women's collections. Prices are standard; free delivery on orders over £35.

Brooks Brothers
www.brooksbrothers.com
In the UK Brooks is one of the first ports of call if you want to rent a tux, but

it only sell onlines from its US site. Consequently you'll need to calculate the import duties and taxes for yourself, and shipping charges start at $35. Prices for their bland, play-safe men's suits begin at $329, so you may find it cheaper to stick to shopping in UK stores, though there are a few good sale prices. Descriptions bizarrely don't include what the suit fabric is, but the photos are much improved over our last visit. Shipping free to the UK on orders over $275.

French Connection
www.frenchconnection.com
Unfortunately the arty opening page and 15-page catalogue of its summer collection gave a false impression, as you can't buy any of the luscious items which are on display. Whether French Connection was just testing the Internet waters only it knows. It was only possible to view the catalogue – albeit without descriptions or even prices – and buy a FC branded T-shirt for £20 with a £3.50 delivery. The site was a big disappointment, but FCUK is only one of a number of high-street names which has yet to fully embrace the Net.

Next
www.next.co.uk
The simple, clean homepage seems to provide everything you need to know. You can browse or use the quick-shop facility. Use the next-day delivery facility and you can benefit from free returns. Sounds too good to be true? It is. You can only buy if you're an account holder and the online registration doesn't recognise all postcodes. If you do decide to register, don't think you can make up time by using the quick-shop facility as you need the codes provided in the Next Directory (£3) to make a search. There are, however, clear and enlarged images, fabric details and easy ordering once you're in.

The following also had websites but no online ordering when we visited...
www.benetton.com
www.kookai.com
www.oasis-stores.co.uk
www.riverisland.com

 Serious streetwear for the hipster in you

Abercrombie & Fitch
www.abercrombie.com
Having been eulogised in many an American rap song, Abercrombie & Fitch clothes have become a must-have with those in the know. Skate and urban wear dominates but, being American, everything is slightly toned down compared to their UK competitors. Inexpensive compared to the UK market, jeans and fleeces are priced at around $50 with T-shirts for $19, though you

LABELLED WITH LOVE

All the groovy kids' clothing in the world is no good if the little darlings have a habit of leaving them lying around. Solve the problem by labelling the lot. The following sites can help:

Penmark Name Tapes
www.nametapesdirect.com

Woven or iron-on tapes in a variety of typefaces cut and ready for use. They also make woven luggage straps for wandering suitcases.

Premier Name Tapes
www.premierservices.co.uk

Woven tapes offered with embroidered pictures or logos too.

J B Ward & Co
www.wardsgroup.co.uk

Traditional school name tapes.

Minilabel
www.minilabel.co.uk

Order or request a sample.

---

should always bear in mind the added costs of importing. For international deliveries add an extra $25 and allow for two to four weeks' wait. You'll also need to sort out any duties and taxes yourself, but it's worth it for something a little more original than a pair of Levi's and a Gap fleece.

AW Rust

www.awrust.co.uk

A fresh and simple amateur site selling all your favourites – Sonneti, Rockport, Gas and Fred Perry. It won't take you long to browse with only a few items listed under each brand, but discounts of up to 50 per cent off retail make up for it. Similar discounts apply to the leather section with snakeskin leather jackets for under £130 and tops at around £40. No delivery charges on orders over £80.

Boxfresh

www.boxfresh.co.uk

If you don't care for the techno music that plays while you browse this site, then this up-and-coming brand probably isn't for you. But even if said music does appeal, this site offers a confusing, cursor-controlled view of a limited selection, poor, undescriptive images and tiny swatches of the available colours. Definitely a case of style over content. On the plus side, some prices work out cheaper than those bumped up by department stores, and delivery is free.

Clothes Store

www.theclothesstore.com

This quirky site has dispensed with the usual catalogue poses to display its wares with clothes displayed flat on a white background. Click on whichever graphic matches to view both men's and women's urban and designer goods. The selection is minimal but popular names include Duffer, Burberry, Replay and Airwalk. Free delivery.

Designer Heaven

www.designerheaven.com

Labels for boys rather than designers for men – the brands include Full Circle, Henri Lloyd, John Smedley and Cabourn. It's a pricey range too – T-shirts begin around the £50 mark and jackets around £100 – but ordering is simple.

Fat Face

www.fatface.co.uk

Surfer bods fill the homepage so it's not hard to recognise the young, fit and funky target audience. Despite their swank status, the clothes are relatively inexpensive, with most items under £35. The online catalogue sells men's, women's and kids' clothes, plus accessories, but when it comes to sizes Fat Face fares poorly, with many women's items only going up to a size 12 or 14.

Iikon

http://shop.iikon.com

Skaters' heaven. Rare and collectible skateboards are sold alongside the only skate footwear to be seen in: Northwave trainers, sold at cheaper than average prices. Use the calculator to convert the various foreign sizes and currency. Order tracking also available.

LondonWide

www.londonwide.co.uk

The essence of London streetwear here, so you can stand out from the crowd with the latest and best in retro chic. Soochi, Burro and Battery Organic are just three of the bizarrely named designers. You pay a price for original designs – £68 for aei:kei's revealing Spider breast top – but there are lower-range T-shirts for men and women, with typical prices around £20.

Rubens

www.rubensmenswear.com

Amateurish graphics and pictures let down this otherwise adequate site, which sells everything from the skaters' must-have label O'Neill to trendy Base footwear and Ben Sherman shirts. Discount prices are available on some stock, but otherwise standard high-street prices apply: £60-80 for Base footwear, £25 for O'Neill T-shirts.

Surf On The Net

www.surfonthenet.co.uk

As the name suggests, this label superstore is dedicated to those who ride the waves, with shirts, dresses and fleeces on sale as well as swimwear. Top brands include Mambo, Rip Curl, Vans and Kangaroo, and there are men's, women's and kiddie sizes. Prices match the high street, delivery is free and you get the added bonus of Surfzine with news, views, schools and cams.

Ted Baker

www.tedbaker.co.uk

Not a site for those in a hurry. Standard men's and women's categories apply but it's a mystery why Lentil and Danish are used as names for skirts, or why Kiwi refers to a stone-coloured pair of trousers. You also have to keep clicking back and forth to see the next item. On the plus side are laundry instructions and size charts for each item. Prices exclude VAT and shipping info is elusive.

Clothes & fashion

Toby Pimlico
www.tobypimlico.com
You might not be familiar with the name, but Toby's range of designs should ring a few bells. All the hot young television stars are shouting about his T-shirts, baseball shirts and underwear blazoned with every slogan from Eat Me Whole to Dirty Girl. Only a small selection is available online and there are a few navigational glitches, but otherwise a fun visit.

Zoo Village
www.zoovillage.com
Sick of wearing the same, tired, old labels as every other Tom, Dick and Harry? This Swedish outfit can put you back at the forefront of urban and street fashion. Names to watch out for include Acne, Dispensary and Kulte. Prices are good, principally in Euros but GB pounds are also listed.

 **From French flair to a Highland fling**

Café Coton
www.cafecoton.co.uk
Don't be put off by your grandad's favourite checked shirts on the opening page: this site promises French flair. Choose from soft collar, button-down, double cuff, French and Italian style collar shirts, all £33 with free delivery in two working days. Difficult to imagine what they'll look like on, as the pictures show just partial views of a folded shirt.

Crombie
www.crombie.co.uk
Crombie has been in business for nearly 200 years, and shows the attention to detail that has kept them going. Sadly you can't buy a Crombie coat online, but a good range of shirts, ties, knitwear and accessories are available for the discerning traditional male. Delivery charges are calculated at the checkout and, since they ship overseas, everything is sent via UPS.

Hector Russell
www.hector-russell.com
A Highland fling can be yours. Kilt-making being a serious business you can't just click and have one sent out, but you can e-mail for details and there are excellent photos and guidelines to the different styles. Secure shopping using an order form is available for accessories like sporrans and clan ties.

Shirt Press
www.shirt-press.co.uk
The answer to all our prayers: shirts that never need to be ironed. Add to this a well thought-out website with button cuffs, double cuffs, dress shirts and

ties in every possible colour. You do, though, pay a price for the luxury of an empty ironing basket – usually £70, or £100 for two shirts.

Thomas Pink

www.thomaspink.co.uk

Thankfully Mr Pink's shirts are slightly more interesting than the site itself, but only just. Shirts, ties and cufflinks are each priced at around the £50 mark, but you can only look at enlarged images of the shirt collar and tie.

The Hom site is a feast for the eyes with its fabulous display of beautiful bods – oh, and they sell underwear too

4XL

www.forxl.co.uk

If you're over six feet tall, you'll be familiar with the problem of trousers that barely reach your ankles. 4XL offers jeans from known manufacturers such as Wrangler, as well as more formal trousers, to cover even the longest shanks. The quality is guaranteed and all prices include delivery.

Underwear Pose in silly frillies or chill in thermals

Agent Provocateur

www.agentprovocateur.com

If the current Agent Provocateur range at your local Marks & Spencer is a little tame, you can buy the real thing here. Both the lingerie and the site are stylish and risqué. Select a complete image, then view before you buy. It's pricier than M&S, though – anywhere between £30 and £60 for a single item.

Ann Summers

www.annsummers.co.uk

Don't be put off by the tacky-looking site – the Ann Summers' site holds an extensive online catalogue with something for every taste. Scroll along, read (if you can) the adequate descriptions and view enlarged images if need be. Only slightly pricier than the high street – £18 for bras – this is a useful site for lingerie that's little bit different but not beyond the average budget.

Brief Look Lingerie

www.brieflook.co.uk

To save time, Brief Look allows you to browse its extensive catalogue according to your own size needs, rather than searching through reams of styles that are never going to fit. Encouragingly, they also appreciate that not all women wear a 34B bra – their sizes range from a 30A all the way to a 50F. The designs themselves are up to date, and prices vary from £3 to £20 for knickers and £10 to £50 for bras. If, like the majority of women, you're wearing the wrong-size bra, the site also offers helpful advice and tips for a better fit. Brief Look also stocks menswear.

Hom GB

www.hom.gb.com

If you don't mind pictures of men's groins thrusting at you from your terminal, Hom GB is worth a look with its large selection of men's underwear and swimwear. Our best advice is to take a few minutes to browse each category; headings such as 'nature', 'fredy' and 'xtras' probably won't leave you any the wiser. Prices are above what you'd pay for your average three-pack from M&S, and postage and packaging can work out expensive unless you buy in bulk, but maybe the pictures of men in tight pants will make up for this.

Kiniki Direct Male

www.kiniki.com

More a peep show than a shopping site, it is all too easy to get distracted in the search for a pair of boxers for Father's Day – especially when the promised 'Spin that Booty' feature arrives. Search through a selection of boxers, briefs, thongs or swimwear and you may be somewhat intimidated. Tamer items include the Charmer boxers in black satin, or for the more adventurous, Jungle boxers in stylish leopard print that come with a matching short satin robe. In shopping terms, the site is easy to use and you can enjoy a 20 per cent discount if you buy online. Not for the faint-hearted but sure to draw a big gay following.

Lingerie World

www.lingerie-world.net

A large selection of well-known brands including Triumph and Sloggi, this site is organised a bit oddly – to get the matching bra to the knickers that you just bought requires going to another section (a direct link would help), but at least they tell you that there are matching sets. Lots of info and a handy bra sizing guide for the 70 per cent of us still wearing the wrong one. Shipping is a flat £2.95.

Midnight Express

www.midnightexpress.co.uk

Finally a site that doesn't seem to believe that selling underwear requires women to be pictured as strippers or treats buyers like voyeurs. Selling well-known brands and designers, this very user-friendly site has gone to some length to make buying online pain-free. Size chart includes a metric converter. Delivery, within 14 days, costs £3.50.

Nile Trading

www.nile.co.uk

Not exactly the sexiest gear going, but doubtless a godsend in the deep midwinter: a complete range of lightweight, thermal underwear, available from a Leicester-based company. All the tights, vests and pants in the collection are made in Britain and since you're buying direct from the manufacturer, the prices are excellent. Now there's no need to shiver ever again. Delivery is calculated at the checkout and your long johns will be keeping you warm within the week.

Toe Rags

www.toerags.com

If your sock drawer is a black hole, fill it up again with a selection of these hardwearing cotton socks in a wide range of colours. Single pairs are £4.99 or invest £6.99 in a twin pack. The site has recently expanded to sell men's and women's clothes as well, with an emphasis on comfortable, outdoor style. Unfortunately there doesn't seem to be any online information about delivery costs, but it's certainly a nice site to look at and plenty of special offers are available when visited.

Victoria's Secret

www.victoriassecret.com

The online version of the US catalogue phenomenon, Victoria's own-brand underwear and lingerie is so popular she can afford to have supermodels on her website. Aside from the standard semi-naked women, the site itself is plain yet stylish, making it simple to navigate. Get your indulgence fix with Deluxe, Miracle, second skin and T-shirt bras to name just a few, or search for wardrobe essentials in the Bra Salon. Once converted, prices are average for the UK market, but you do need to take into account shipping fees – $14.95 for the first $75 spent and so on. They also offer a useful info section on international duties and an e-zine section on what's happening in the bra world. Hosiery and clothing also available.

Victoria's Secret has been let out of the bag and now you too can indulge in itsy bitsy pieces of satin and lace

Coffee & tea

Caffeine is one of the few addictive drugs you really can buy over the Internet. And the choice is all yours: you can buy it from Baltimore, Chelsea or the island of St Helena

Baltimore Coffee Company
www.baltcoffee.com
According to the rather dull homepage this is the most comprehensive tea and coffee site on the Web – certainly the range is vast and each comes with no fewer than six different types of grind. The payment screen is untidy but you are assured it's safe and you can have your order confirmed by e-mail.

Barnie Coffee
www.barniescoffee.com
This is a mercifully simple site and navigation is clear and easy – but everything falls apart during registration. This takes ages, is way too complex and once you are through, hits you with international delivery at $50!

Clipper Teas
www.clipper-teas.com
Masses of information on the company, and tea in general but the store is not immediately evident on the amateurish homepage and some text is obscured by pictures on the rest of the site so no gold star for graphics. The selection is good, though, with a definite ethical bias in favour of fair trade and organic teas. There's some intriguing product info and you can request free samples.

Coffee Compass
www.coffeecompass.co.uk
Those who struggle when faced with making choices could be in trouble here, given the 45 different single-varietal coffees on offer including the hard-to-come-by Australian Skybury. Pick a £15, £22.50 or £33 selection and indicate which coffees you'd prefer. Not the slickest site in the world but worth sticking with for the product. Delivery costs from £5; payment has to be by cheque.

Coffee, Tea and Spice
www.coffeecoffee.com
Coffee, Tea and Spice is a small firm operating out of one shop. There is no mention of a secure server and the request to log in seems a bit unnecessary. However, when you know that Myrna Blaine is preparing your coffee herself, who cares? The purchase process itself is clear and logical and delivery charges are ridiculously low, easily eclipsing most of the big players.

Coffee World
www.realcoffee.co.uk
This site claims to be the "No 1 Coffee Resource on the Web" and while that might be open to question it has a reasonable selection of coffee and tea – and offers the peace of mind that comes with dealing with a *Which?* Web Trader. You can order online, or by fax, phone or snail mail, with the order dispatched the day you make it.

Java Johns
www.javajohns.com
They gain some credit for not blaring out the Ink Spots' *Java Jive* as you access the rather spartan homepage. But they haven't skimped on the product range. They do deliver to the UK but there's nothing to confirm that you are on a secure server. You will, however, find a link to the espresso top 50, a site network coffee addicts may not be able to live without.

Starbucks
www.starbucks.com
Starbucks is one of the best known names in coffee but the closest it gets to delivering to the UK is shipping to Canada which isn't really that close at all.

St Helena
www.st-helena-coffee.sh
This site doesn't seem like much from the homepage but delving further reveals some stunning images of the island. The range is limited but there's a secure server and worldwide delivery is included in the price.

Whittard of Chelsea
www.whittard.co.uk/start.jsp
The coffee and tea shop for people who know which finger to raise when they're having a cuppa has an impressive range of products, extremely clear advice on how to buy (including reassurance that you're on a secure server) and an exhaustive FAQ for first-time buyers. There is even free advice of the 'how to make a perfect cuppa' variety which concludes with the baffling advice: "Teapots should never be bleached." The customer testimonials have to be read to be believed: one satisfied shopper compares a member of staff to a "modern day ship captain" while one visitor rhapsodises over the "incredibly beautiful" website. Some Netheads really should get out more.

Collectibles

Collectibles

That's collectibles as in shark's teeth, corkscrews, Monkees memorabilia.. oh, and a few old coins and stamps

General | Including one Eastern Airlines coffee pot

Acubid

www.acubid.com

A rather respectable homepage doesn't quite conceal the sheer gaudiness and oddness of many of the goods up for grabs on this auction site. Among the bizarre range of collectibles on offer when the site was inspected was a figure of Barbie's Ken as the Tin Man from *The Wizard of Oz* (probably a shrewd investment at $50) and an APC Smart UPS 420 uninterruptible power supply for your computer at $25. Stronger on stamps than coins and stronger on sports memorabilia than stamps. As a well-established site, you will have few security worries when bidding here.

Christie's

www.christies.com

Ever since Christie's bought Spink, the world's oldest coin dealer, in 1993, it's been impossible for serious numismatists to give this site a miss. Spink still has its own site (www.spink-online.com) but Christie's is also worth visiting if you're collecting anything from sports memorabilia to corkscrews (it's no joke – a good corkscrew can fetch £5,000 these days). Given the company's policy of only accepting bids in person or over the phone, this is strictly window shopping, but it's one hell of a window.

Dibit

www.dibit.com

Exonumists (to you and me that's people who collect tokens and medals which resemble currency but were not intended to act as currency, got that?) may be somewhat disappointed by this site. It doesn't always have the range of bigger auction houses like eBay but the search facility is pretty nifty and it's a bit like going through a January sale: amid all the tat you'll probably find something to reward your patience.

eBay

www.ebay.com

The best known online auctioneer has an extensive range of coins, along with banknotes, stamps and autographs. You may want to avoid the registration process if you're just browsing, both on principle (why should you have to bother?) and because it takes a while. Besides, all that form filling is an unnecessary distraction from searching the site which can contain such curiosities as an Eastern Airlines coffee pot ($9.99) or a selection of rare condom tins (on which bids swiftly rose above $200). As at an offline auction, you have to know what you are doing before you buy.

QXL

www.qxl.com

Few sites more effectively contradict the stereotypical image of online auctions than QXL. Far from being cyberspace's answer to a smoky back room in which items of dubious origin are traded, this site is packed with clear, in-depth information about each lot. One of the best auction sites for coins and tokens, QXL also has a fair range of stamps and memorabilia. Every so often you come across something like an *Eighth Army News* issue for £1, which is so cheap and so odd you just want to snap it up there and then.

Sotheby's Collectibles

http://search.sothebys.com/search/collArea/
collArea.jsp?code=ca004&type=C

This is the address for the Sotheby's collectibles section, worth knowing because, on a bad day, the journey to here from the dotcom page (which ought to be the cyberspace equivalent of a walk in the park) can take aeons.

Coins & stamps   "Buy them while they're hot"

Franklin Mint

www.franklinmint.com

This is a specialist collector's site that seems to have dedicated itself to tack. It's not that fast to navigate but there is a guide to what is selling best. International orders are only accepted by phone and mail which is a disadvantage, but the amount of top-notch Elvis merchandise could make up for your disappointment. For a company with Mint in its title, there isn't a lot for coin collectors here. At best you'll find a Princess Diana coin set; at worst, the Star Trek calendar medal which, naff as it sounds, costs £135.

Harlan J Berk

www.harlanjberk.com

This is probably the most professional site for numismatists on the Web, but given the homemade nature of some of the other sites out there, that's not saying much. The range of coins available covers a huge period of history and spans the globe (it even lists Alaska as a country) and tends towards the very expensive. But be warned: if you want to actually view a coin online, the process of clicking for an image sends the company an e-mail.

Ice-coin

www.smart.is/ice-coin/ice.html
A site dedicated to the coinage and coin-based merchandise of Iceland. The product range is therefore a little limited. The shop is simple to use and is relatively inexpensive, but as the slightly questionable English proclaims, perhaps with unintentional candour, "discount is a question about quantity". To make the site even more one of a kind, it tends to lapse into Icelandic without warning.

Online Coins

www.onlinecoins.com
Backed by a network of US dealers, this site has a searchable archive of coins in various categories from nickel to gold and silver bullion. Once you search for an item you are presented with a list of what's in stock and a phone number and e-mail address for the dealer. At least that is the theory. What actually happens is the search engine seems to go into temperamental overdrive when you can almost hear it shrieking: "Coins? You want coins? And what makes you think I've got any of those?"

Princess Diana stamps

www.princess-diana-stamps.com
URLs don't come much more descriptive than this. The site is, unsurprisingly, American and very amateur in terms of both design and navigation. The saving grace is the extensive product range. The shipping form is quite complex but there is a choice of secure or non-secure servers, depending on your browser.

Royal Mint

www.royalmint.com
As you might feel entitled to expect from the Royal Mint, this is a clean, well-structured site (although you need to tell it which country you are browsing from before you can go any further) with an impressive, well-presented stock of coins on offer. The gold bullion sovereign and half-sovereign, produced to commemorate (what else?) the Millennium, at £69 and £35 respectively (with free delivery in the UK), seem like they could well turn out to be a good investment.

CELEB eBAY

On a typical day on eBay this is how many items were up for sale for these giants of popular culture

1 The Beatles had 7967 items up for sale, 34 of which would go within the next hour

2 Mickey Mouse had 6369 lots, also with 34 closing within an hour

3 Elvis Presley had 3248 lots, with 11 closing in the next hour

4 Marilyn Monroe had 3197 lots, 13 closing in the next hour

5 Britney Spears had 2135, six closing in the next hour

Bubbling under: John Wayne (2124, 6) and Princess Diana (1619, 5)

Memorabilia No such thing as a free lunch box

Fun45s

www.fun45s.com

You can find records for your next *National Lampoon Animal House* 'Toga! Toga!' tribute party (go ahead and organise one, you know you owe it to yourself) at this site which, with perhaps a dash of hyperbole, calls itself "the Internet source for classic vinyl". The invitation to search the archive by 'fun category' may sound inappropriate for those who think that the words 'fun' and 'category' should never be that close together, but it's hard not to smile when you scroll down to see categories like: 'Caution! Power ballads ahead'. International shipping costs are available on application by e-mail. There is one slight drawback: the site's no-returns policy. Pricing is wonderfully simple: "all records cost $3 each everyday". An unpretentious site which also sells accessories like a record player, white single sleeves, and (back by popular demand, at least that's what the site says) those classic red, blank jukebox title strips. And there's secure ordering direct from the site on your credit card. What are you waiting for?

It's not hard to figure out the main line of business here but if you're into, fossils of, say, whale ribs, rather than your common-or-garden shark, they can probably sort you out there too

Collectibles

Prince! The artist formally known as HRH on the Web

Children's video
www.amazon.com
If you head for Amazon.com desperate for a copy of the video of *the Old Man of Lochnagar*, written and narrated by the proper Charlie, you'll be out of luck because they haven't got any. But they'll get a secondhand copy for you if they can. Just fill in the handy pre-order form and keep your fingers crossed.

Clematis
www.roselandhouse.co.uk
UK gardeners can now get the Prince Charles clematis online. The plants can be yours for only £5 apiece – though delivery will cost you a further £7.85. And you'll need to send a cheque to the nursery first.

First-day cover
www.qxl.com
That's stamps, to the uninitiated, these particular ones having been minted to mark the investiture of the Queen's oldest son as Prince of Wales in Caenarvon way back in 1969. Yours for the less-than-princely sum of £2.

Fridge magnet
www.politicos.co.uk
Impress your republican *Observer*-reading friends by ordering a *Spitting Image* fridge magnet of the heir to the throne, available for just £2.99.

Drinks tray
www.royalcoll.fsnet.co.uk
Load your Royal Collection mugs on this Charles and Di tray for just $19. Featuring the 'engagement photo', it comes complete with "surface scratches".

Commemorative bust
www.ebay.com
One of 141 Prince of Wales pieces on eBay, this black, basalt, Wedgwood bust is nine-and-a-half inches tall, is in perfect condition and was up for grabs for $85.

If you can't flog that Chas and Di wedding mug your auntie gave you on eBay, someone may want it here

Lunch Box Bonanza

www.cassidyframes.com/box

A genuinely weird site by an American called Jim Cassidy who has never got over his school/golden rule days. You click on the lunch box in the picture to enter a site which, judging from the variety of colour type, is run by someone who, as a kid, would use every crayon in the set to draw. Just when you are about to conclude that this kind of insanity can only happen in America, you scroll down the list of lots for sale and see that one item is quoted at over £100. Time to send dad into the attic.

Monkees Collection

www.themonkees.com

Here they come, still getting the funniest looks even in cyberspace. The manufactured group, whose reputation has outlived many of the genuine ones from the 1960s, have their own collectors' page where, after an electronic rendition of *A Little Bit Me, A Little Bit You*, you are invited to inspect a little bit of Monkees memorabilia. Sadly, the only item of Monkees memorabilia most fans really want – Mike Nesmith's woolly bobble hat – isn't here but you can console yourself by perusing the list of rare bootlegs, books and comics.

Paper Antiques

www.paperantiques.co.uk/forsale/postcardcig.htm

No Flash plug-ins, no animated graphics, not even a homepage with a bogus corporate message on it, this Amazon-associated site devoted to all kinds of paper antiques cuts straight to the chase with an invitation to search its archive of cigarette cards, magazines, Acts of Parliament etc. This approach doesn't seem to pay off as the site had a 'For sale' sign posted.

Sharks Teeth

www.sharksteethforsale.com

Captain Al Williams doesn't actually extract the teeth from live sharks you understand (although that sounds like a suitable punishment for errant dentists); he waits until they have been dead a few thousand years and picks them up off the sea bed. An odd way to make a living but a good tooth (from the extinct Carcharocles Angustidens or giant white shark to you and me) can fetch $250. You can order online and phone in your credit card number.

World War II stamps, coins, propaganda, posters

www.wwII-collectibles.com

As the title suggests this site is dedicated to WWII. The site layout is not that brilliant but if you look hard enough you can find real treasures. Coins, stamps and memorabilia are all present. The site has a unique 'secure' ordering system: you send one e-mail in which you list the usual details and all but the last four numbers on your credit card. Then send a second e-mail with those four numbers, the expiry date, and the key words: "I am the authorised card holder for this account." It's ingenuity like this which won the war.

Comics

They may be
very collectible
but fans could be
disappointed by what they
can actually buy over the Web. Still, among
all the sites which have a 'look but don't buy'
policy, you can find a few bizarre curios

Comic Shack

www.comicshack.uk.com
Simple site offering a huge array of commercial and independent comic
books. Start by selecting a publisher from a list including old favourites,
Marvel, DC and Golden. Then you'll be led to lists of comics and issues
available, with prices and condition information. Head to Bits & Bobs to
translate the condition codes. Prices are good – we're talking pennies in
some cases – with postage starting at £1. They don't currently operate a
fully fledged online order form but you can e-mail requests.

Books 'n' comics

www.booksncomics.co.uk
This is one site where you can order online, over a secure server, and which
spells out its terms and conditions very clearly indeed. All that said, you're
more likely to find comic books here (everything from *Buffy* to *The Simpsons'*
seminal tomes and *2000AD*) than issues of your actual favourite comics.

Comics International

www.comics-international.com
A useful gateway site offering a virtually definitive directory of UK stockists,
rated hyperlinks to great comic sites, reviews of hundreds of comics and an
FAQ on comic trivia which, among other interesting things, tells you which
sets of Marvel Comics are almost worthless.

Comics Unlimited

www.comicsunlimited.com
A site which almost lives up to its title, with an impressive array of products
from Marvel, DC and Chaos, a resumé of the latest comic news and even an
issue of a psycho circus magazine based on the rock band Kiss. And, by
God, it even delivers outside the good ol' U S of A.

English Magazines

www.englishmagazines.com

This site comes with good word-of-mouth backing and enables you to subscribe to a range of comics including such immortal works as the *Beano* and *Sabrina The Teenage Witch*. Not for the collector because it focuses on the here and now rather than classic titles and issues of yesteryear.

Vault Comics

www.vaultcomics.com

Despite its guarantee to hold at least four auctions each year, on our last visit the site hadn't been updated since the last one closed. But it's still worth a look if your spine tingles when we tell you *The Adventures of Wonder Woman* (Vol I), available on our last visit, sold for £609. Comics are divided into bronze, silver, golden and British, selling from between £5 and £700. Bids can be made via e-mail, post or fax using the handy online bidding form.

Vintage Magazines

www.vinmag.com/vintage.htm

The Vintage Magazines Company has a fantastic selection of classic comics in its online back catalogue. Sadly the closest you can get to instant shopping gratification is to e-mail them about an issue's availability.

Other sites you might want to consider:

www.acmecomics.com runs auctions on e-bay and is in the process of adding an electronic archive of issues.

www.comicshack.uk.com is a good British site with a strong archive but, as yet, no online ordering.

www.comic-store.com for persistent DC Comic fans only. If you're not ordering from the US you have to e-mail details of the DC title or issue you want and send a money order.

www.amazon.co.uk has a significant stock of books about comics.

www.whsmith.co.uk has a fund of the same and you get the chance to reserve the latest issue of the *Beano*, *Dandy* etc.

If you're always on the lookout for comics, it's worth keying the magic c-word into a search engine or two as there always seems to be a weird car boot fair or auction where a collector is selling their complete Dan Dare back catalogue.

It's a bold claim to suggest that you've got the lot but Comics Unlimited do a pretty good job of living up to it

Computer games

There's no better (or cheaper) place than the Internet to get gamed up, whether you're into aliens, zombies, Ecco the Dolphin or golf

General — Jungles, Amazon but no rainforest

Amazon.co.uk

www.amazon.co.uk

Amazon has added a new section for games with a cross-referenced database and some abbreviated charts to give you ideas. Practical info on availability and age restrictions is clearly marked, but what sets Amazon apart is the number and quality of its reviews. These are written by real people and Amazon is not afraid to criticise (of one title the reviewer says simply: "I'd rather watch paint dry."). First-class deliveries are £1.40, plus 42p per game.

BOL

www.uk.bol.com

Along with books, music and film, the UK arm of bol.com has now extended its range to include software – both gaming and business, education and reference titles. Browsing can be done by game genre or console type, or you can go straight to the bestsellers, value titles (all under £10) or check out the downloadable demos before you buy (PC games only). You can even ask the editor for recommendations – just let them know the platform you are buying for, the age range and how much you want to spend.

Toys "R" Us

www.toysrus.co.uk

This famous high-street toyshop has a section dedicated to video games, and includes Playstation (1 and 2), Gameboy, Dreamcast and PC platform games, as well as some hardware. There's a lot of choice and the kids' games (such as Tweenies. Pokémon and Buzz Lightyear) are particularly good. Delivery is £3.50, mainland UK only, with orders delivered within three days.

Jungle.com
www.jungle.com
A decent site from one of the biggest names in Internet retailing which specialises in electronic goods and which also happens to be *Which?*-approved. The homepage is inviting although the site's determination to convince you there's a lorra, lorra stuff here does tend to have an adverse effect on clarity. The best way to steer yourself through the busy pages is to click straight on the games icon and you can search by genre and platform. There is also a list of top sellers and you can add your own reviews. Delivery is included in all prices.

Games without guns   "Peace, man!"

Chicken Run
www.eidosinteractive.co.uk
Fast and furious game based on the film. Just pull down 'Select a game'.

Ecco the Dolphin
www.sega.com
Ecco falls through time and has to restore the human/dolphin paradise. Gorgeous graphics with an eco-friendly theme. Only for Dreamcast.

Hello Kitty's Cube Frenzy
www.nintendo.com
Brightly coloured, Tetris-like puzzle game for little ones with a Gameboy.

Myst and Riven
www.cyan.com
Extraordinary brainteaser games and fiendish logic problems to solve.

Starship Titanic
www.starshiptitanic.com
Hilarious game from the endearingly knotted mind of the late Douglas Adams. Rescue the starship using only wit, hopeless robots and some roast chicken.

Super Mario 64
www.nintendo.com
The official homepage of the gent who started all this, and for what? A cake, that's what. This URL is attached to the official Nintendo address and has plenty of strategy tips but you can only order if you're in the US.

Computer games

Argos

www.argos.co.uk

Argos' website is warm, friendly and full of places to explore. If you know what you want, head straight to the product search; otherwise browse the catalogue using the other link on the left. For computer games, you'll confusingly have to click on the consoles link before opting whether you want to purchase a machine or a game. Games are only available for Playstation, Dreamcast and handhelds and there isn't a great deal of choice, but the prices can be surprisingly good – and, though you'll struggle to reach it on games alone, any orders over £100 are delivered free.

Dixons

www.dixons.co.uk

Dixons is one of the best known brands in the high street, and its website comes across as cheap, cheerful and colourful. The homepage is packed with flashing bargain signs, as well as links to best buys and special offers. The games section is split into those that are suitable for consoles and those you can play on your PC, which can be annoying if you just want to look at all the available versions at the same time. The purchase process is logical but trying to register from a Mac was a frustrating experience. You can find a decent range of product, in a slightly more relaxed online environment, at **www. freeserve.com/games** – Freeserve being the free Internet Service Provider launched by Dixons in another century.

Electronics Boutique

www.eb.uk.com

Once the site loads, you are confronted by an annoying loyalty-card pop-up, but once you've got rid of this there are some featured games, a list of top sellers and a pre-ordering service for those much-hyped titles you just can't wait for. Games are listed by hardware (Nintendo, PC and so on), all of which can be accessed via the funky-looking

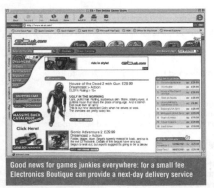

Good news for games junkies everywhere: for a small fee Electronics Boutique can provide a next-day delivery service

sidebar. You can read thorough reviews and search for your local EB high-street store so you can trade old games you've had enough of. An excellent ordering process, and no need to register tops it all off. Delivery is free within the UK, although if you're desperate you can pay £4.95 for an overnight service.

Game
www.game.uk.com
You would expect to find a good online store when you're dealing with one of the best games retailers in the real world and you won't be disappointed. Once again, however, the site starts off with that ever unpopular feature known as 'Loyalty pop-up time!' which confronts you even before you access the homepage – it feels a bit like going to a restaurant and being asked to order before you've been given the menu. Games are grouped by machine and there are excellent descriptions of each title, some complete with examples of the graphics. The charts and featured titles offer plenty of ideas; the news stories will satisfy gamers anxious to find out about upcoming releases, and there's an A-Z list for those who know what they are looking for. When you come to buy, do be careful with your clicks as you don't get any confirmation for each addition, though your titles are added to a shopping cart which remains on the left of the screen. Delivery starts at £1.95 but is free if you spend more than £75.

HMV
www.hmv.co.uk
Soon after you enter this site it becomes pretty clear that HMV regards itself primarily as a music retailer and everything else is a bit of a bother. Music fills the homepage, and you have to hunt for the games section. Even once you're there, getting to a list of titles is hard. News stories are provided but scrolling and navigation are slow and registration is lengthy and complicated.

PC World
www.pcworld.co.uk
PC World has a similar site to that of Dixons – can

THE EVIL EMPIRE?
Rather like a virtual baddie, the Dixons group is establishing something of a gaming empire with some of the strongest names under its wing.

PC World and Freeserve are involved with the high-street giant, and the purchase of a stake in Gameplay furthers this trend, making it feel as though all consoles lead inevitably to Dixons.

Whether this is good for the gamer or not is a matter of opinion, though at least online ordering saves you waiting for hours to talk to a monosyllabic and uninformed salesman in one of Dixons' shops.

And while the 'bargain basement' approach might not suit everyone, the sites are all secure and quite easy to use.

----

www.dixons.co.uk
----
www.freeserve.com/games
----
www.gameplay.com
----
www.pcworld.co.uk

this be a coincidence? – with the same 'bargains galore' image. Only PC and Playstation 2 titles are available, and there's a limited choice of those. But once you have selected a game there is plenty of descriptive and technical information. Pricing is clear and, as with Dixons, ordering is safe and simple.

Special Reserve Discount Club

www.ukgames.com

The online games arm of the Special Reserve Discount Club is probably the most cluttered homepage of any of the games sites. There's far too much information there to take in properly, even if you do keep scrolling all the way down. A bit of careful editing would help immensely in this respect. Getting to the checkout is equally difficult, but the hefty discounts for members might just make all the effort worthwhile.

WHSmith

www.whsmith.co.uk

Another high-street retailer whose heart, at least based on the evidence of this site, is not really in computer games. Having said that, the search facility is quite speedy, with plenty of fields to help you narrow your search. The red-hot sale section also offers discounts of up to 50 per cent, although the game section of this bargain basement is quite limited. Delivery will cost you a minimum of £2.74 and a maximum of £15 in the UK. Serious users would probably prefer to use the site for Games Paradise (see facing page), part of the WHSmith group.

Online retailers Out there in cyberspace

Chipsworld.co.uk

www.chipsworld.co.uk

Not a site dedicated to the multifarious uses of potato but a rather good games site. It looks pretty and is easy-to-navigate, two characteristics that don't often go together. Along with games listed by machine, there is a featured title, a section on recent releases and cheaper second-hand versions of most of the games. There is clear pricing information on products and e-mail confirmation for both receipt and dispatch.

Computer Exchange

www.cex.co.uk

CEX claims to be the largest online retailer and the range is certainly good. It can be unreasonably hard to find what you want, however, if it happens not to be a featured item or in the charts. When you have found what you're after, clicking through gives you a brief description and then the buying process is pretty simple. The most useful feature is the five-step ordering process which shows you exactly how far you've got and ensures that you don't get lost.

Postal delivery is free in the UK, with a £3.80 charge for a next-day service.

Gamesparadise.com

www.gamesparadise.com

Another homepage with too many options hides the fact that this site doesn't seem to have a full range of titles. Featured and new games dominate. You have to do a lot of scrolling to get anywhere. There's a lot of news and info here but it's not quite the paradise the URL suggests.

Gamesstreet

www.gamesstreet.infront.co.uk

This site is organised primarily by the various platforms, each of which you reach through a button on the homepage. The well-designed graphics and clear symbols allow easy navigation but you find you have to scroll way down each page for featured products and the latest chart. What is good, though, is the very clear indication of games' age restrictions – useful for adults searching for suitable titles for the family. The registration process necessary before ordering is tedious, but delivery is free and takes between one and two days.

First choose your platform, then choose your game. It sounds simple and it's made simpler by the provision of handy hints over what games will hit the spot for different-age gamers

Computer games

Not just a site to help boost your games collection, GamesWire also does its bit to keep you informed

Games Console

www.games-console.com

The site's not much to look at, and it does take a while to find what you want – opt to enter the secure shop from the homepage and then click on the platform of your choice, before selecting whether you are after software, hardware or accessories. There's no straightforward search facility so be prepared to do a bit of browsing, and there isn't a great deal of information available on the games. However, there are some real bargains and good secondhand deals to be found here if you are prepared to look. Unfortunately delivery starts at £3.80 for small items, going up to £10 for bigger items – although that is guaranteed next-day.

Games Wire

www.gameswire.com

This is more a portal than a shopping site (although there are games to buy) and it has plenty of information on the world of gaming. There is a news section and some very interesting editorial features, such as an article on violence in games, although (predictably enough) they don't regard it as any kind of problem. Finding games and specific information for your chosen machine is done by clicking on the desired platform. Symbols are provided but they could be clearer and are no good for non-gamers and newbies. Or you can scroll down the homepage for fuller listings. The ordering process is simple and works on a step-by-step basis, with free delivery on all orders unless you want the 24-hour service which costs £3.80.

The Game Zone

www.thegamezone.co.uk

Only games for Playstation 1 and 2 and PCs here, with the emphasis on cheap prices. There's not a great deal of choice, and the site doesn't look particularly inviting, but it's easy enough to see what they're offering and if you're after a good deal, it's worth a look. There's also a pre-ordering facility and delivery within one or two days is free, though there is an additional charge for Saturday drop-offs.

Simply Games
www.simplygames.co.uk

Fun, nicely designed site that offers nothing but gaming products so die-hards won't be distracted. The site looks good with clear graphics, links to each platform along the top of the pages and the best bargains of the moment flagged up straightaway. The search facility, which is easy to find on the homepage, lets you search for any title by format, genre or price. The prices are excellent (savings range from £5 to £30), the site is secure and delivery is free to anywhere in the world by air mail, first-class mail for the UK.

Softwarefirst.com
www.softwarefirst.com

Although sometimes slow to load and occasionally temperamental, this is a pretty simple site which lists games by machine, including Game Boys and Apple Macs. There are some featured titles and news stories about the most popular games, and once you've placed an order through the secure server you can make use of the tracking service, although it may sometimes simply tell you that your order is being processed. They also sell DVDs and have a pre-ordering service on forthcoming titles for impatient gamers.

Software Savings
www.softwaresavings.co.uk

This is a grown-up site featuring primarily professional software but you can buy games as well. There are no funky images or graphics, but the site does offer very good prices on the limited range of titles (mostly flight simulators and other strategic games). The ordering process is mercifully short and shows clearly what you have chosen. First-class recorded delivery is free on all orders, or they offer a next-day service at an extra cost.

Softwarezone
www.softwarezone.com

The spartan design of this site is great for no-nonsense shoppers who like to download their software direct from the Internet, with game demos

---

"TWO FAT LADIES..."

For those of you who find computer games a bit like trying to understand the difference between garage music and grunge, Yahoo Games has kindly provided a relaxed environment where you can play electronic versions of such classics as mah jong, Chinese checkers and, erm, bingo. Yes, even on the Net there is the equivalent of an electronic voice shouting "Clickety click! Sixty-six."

Thankfully, chess and backgammon have proved more of an online mecca than Mecca's favourite. To join in the fun, just log on to *http://games.yahoo. com*. You'll need to have a browser which can handle Java software. After that, you're on your own.

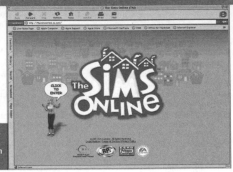

With the Sims you can simply set up your very own domestic hell, then sit back and enjoy...

and shareware options. You can see straight away that any purchase you make is secure and the process is easy and fast as long as you choose the correct download for your operating system. The range of titles is mind-boggling, even extending to some out-of-date (but still dearly beloved) machines such as the Sinclair Spectrum – yes, really. At first the site can appear difficult to browse, but either head towards the 'top 20' or 'staff picks' links if you want to look at the best, or alternatively search by keyword if you know what you're after. Clicking on a title gives you such details as how long a game took to download and what operating system is required for a selected range of titles.

Specialists If you already know what you want

Eidos
www.eidosinteractive.co.uk
The people who brought you Tomb Raider have an e-store which allows you to buy their games and merchandise and play online. Delivery normally takes five days but you're asked to allow up to 28 days, which sounds like the bad old days of 1970s mail-order catalogues. Delivery charges, which seem to work out around the £5 mark for the UK, are displayed early on in the checkout process.

Electronic Arts
www.ea.com
Electronic Arts has been making some of the best sports sims in the business for a while and this site is dedicated to its range. As long as you're not visiting via a Mac, you can search by brand, genre or machine, plus there are some

features and 'hotspots', but the range is limited to EA and associated products and isn't what you might call impartial. Make sure that you select the European store from the bottom-left menu or you'll be lost in the US version before you know it. The ability to search specific categories on the site (such as support) is a nice touch. Delivery charges are calculated by the contents of your shopping basket.

GameSpy Industries
www.rpgplanet.com
As the name suggests, this is a massive portal for fans of role-playing games. It's all a bit dark and scary for the uninitiated and you almost have to be an expert to get the best out of the site. The navigation bar has all the options you need to join a game or set up your own for others to join, but the text is tiny, so read carefully before you commit. As on other game-centric sites, shopping is provided by links elsewhere and can be hard to find.

Sega
www.dreamcast-europe.com
The official site for Dreamcast and Dreamcast players is where you need to come to enjoy playing online with other users. It has a slim range of titles available to buy through the site, but make sure you're actually in the shop section, otherwise you'll be surfing around aimlessly wondering how to order. The advantage of this is less clutter and more up-to-the-minute information, but you won't get the discounts that dedicated retailers offer. All orders are subject to a delivery charge of £2.50.

The Sims
www.thesims.com
Fancy a cup of tea? Well, type this URL into your address bar, go milk a cow, pasteurise the milk, put the kettle on, do the necessary and then come back to your browser page. Chances are the homepage for this genetic mutant (X chromosomes from computer games and Y chromosomes from soap operas) will just about have loaded. It's worth the wait, however, because the Sims allows you to build a virtual family – only unlike your real family, you actually have some shred of influence over what they do because you can, for example, stick an aggressively untidy character into a house full of control freaks and wait for the fireworks. Go here to understand what all the fuss is about, download videos of the characters and buy the CD-ROM.

The Station
www.everquest.com
A site dedicated to the game which mirrors its gothic-style graphics and scantily-clad female warrior characters. It isn't immediately clear where to buy but there's a 'Buy EverQuest' option on the left-hand menu. The retail service is from Sony's Station.com, which is easy enough once you're there. There is also an online forum that allows you to chat with fellow fans.

Computers

So can you get good deals
on a PC online? Is bargain
software hard to find?
The Net can deliver,
and we're here to help
you carve a path through the
maze of conflicting data

General Where do you start?

Buy.com

www.gb.buy.com

From computers and software through to digital imaging and net-
working, this site has it all, with plenty of information on the 35,000 products
available and competitive prices too. The selection is huge and each item
comes with full specs whether it's the latest desktop PC or just a replacement
cable. There's also a low-price guarantee in operation – if you find your purchase cheaper at any other UK store (online or off) within 24 hours, Buy.com
will promise to beat that price by £1. Buying online is straightforward and
next-day delivery is free for all orders over £50 (it's £4.95 for those under).

DABS

www.dabs.com

Dabs is the name on every aficionado's lips when it comes to online computer
buying. This Bolton-based site can offer the goods more cheaply than most
because it takes less profit than competitors and therefore shifts its stuff
in greater volumes. No 'proper-beige-computers-only' attitude, either:
Dabs sells Macs as well as PCs, and at prices very competitive with Mac
Warehouse the last time we looked. All the big PC brands are there, plus
software, peripherals, components and audio-visual gear. Colourful and easy
to click round, the site is secure, although it could have more information on
delivery times (usually pretty rapid and often next-day).

Insight

www.insight.com

Another little goldmine, though this pure-PC site is stronger on components and peripherals than on complete desktop PC systems – its partners here include Toshiba, Hewlett Packard and Compaq. It's American, but you click through to the UK site with no fuss. The main attraction here is what Insight calls its Stock Blowout – a bargain basement where you could pick up anything from a still-boxed IBM notebook to a slightly scuffed AMD K7 motherboard for a fraction of the original cost. No refunds and no returns here, matey. As with most computer warehouses, (free) delivery depends on whether what you want is in stock, but it's generally within four days and often next-day. Insight's is an SSL site.

PC World
www.pcworld.co.uk
This is the non-techie end of the online buying spectrum. The well-known real-world warehouse site is for those who know they want a computer but don't know much more than that. The friendly design is particularly friendly to the PC novice. There's no bewildering depth or range, just well-known names and a brief selection of everything, from complete packages to monitors, printers, peripherals and software. First-time shoppers should head to the customer services section to check delivery details and after-sales care, while *PC World of Computing* provides sound advice on taking the plunge into technology, including reviews, hints and tips, and a handy jargon buster. Each product comes with a full spec sheet, images and a competitive price tag.

 Briefly Sites where the consumer is king

Capital
www.capital.uk.com
Clear and easy-to-navigate, with a handy panel listing all the categories carried. Essential items such as computers, laptops, handheld devices, monitors and scanners all included, now that they've stocked up the shop.

Comet Direct
www.comet.co.uk
A limited range of PCs and accessories, as you might expect, but pictures and specs for each product are available and the prices are competitive. Comet offers brief tips with most products – one being refreshing: "ask yourself whether you actually need that laptop before you buy…"

Dixons
www.dixons.co.uk
Much what you'd expect from Dixons, with top brands, brief information and easy navigation. If you're lucky you may pick up a free printer or a scanner with your PC. Prices, along with model specs, range across the spectrum.

It is _so_ a proper computer

Apple Store
www.apple.com

With products this glossy and seductive, it's no wonder Apple offers its own loan or lease scheme; the temptation factor, heightened by great site design and photography, is enormous. Choose UK from the pop-down list at the bottom of the page, then check out the spec sheets and helpful advice. Caveats: Apple is a bit mean with the RAM at the lower end of the range. No, we didn't care, either. Delivery can take 14 days, but is usually much quicker.

Mac Warehouse
www.macwarehouse.co.uk

Good site for Mac-compatible peripherals, plus you could pick up a titanium PowerBook G4 with 256 MB SDRAM for less than the official Apple site price when we visited. Everything comes with a spec sheet and it's good for speed as well as price: they will try to deliver next day if you order before 4pm.

 From the big names to the little guys

Aria
www.aria.co.uk

You can now order online with Aria's secure credit card server, but the product info is still as tech heavy as ever. If you know your MTBF from your CMOS, you'll be fine; if not, you may want to come back when you know exactly what you want. On the plus side, you should at least be able to find a top brand model to suit your price bracket and the helpful quick link to their price directory means you can see what deals they can do before you trawl the site.

Big Red
www.bigred.co.uk

Big Red's no-nonsense site gets you to what you want right away, whether you want a hot deal on a top spec PC or to build a machine to suit. You can design your own standard notebook and PCs, for business or pleasure, and you can also top up on all the software and components you'll need. Delivery is free, and while they ask you to allow ten working days for your order, they admit it usually only takes half that time.

Computer Manuals
www.compman.co.uk

If you're going to operate something with a 1Ghz processor and the kind of software something so fast can run, you'll need to RTFM (Read The Flippin'

Manual!) to get the best out of it. Here's where to buy. Particularly good are the O'Reilly tomes – there's probably even one to help program your juicer.

Dan

www.dan.co.uk

An oddly constructed homepage gives pride of place to news columns, only one of which is dedicated to the doings of Dan, but the machines have a good reputation and the site is easy-to-navigate with separate business, home and education user sections. Pick up a starter family PC for less than £800, or customise your own. Delivery should take five to ten days.

Dell

www.dell.co.uk

Efficient and businesslike, online sales specialist Dell aims to provide a desktop, workstation or notebook to suit your needs, whether that's home office, small business or large conglomerate. Pick a specific model or select a basic model and customise it to your heart's content. The site has been revamped and extensive product descriptions, spec sheets and guides now help you buy. Prices obviously aren't bargain basement but there's an auction link to the Dell factory outlet section advertising models for as little as £1.

Gateway

www.gw2k.co.uk/

It's great that you can customise your Gateway model to suit your needs but not quite so great if you don't know the difference between a 3.5 diskette and Superdisk LS120. It also failed to function using IE4 on a Mac when we tried. The site has, though, taken a step away from the US version and taken on its own identity. And from the sales advisors waiting to take your order to the legions of Gateway staff keen to 'chat' to ensure your wads of cash get you just the right package, they also seem big on customer service.

IBM

www.ibm.com/uk

You can buy PCs, laptops, handhelds and accessories direct from IBM's website or, for more choice, there's a fuller list of all the products available from their partners. Search results can be sorted by price or spec, depending on your priority, and all the products come with thorough details and photography. There are loads of helpful features – such as the

You'd expect Dell to have something for everyone and the newly revamped site doesn't disappoint

ability to compare models, find a local dealer and source technical support. The only downside is that some of the menus use an illegibly tiny print.

Simply
www.simply.co.uk
East London company selling its own Systemax PCs in desktop-ready, customisable or no-monitor, pre-built versions. At the bottom end of the home range the C7665R with a 766 MHz Intel processor would set you back a mere £586, with a top-end P1500R with a 1.5 GHz Intel processor, 20 GB hard drive, DVD and CD-RW, steaming in at £1,761. There are plenty of hardware peripherals and software. The site is SSL-secure and you can pay by credit card. Orders over £50 are postage-free.

Viglen
www.viglen.co.uk
Click straight through to the latest special offers from the homepage, or choose 'buy online' to select your desired model from the popular Genie range. The site is full of constantly changing special deals, great if you're a bit of a bargain hunter, and each PC can be configured to suit your needs.

Watford Electronics
www.watford.co.uk
Watford is named after its company base and has been manufacturing and selling its own-brand Aries PC for nearly 30 years (it gave us the first electronic TV video game – 'Pong' – in the 1970s). You should be able to pick up a PC Lite without a monitor for less than £300. There's a wide range of competitively priced desktops and notebooks, though annoyingly many models seemed to be sold out. Delivery (free if your purchase is over £50) is within three to five days. Keep an eye on the B-Grade section for bargains.

It's well worth keeping a very close eye on the Viglen site as their 'special deals' keep on rolling in...

W Store
www.wstore.co.uk
Although a "helping businesses to buy smarter" slogan is visible (just) on the homepage, it is not immediately obvious that this means only businesses can buy here. The prices are competitive, but you need to enter all your company details to register and buy. The site's search facility is directed around manufacturers, with each having their own store here; to search by product, use the keyword search.

Accessories For the tastefully garnished PC

If you thought the man in your life had finished spending your mortgage repayment money on his new computer toy, here's the bad news. The spending has probably only just started. Your house may now be home to an entry-level PC, complete with all the essentials, monitor, keyboard etc but chances are it will look like everyone else's – so why not put your individual stamp on it. Start off by customising the keyboard. Both Access Keyboards and the Keyboard Company sell customised keyboards to your specifications, or you can simply choose one from their range of large, small, waterproof and industrial models. If the South Park mousemat you got free with your PC just doesn't give out the right message, pick up a sophisticated mouse kneepad rug from PC Mouse for £11.99, or advertise your Irish heritage with religious, historical and legend designs, including Mollie Malone, from Casey Designs for £6.99. A must-buy are the wrist rests for £11.95 and the photomats for £7, both from Inpace. Face it, once you get going, you can say goodbye to any spare cash you thought you had.

Access Keyboards
www.accesskeyboards.co.uk
Cartridge Shop
www.cartridgeshop.co.uk
Casey Designs
www.caseydesigns.co.uk
Cover Tec
www.covertec.com
Inpace
www.inpace.com

Keyboard Company
www.keyboardco.com
Mouse House
www.mouse-house.co.uk
PC Mouse
www.pc-mouse.co.uk
Technofilter UK
www.antiglare.co.uk

Novelties Computer trinkets & Hazzard-ous mousemats

Cybertrash

www.cybertrash.org

At last, girls! Bits of old computer recycled into jewellery, wind chimes and fridge magnets! Surprisingly attractive, too, particularly the earrings made from pre-loved inductor coils, resistors, diodes, head amps and switches, among other components. Ordering is secure and all major cards are accepted. What happens with overseas delivery isn't too clear, but Cybertrash is set up to automatically convert foreign currency for credit cards, adding however much is necessary for the bank's fee. At an average of only $5 per item, it must be worth a try just to see what turns up.

Computers

Stardust
www.kitsch.co.uk
How much do you want a pair of computer cufflinks? Or Farrah Fawcett's head on a pencil? A Dukes of Hazzard or Elvis in Vegas mousemat? Some chilli lights to drape round that boring beige monitor? A Drinking Bird for your mug…? You're there already, aren't you?

Red Light Runner
www.redlightrunner.com
Apple collectibles, from towels and sandals with the Apple logo to mugs, pens and even a 'Steve Jobs for President' sticker. Red Light Runner also sells those classy 'Think different' posters, featuring Miles Davis, Callas, Lucy & Desi and Martha Graham, all at classy prices. Shipping is international.

PDAs — The world in the palm of your hand

21 Store
www.21store.com
From the Handspring Visor to the wafer-thin Rex Pro DS-5, 21 Store – now also incorporated into www.expansys.com – has the compete range of PDAs and palmtops, with both Palm and Windows CE platforms. It's cheerful, fast and well organised, and you can search the complete store or head straight to one of the sections, which include global positioning systems, and binoculars and night vision departments. Good images, descriptions in plain English, and overnight delivery is promised if you order before 3pm.

Widget Software
www.widget.co.uk
Selling all the latest handheld systems, EPOC devices, Palm OS, Windows CE and a selection of mobiles, this is a site that offers enough additional information to allow you to feel confident about your new purchase. Psion, Compaq, Hewlett Packard and Handspring dominate each section with high-street prices throughout. There's also a bargain bin with an extensive list. Secure ordering is available and gadgets are dispatched within seven days.

Yahoo Handhelds and Palmtops
http://fullcoverage.yahoo.com/fc/Tech/Handheld_and_Palmtop_Computers
You can't buy palmtops here but check this site out

Widget has plenty of big names to choose from as you search for the perfect handheld number – and a bargain bin for a low-cost route to going high tech

before you do, as Yahoo gives you the dirt on whether the shiny now toy (sorry, business tool) you want is about to be rendered obsolete by a successor. On busy days, four new palmtop-related stories are posted and there are loads of vital links.

 Before you splash the cash, read this...

IT Reviews
www.itreviews.co.uk
If you need more info than the single-line captions on most resellers' sites, there is a wealth of online technological support and advice via the Net. IT Reviews is one of the best, with independent reviews by professional journalists. Hardware, software and games are all included, and the reviews are consumer-friendly. The analyses and concise final verdicts of the group tests are the most useful of these.

You might also want to take a look at…
Computer Previews http://compreviews.about.com/compute/compreview
Tech-review.com www.tech-review.com
Review Finder www.reviewfinder.com
Ziff Davis www.zdnet.com

Crafts

Okay, crafts have never been what you might call groovy, but the Internet is helping them finally shake off that Women's Institute stereotype. Slowly...

Candle Makers Supplies
www.candlemakers.co.uk
Although you can't order online, as Europe's largest candle-making supply store this simple, well-organised site deserves a mention. Experts, novices, adults and kids are all catered for. Prices are good (a complete kit is around £24) and there are plenty of hints to help you create more intricate designs.

The Crafts Council
www.craftscouncil.org.uk
Packed with news on craft shows, events and exhibitions, plus an education section detailing workshops and seminars all over the country. There's also a list of craft shops with links to those with websites.

Crafty Chick
www.craftychick.com
Don't think you've tumbled across a Playskool site: Crafty Chick offers both materials and inspiration to go beyond toilet-roll-tube pencil pots and scary masks. Crafts include glass painting, découpage, stencilling and gilding. All the necessary tools are available, alongside advice to get started, including a *Changing Rooms*-style guide to rag rolling, bagging, sponging and crackling.

Economy of Brighton
www.economyofbrighton.co.uk
Specialising in decorative rubber stamps and hole punches, this site also sells a vast range of other art supplies including powder paint, modelling clay and Plaster of Paris at excellent prices. Accounts are available for schools, and delivery is £5 for any order up to a max of 30 kilos.

Encaustic Arts
www.encaustic.com
Large site full of tips and ideas for projects involving heating wax to make

pretty pictures. It sells a rainbow of coloured wax blocks plus card, rubber stamps and even the right sort of iron for creating the best result. Postage is free on UK orders which are dispatched within two days.

Heaton Cooper

www.heatoncooper.co.uk
Site run by Cumbrian artists selling high-quality paints and art supplies, including specialist items like gold leaf. Postage is free on orders over £35, though there are special delivery options if you're having a watercolour crisis. A test order arrived well-packed and complete within three days.

Hobbicraft

www.hobbicraft.co.uk
A huge range of hobby and craft supplies here. Airfix models (remember them?), glass engraving equipment, beads, and painting-by-number kits to mention just a few. You need to know what you're after, though. Delivery is promised within five working days and there's a 14-day no-quibble refund.

Hobby's

www.hobby.uk.com
Online version of weighty craft supplies catalogue specialising in model-making, but now featuring other creative kit like glass cutters and dolls houses. All orders over £10 are sent by Parcelforce.

Scottish Wood Craft

www.scottishwoodcraft.co.uk
Simple but effective site selling woodworking tools as well as delightful handmade wooden items from chairs to bird mobiles. We particularly like the spurtles (that's a porridge-stirring stick to you sassenachs). Prices do not include VAT, and delivery can take up to two weeks (longer for the larger items), but everything comes with a 30-day money-back guarantee.

Sunflower Fabrics

www.sunflowerfabrics.com
Impressively forward-thinking site, established for more than three years, with a comprehensive help section. It specialises in quilting and other needlework supplies, and offers a lovely selection of patterns and complete quilt kits. Orders under £10 incur a £1.50 handling fee, but they'll ship abroad if you want. As the company reckons it could take you months to browse the 2,000 images and 1,000 products on the site, its catalogue is now also on CD-ROM.

Sybilla Davis Designs

www.sd-designs.com
Professional looking site selling a limited range of cross-stitch designs displaying picturesque scenes from Devon and Cornwall. Most are priced at £14, with a number of simpler designs around £5, all with free UK delivery.

Crazes

With each new craze lasting about as long as a goldfish's memory span, the Internet is a wonderful tool to find the best, the worst and the weirdest

Modern "The trouble with kids today..."

Beanie Babies

http://shop.store.yahoo.com/walloffame/beaniebabies.html

It's easy to forget that it's only a couple of years since the Beanie Babies craze was a Threat to Society As We Know It. New babies continue to pour out of the toy industry as this Wall Of Fame site proves. There's even a video called How To Spot A Counterfeit Beanie Baby, released in 1988, which resurfaced on the Web last summer.

Digimon

www.digiexperience.com

These are cute cartoon characters that have their own special powers, now available as cards that kids can collect and swap and fight over in the playground... yes, the successor to the Pokémon craze is itself about to implode (first few sites checked have now shut down due to boredom of the creators – not a good sign). But a few out there are still fighting the good fight, and with an episode-by-episode show synopsis, message board, videoclips and complete character bios, and so, so much more, this site must surely be the (soon-to-be) last word on the critters.

Microstars

www.microstars.co.uk

If you have a young child, these hand-held heroes that come in Powerpodz Chocolate Podz are probably already scattered about your living room. Find out all about these mini players from this official site. It doesn't sell the figures direct, but will link you to www.webswappers.com where you can complete your collection. Each player comes with a skill rating and the players can come with six different coloured bases with different ratings. Then you play some kind of game where total rating doesn't matter anyway. No, we don't get it either. Plus our stomachs hurt from having to eat all that chocolate.

Pokémon

www.pokemon.com

The official site isn't a merchandise shifting operation but a useful source of downloads if junior has a computer, and an even more useful source of info for parents who find they can't stomach the contemptuous look in their kids' eyes when they inadvertently confuse Clefable with Clefairy. You can find the official card game site on www.wizards.com/Pokemon and the official online store on http://store.wizards.com but by the time you've figured out the ordering process you could have gone down to WHSmith, bought the starter pack, read the rules booklet and be lurking outside schools trying to make trades. You will lose all that hard-earned street cred unless you get your mitts on the interactive THINKChip computerised battle stadium – out now!

Scooters

www.streetscooters.co.uk

Okay, not so much a craze as a sign of an early mid-life crisis, as even your boring banker uncle has one of these folding aluminium scooters (and now that he has spent the last six months of Saturdays practising in the driveway you are not so ashamed to be seen out with him). Check out this site to get him an upgraded model or an accessory like a holdall for that office commute. Clearly laid out and shipping is free in the UK.

Tamagotchi

www.ridhughz.demon.co.uk/tamagotchi

The world's most famous virtual pet may already have its own set of anti-sites but the epitome of "cuteness on a keychain", as it's billed, is still damned hard to get hold of. This site has links to online stores such as Toys "R" Us which might still have a few in stock. It also has tips on how to make it age quicker, which cynics may think might best be achieved with a hammer.

 Stuff that's no longer really happening, man

Space Invaders

http://spaceinvaders.retrogames.com

The classic arcade game of the late 1970s has its own e-shrine where you can download stuff. It has also been regenerated as a computer game you can buy from www.activision.com/games/spaceinvaders.

Tablesports

http://members.aol.com/tablesport/INDEX.HTM

Table football has entered the design sweepstakes with these Italian-made games. Choose from elegant art deco or formica briar wood, to pub-quality coin-operated tables if you want to spite your flatmates. They'll set you back several hundred pounds, but it's a small price to pay to impress your mates.

Department Stores

Traditional high-street names have
taken to the Net the way porcupines
make love: very carefully indeed

High street | Old names and new technology

Allders

www.allders.com
'In development' probably sums up this Allders online effort. New sections are
gradually being added to the store but they should have ensured everything
was in good working order before they spread their wings. Currently selling
housewares, fashion and electricals, navigation is annoying – the scroll-down
menus frequently disappear and reappear ad hoc – and descriptions are poor.
And although images can be enlarged, the poor quality makes this a pointless
exercise. Room for improvement.

Debenhams

www.debenhams.com
A sensible site for a sensible store and a safe bet for Debenhams. No flashy
graphics or elaborate colour schemes, it's staid to look at and to search.
You'll find fashion, gifts, flowers and wedding items: search for a gift in your
price range or check out fashion by brands. Top names include Jasper
Conran, Pearce II Fionda, Boxfresh and Warehouse. On the downside there
are minimal descriptions and poor images that make it hard to feel confident
about your order unless you've seen it in store, and the pink type is hard to
read. The wedding section is a complete department in itself with dresses,
suits and hymns, and the capability of registering your own wedding list.

Littlewoods

www.indexshop.com
Traditionally backward in coming forward, Littlewoods currently offers two
online shopping schemes: Index, the online equivalent of the Index catalogue,

and Shop-!, an online and interactive television service. The Index site is busy, yet easy-to-navigate with standard categories like Sound and Vision, Gifts and so on. Cheap and cheerful, Littlewoods beats many on price with monthly sales and three months' interest-free credit, delivery guaranteed in 48 hours, and with a large collection of their paper catalogue featured online.

Marks & Spencer
www.marks-and-spencer.co.uk
Recently revamped M&S no longer sells food online, sticking to clothes and housewares. The site has improved greatly in recent months with clear, enlarged images and descriptions of each item. Standard ordering system with a £3 delivery charge and guaranteed 72-hour delivery.

 **Cyberstores**

Best of British
www.thebestofbritish.com
An online department store with clothing, gifts and household items from top British designers. Search by brand and product type or simply browse the designers' own collections. Top names include Mulberry and Lulu Guinness. No discounted items but delivery is free, taking up to 21 days.

Big Save
www.bigsave.com
Big Save has gone for a busy design with as much information crammed onto one page as possible. The images and text are too small, although the site is easy to navigate with distinct categories. Not your traditional department store, it still sells everything from blenders to pashminas, designer luggage and insurance, with up to 50 per cent savings.

Shoppers Universe
www.shoppersuniverse.com
Having long ago established itself in the online shopping market, Shoppers Universe has ironed out all the creases to bring you a well-organised store, packed to the brim with items for you, your family and even your garden shed. Navigation is smooth and simple. Delivery is charged at a standard £2.95 no matter how many items you order, and is free if you spend more than £100.

SLOW STARTERS
Despite the one-stop nature of the Net, high-street department stores have been slow to embrace the technology.

Big names such as House of Fraser and Dickins & Jones have as yet failed to set up a cyber equivalent. Harrods, on the other hand, has a comprehensive catalogue – but only for the US and Canada. And Liberty, after a initially successful trial, has now folded its online service.

Gradually, though, more and more stores are jumping onto the bandwagon with John Lewis (*www.johnlewis. co.uk*) selling many of its lines online and Bhs (*www.bhs.co.uk*) establishing a presence.

Drugs

The legal variety. For illegal ones you'll have to buy a different kind of guide book. Prescription and over-the-counter medicines are popping up all over the Web, and despite dire warnings, there are plenty of reputable sites which don't allow customers to flout the rules

General   Equipment and sports products

Academy Health

www.academyhealth.com

Stylish and calming, this site has a wide variety of products on sale: vitamins and supplements, sports nutrition, herbal remedies, skin and body care, family planning, and some over-the-counter medicines such as aspirin, and, oddly enough, fine wines. You have to do a lot of clicking to get to the products, but there are some attractive discounts over high-street prices, and, except for the wine, delivery is free within the UK, promised within three to seven days, which makes this a good-value alternative to battling the throngs on the high street if you can wait.

Allcures.com

www.allcures.com

This is currently the UK's only full-service online pharmacy, dispensing both private and NHS prescription medicines. Also on offer are the usual beauty products, toiletries, herbal remedies and vitamins, and even films. There are comprehensive sections on health information, plus news and FAQs on medicines and other Allcures products, though you have to scroll down a very long list of questions set out in no apparent order. Postage and packing is £3.49 for standard delivery in four days, free for orders over £35, and overnight shipping is available for those in pain. Minimal savings off high-street prices. With some medicines you may have to fill in a health questionnaire to proceed with your order.

Wellbeing

www.wellbeing.com

Wellbeing has joined up with high-street retailer Boots to offer an overall health site featuring not only pharmaceutical products but lifestyle items as well, many not available from the offline shop. Ranges include the usual beauty and health products plus nutritional supplements, a mother and baby section and fitness equipment. There are also plenty of articles, a discussion forum and even a Wellbeing television station for those with the technology. A recent addition is an online magazine. The Boots brand lends credibility, and you can earn Advantage points on some items as you shop, with special online-only deals. Shipping charges are £2.50 for second-day delivery, with next-day and Saturday delivery options.

Direct Response Marketing

www.propecia.co.uk

A very uninspiring name for a company – rather puts the emphasis on parting you from your dosh. Offering Viagra, Propecia and Xenical (the latter two being for baldness and weight loss respectively, the former for you-know-what troubles), this bold and brash site wins no design awards but all the info you need is right up front. To order, you fill in a medical questionnaire, including the name and address of your doctor, who will be informed by DRM, unless you declare that you will do this. The price of four Viagra tablets is £70, including postage and packing, so use them wisely. Delivery within the UK is promised in seven days by recorded post. The site's medical credibility is undermined by the offer of Lure 2000 which will "increase your desirability to women, or your money back".

Getfit

www.1getfit.com

You may be in need of a lot more drugs than you originally thought after browsing this site which has vitamins and supplements to halt the ageing process, give you the body of a god(dess) and the stamina of a Duracell bunny. If you don't already know how Gen Dhea halts the ageing process you won't find out here either, but you can buy it online. At a very high price.

Drugs

The UK's first online pharmacy will try to cure what ails you with the help of online chemists in just a handful of clicks

MED Clinic

www.ukyes.com

You can buy Viagra, Propecia, Rogaine (also for baldness) and Xenical here. Answering a simple medical history questionnaire is all you need to do before buying. All prices are displayed on the homepage and appear competitive with other online sources. The back-up clinical data will make your head hurt, and it is not entirely clear who conducted the research. Delivery is free and you receive a 10 per cent discount on refills.

On-Line Medical Center

www.on-linemedicalcenter.com

This US-based site sells a limited range of prescription-only 'lifestyle' medicines, including Viagra, Propecia, slimming pills and other life-enhancing supplements. You need to have an online consultation with a doctor (licensed in the US, a claim they can document on request) before your order is approved and an adult signature is required on delivery, via UPS Second Day Air for outside the US. Delivery is included in the prices which, as you might expect, are about half what you'd pay in the UK. More professional looking than equivalent UK sites.

Pharmacy2U

www.pharmacy2U.co.uk

The UK's first online pharmacy sells prescription medicines plus the normal range of personal care products. Attractive and easy-to-use, this site even offers e-mail advice from trained pharmacists – just as you (sometimes) get in a high-street pharmacy. Pharmacy2U also offers over-the-counter medicines, healthcare, beauty, and disability aids. Postage and packing is £2.50 (free on orders over £30 and for prescription medicines). These items cost the same as in the high street, though there are a few specials. Delivery of medicines is next day if ordered before 11am and within five days for other products.

Online prescribing — The debate never stops

Prescribing drugs over the Net can be easily abused but the Royal Pharmaceutical Society of Great Britain has laid down a code of practice to ensure the public receives the same quality care from online pharmacies as from a high-street chemist. (Obviously the RPSGB assumes you get high quality care from its members. You may not agree.) The main points are:

Security and confidentiality of patient information has to be assured by encryption of data transmission.
The e-pharmacist must advise when a patient's symptoms suggest a face-to-face consultation would be better. (Most of the e-pharmacy business is for repeat prescriptions where you often don't need to see a doctor.)
A questionnaire must be filled in if you want a pharmacy medicine (the ones kept behind the counter in the chemist's shop).
The online pharmacy must keep proper records of medicines prescribed. An online pharmacy can only operate from registered premises open to inspection by their officers.

Meanwhile, the tricky issue of online doctor consultations (where you e-mail your symptoms to a doctor who prescribes in response) is under debate at the British Medical Association. Some say there's no substitute for a face-to-face consultation (although this could be achieved with videoconferencing technology) and there's a danger of missing a serious condition if e-mail replaces a trip to the surgery. But for people waiting up to a week for an appointment, you can see why e-mail is an appealing option.

Brands — The usual names: aspirin, Viagra, Lockets

Aspirin

www.aspirin.com
No online buying but you can read the history of the little white pill which Neil Armstrong took to the moon. You can also read how pain passes around the body so you can speak fluent medical-ese: "It's like this doc, I've got these sensor tissues right? I know they're only a millionth of a millimetre in diameter on average, but they're hurting like hell... can you give me something?"

Lockets

www.doubleaction.co.uk
Presumably if you have a cold you should log-on to the Locket site for some light relief or helpful advice to get rid of the nasty bug. Pick up a 'fun' sick

certificate to send to your boss or join the chat room. As for cures, the best they can do is give advice like "keep warm and drink lots of fluids". No double-action cures to buy here, but there is a talking koala bear.

Savlon

www.familyfirstaid.co.uk
None of your favourite-smelling first-aid treatment but a family-friendly guide to all those minor problems we all endure and that only Savlon can help remedy: cuts, bruises, grazes, burns and allergies to... close relatives. The online guide to recognising the difference between a child's graze and a life-threatening stitch job doesn't tell you anything your mother doesn't know.

Viagra

www.viagra.com
Don't be put off by the cheesy image of a couple with a new! improved! sex life (the wife looks so happy you expect her to break into a Volaré-style chorus of "Viagra! Wo-oh-oh-oh!"). The site itself is full of self-evaluation questions, success stories and info but you have to buy elsewhere (see above).

 **And finally** For hypochondriacs only

Patient UK

www.patient.co.uk
The aim here is to help you get the best out of the NHS. You may think this is a job big enough to occupy the chap who took just six days to make the world but no, this task has fallen to a humble website. The medicines section links to the British National Formulary will help you find out what you're feeding into your body. You should be warned of two things: the guidelines on everything from hepatitis to osteoporosis involve words only someone with an advanced medical degree will understand; and you may also feel more than slightly paranoid after your visit.

Eco living

You don't have to be Swampy to live an environmentally sound life. Online you can find anything from "clothes with a conscience" from Canada to magnetic water softeners and solar-powered energy systems

The Centre for Alternative Technology

www.cat.org.uk

Primarily an education and research organisation, CAT's online shop is a virtual treasure trove of everything a person could need in order to live an environmentally-friendly life. Many of the products will save you money in the long run, too. Lots of gift ideas for children to get them interested in eco-concerns, like a paper-making press and a kit to help them construct their own solar-powered models. Shipping and handling charges vary depending on the item and are calculated on site.

Eco-Fibre

http://freespace.virgin.net/eco.cellulose

This Nottingham-based company called Save It has developed a fibre from recycled paper that has several industrial uses like soundproofing panels. The site is full of technical data, but the loft insulation section is easier to use, outlining the fibre's non-toxic, non-irritant properties and its compliance with the British Standard for thermal insulation. E-mail for further details.

Eco Shop

www.solar.org.uk/ecoshop

All kinds of solar-powered devices, from bike lamps to garden power stations that run your pond pumps and outdoor lights. There's even a sun-powered baseball cap with integral fan to keep you cool when the globe really warms up. Every item comes with a warranty and delivery is free in mainland UK.

Ethical Junction

www.ethical-junction.org

Limited choice at the moment, but this online mall is set to house an entire high street of fair-trading, earth-conscious retailers. Divided into categories like Ethical Trading and Conservation and Energy, current shop links include The Fresh Food Co, The Pure Wine Company and Swaddles Green Farm. So eating and drinking it is, then.

Friends of The Earth

www.foe.co.uk

A great starting place for those looking to green up their lives. There's nothing to buy, except membership and a subscription to their magazine, but there's plenty of information on recycling, food issues and green energy, plus shedloads of links to other environmental sites where you can get all the kit you need to feel good about your impact on the planet.

Greencare

www.greencare.co.uk

A wide selection of recycling options for offices is offered on this laudable but sometimes temperamental website. The company offers a collection service for items like fluorescent tubes, toner cartridges and drinks cans which they clean and sell on rather than letting them end up as landfill. There are also franchise opportunities for those looking to make money from being green.

Mad River Clothing Company

www.madriverclothing.com

Canadian firm selling "clothing with a conscience" for kids from six months to 14 years old, made mostly from locally produced organic cotton, hemp and eco-spun fleece. The clothes are stylish and look hardwearing, with the bonus that no one will have anything similar. Mad River will ship internationally (charges start at CAN$9.50) and donate part of its profits to Unicef.

The Natural Collection

www.greenstore.com

Glamorous catalogue of products for home and personal use that promise to have minimal impact on the environment. This is a brilliant place to come for unbleached cotton bed linen or magnetic water softeners for your washing machine. The hemp section is packed with items made from the new-age crop, from socks to soap. Delivery starts at £1.75 but is free for orders over £100 – though if you want next-day delivery it will cost an extra £5. Customer service is excellent and orders almost always arrive within five days.

The Recycled Bottle Glass Centre

www.rbgc.co.uk

Just a quick look at some of the glorious, stained-glass panels that this community venture in Plymouth has produced from locally collected bottles, will convince even the most cynical of the advantages of recycling. Using a patented process, old bottles are turned into recycled glass in a variety of colours which you can then purchase in sheets for your own project, or commission a unique stained glass piece for yourself. There's an online enquiry form, or you can phone for price details and further information.

Educational

The Internet really started life as an
educational tool for academics. Of
course these days, the definition
of learning has broadened somewhat
to include detective stories starring
Barbie and "Epidemic Simulation"

Art Education

www.art-education.co.uk
This is a shockingly inartistic site for a business that specialises in art tuition
videos, but worthwhile if you're dying to master airbrushing, oils, drawing,
pastels, watercolours etc. You'll find a pretty large range of three-hour VHS
videos on offer, each costing £15.95, including postage and packing.

BBC Shop

www.bbcshop.com
The Education section sells books, videos and CD-ROMs, poorly organised
in an A-Z listing of titles. The range is heavily influenced by what's on the
national curriculum and though you'll find decent, well-produced stuff, with
the likes of a Hamlet CD-ROM costing £88 you won't find too many bargains.

Berlitz

www.berlitz.com
Berlitz asks you to select a website language (which might be one way
to practise that rusty Finnish) before you go on to browse or search its
impressive selection of language books, tapes and CDs. Decent product
descriptions help prevent you being overwhelmed by choice, and the site is
admirably clear. So far so good – until you reach the checkout. Should a
$8.95 phrasebook really cost $17.28 to ship to the UK?

Brilliant Publications

www.brilliantpublications.co.uk
Much improved design-wise since our last visit, this site is now clear and
focused, with sensible organisation. Brilliant has an attractive selection of
posters and books, broken down by age group and the area you want to
improve (literacy or maths, for example). If your order comes to less than £5,
you should add 10 per cent for postage and packing.

Discovery School

http://school.discovery.com

The Discovery Channel has teamed up with the US's largest school supplier, JL Hammett, to sell a huge range of educational videos, books and software aimed at adults as well as children. If you can stomach entering the Family Learning Store, you'll quickly find yourself browsing through hundreds of products including craft activity kits and the rather more exciting-sounding Epidemic Simulation Kit. All in all, a plush, well-designed site. Postage and packing to the UK will add from 15 per cent of the checkout price to the total.

Dorling Kindersley

www.dk.com/uk

DK's top-quality range of books and software are on sale here. Categories include arts and crafts, languages, DIY and science. You can select your age range (child to adult) before you start searching. Plenty of small but clear pictures help make the site a rare pleasure to use.

Europress

www.europress.co.uk

This simple but well-designed site offers the usual educational categories (science, maths, English, etc), mainly for primary, GCSE and A-level pupils, with products allied to the national curriculum. Free delivery in the UK.

Green Board Game Company

www.greenboardgames.com

This range of educational board games is aimed at primary school ages and up. Categories include nature, maths and history, which features Sophie's World, a game based on the best-selling novel. For bonus points, precocious kids can talk for a minute on a "big question debated by philosophers for centuries". If that doesn't put you off, you'll love the small but high-quality selection of games on offer.

Learning Store

www.learningstore.co.uk

Search more than 1,000 educational politically correct software titles at this very easy-to-navigate site. The CD-ROMs are arranged into subject and age categories and there are plenty to choose from. The educational value of the products isn't always clear, but who could resist *Detective Barbie's Mystery of the Carnival Caper*? Savings of at least £5 are on offer and shipping takes from 24 to 48 hours.

Linguaphone

www.linguaphone.co.uk

Simply fill in the boxes: "I speak_____. I want to learn_____." It's that easy. Or is it? You'll have to decide which of the staggering selection will suit your needs. If you want to learn French you could pay anything from £12.99 for a

Your kid may not know what these are – just explain that in the days before computers and TV, this was entertainment

travel pack to £349.99 for the combination course. Descriptions could be better but ordering is simple. Delivery takes up to five working days and costs £7.90 (£4.95 for a travel pack).

Nishat Books

www.nishat.com

Nishat has 15 years' experience in exporting educational titles from "all major UK publishers" around the world, and a large selection of books on every subject area from primary to university level is featured on this clear, simply designed site. But you have to register to search and even then you have to enter a title, author or ISBN number – you can't search by subject.

Osborne Books

www.osbornebooks.co.uk

Based in Worcester, this small bookseller specialises in business, accounting and finance education. The site is neatly designed and simple to use, but the range is not that extensive. Browse through what's on offer and you'll find titles ranging from *Costing Reports* to the more mysterious *A Fiery Glow in the Darkness*. There's also a resource section of financial documents suitable for accounting courses that are free to download.

Proops Educational Packages

www.proops.com

Proops sells an eccentric selection of educational science, technology and construction kits. Want to build a water-powered rocket? You'll find the parts here (though you might also want to buy the instruction brochure). Also on offer are kits teaching basic laws of physics, solar power parts, flight motors, etc. Great for that budding engineer in your family. VAT is added along with shipping (Royal Mail rates) at the checkout.

Show How To

www.showhowto.com

Log on here for "Fun Modern Learning!!!". Search through a vast selection of videos in categories ranging from martial arts to theology. The videos aren't cheap (averaging around $40 with shipping from $7.75). But shop carefully and you can save money on the right title. The gambling title *Beat a Cheat* has to be a bargain at $29.98.

Films, video & DVD

Let the Web help you buy cult horror classics (the *Carry On* collection), documentaries (*Dr Goldfoot And The Girl Bombs*) or light viewing (*I, Claudius*)

General   Mainstream movies and a cast of thousands

Black Star

www.blackstar.co.uk

Exemplary home video and DVD site with a huge catalogue to help you find that movie you sort of remember where Dustin Hoffman is a seedy pimp (*Midnight Cowboy*, if you're interested). Search by title, star, or director and each film has a mini-synopsis to help. The Instant Video Library section where popular and classic films are on sale for only £5.99 each is particularly good. Other prices vary but shipping is fast and free on UK orders.

Britannia Video Club

www.britannia-video.co.uk

This simple and well-organised site offers the same deal as those annoying Britannia pamphlets which cascade from your paper – though, online, there are far more videos to choose from and an immediate contact point to resolve any problems. The usual deal applies, five videos now for just £13.99 on the condition you buy six more within two years. Always a good deal.

DVD Street

www.dvdstreet.infront.co.uk

This site claims to sell the biggest online selection of DVDs and also has an outstanding technical guide to the issues of aspect ratio and DVD territory codes. The site features video-streamed trailers playable through Real Player 8 Basic, which you can download for free, and there are loads of good special offers which change every week. Prices include delivery within the UK.

DVD World
www.dvdworld.co.uk
This site claims to stock every DVD available in the UK, with some prices heavily discounted. Interesting ideas include a bargain bundles section (*Pretty Woman* plus *Runaway Bride* for only £25.99). You can also buy DVD players or drool over other expensive home cinema gear. UK delivery is free and if you order more than five discs, they will send your choices by registered post at no extra charge.

Film World
www.filmworld.co.uk
The online shop of this excellent news and review site sells videos and DVDs at around 20 to 25 per cent less than on the high street. The emphasis is on smaller independent and foreign films, with honest reviews of every title. Shipping costs £1.25 per video or DVD and they will e-mail you with an order confirmation and expected delivery date.

HMV
www.hmv.co.uk
Despite even the website leaning more towards music, HMV both online and offline is always a good bet for bargain videos and DVDs. Select a suitable category, and either use the alphabetical bar to make specific searches, or take your time and browse aimlessly. You'll be hard-pressed to find a time when there isn't a sale going on, so one to bookmark.

Red Hot Monkey
www.redhotmonkey.com
A DVD specialist which offers excellent prices, with particular savings in the Hot Deals section. There's a pre-ordering service with a 20 per cent discount on upcoming releases, and a Director's Chair movie review section is promised. Delivery anywhere in the world is free; UK orders are sent by first-class mail.

UK DVD
www.ukdvd.com
Despite this chaotic looking DVD warehouse being proud to announce the release of the entire *Carry On* film catalogue there's more to UK DVD than Sid James and friends. One of the cheapest sites around with Under £13 and even Under £6 categories to browse, ordering is simple and membership brings with it reduced delivery charges.

Films, video & DVD

Video Empire
www.videoempire.co.uk

Efficient and user-friendly site, selling new and used videos at good prices. They have an extensive catalogue, including a section of Japanese Manga videos, and a good help section if you're confused about video formats. There's also an online form to complete if you want the site to track down any title you can't find listed. Delivery costs £1.75 for the first video and 50p for each extra item, and your order should arrive within five days.

Video Paradise
www.videoparadise.com

As a division of WHSmith, Video Paradise offers the professionalism of its owner, but the prices of an independent venture. Browsing isn't really an option unfortunately, it's more a case of looking for specifics, unless you head for the special offers section which we highly recommend anyway. Our last visit produced bargain finds on notable classics *Seven, Long Good Friday* and *Play Misty* for as little as £3:29. Don't forget delivery starts at £2.74.

Make mine a DVD An online ordering story

US film fans have it good compared to us. The number of movies available in America far exceeds those in our own fair land and because films come out in the States first, the DVDs come out sooner, too. *High Fidelity* could be bought on DVD in America at the time of its cinema release in the UK. And US discs often carry juicy added features or come in special editions. However, thanks to the Net, we can now buy DVDs direct from US online stores.

Buying DVDs online though is a tad more complicated than buying CDs because of region codings, which film-makers have brought into force to stagger movie releases around the world. In short, the US and Canada are represented by Region 1; Europe, Japan, South Africa and the Middle East are in Region 2; and so it goes on (*www.dvddebate.com* is a good source of info). Technically, a Region 1 disc won't play on a Region 2 player, but the availability of multi-region players and globalisation of the market mean this is becoming less of an issue. UK stores can only sell Region 2 discs but sites such as Play 247 (*www.play247.com*), a British-based Region 1 and 2 store, gets around the legality of selling Region 1 discs by being based in Jersey.

Consumer Internet magazine *The Net* conducted an online buying exercise from both British and US stores. As you'd expect the US was cheaper but delivery charges often wiped out any savings. That said, US store Movietyme (*movietyme.isys.ca/index.shtml*) came up trumps by charging only £2.95 p&p on two discs. They arrived in 11 days and while most UK stores in the test delivered in one or two days, it's a lot quicker than the typical six months we wait for US films to go on general release over here.

Video Shop

www.videoshop.co.uk

This site is clearly run by enthusiasts. There's an excellent selection of unusual films and the catalogue is divided into genres for easy browsing, and they offer to track down old and out-of-print tapes for £13. They accept euros and can deliver worldwide. Shipping in the UK is £2 for up to four tapes, with every subsequent tape costing 50p, but DVD postage is free.

VideoZone

www.videozone.co.uk

This works via a search engine, rather than having pages you can browse and enjoy along the way, but if you're in a hurry, you might appreciate the direct approach. Be careful, though: if you click on a title after you get your search results it goes straight into your basket. Delivery is calculated online.

Woolworths

www.woolworths.co.uk

You just can't beat Woolworths when it comes to finding a bargain. Like a number of their competitors it's unlikely you'll find a time when they're not promoting their latest sale, but prices are always good, particularly on classic films, so take advantage. Delivery charges start at £1.50.

The following sell a range of films on video and DVD, plus other items like books and CDs. Their catalogues may not be extensive, but if you stick to the mainstream, they're certainly worth checking for price comparisons:

www.amazon.co.uk	Amazon
www.gameplay.com	Game Play
www.jungle.com	Jungle
www.towereurope.co.uk	Tower Records
www.whsmith.co.uk	WHSmith
www.yalplay.co.uk	Yalplay

 **Specialist** For the 'cognoscenti'

American Film Foundation

www.americanfilmfoundation.com

The AFF makes and sells videos of independent features and short documentaries which often pop up at the Oscars. Based in California they will ship abroad – but make sure you get the UK-compatible PAL format.

BBC Shop

www.bbcshop.com

Find your favourite Beeb programmes on video here, whether it's *EastEnders* or *I Claudius*. Some productions are also available on DVD. Easy-to-use and

postage charges start at £1.95 for a three-day service or £2.95 for next day, but if you buy more than five items, delivery is free.

Carlton Video
www.carltonvideo.co.uk
The online store for videos of Carlton Television's TV programmes, from *Monsignor Renard* to cult classic series like *Thunderbirds*. Delivery costs £1.90 for the first item and £1.30 for each subsequent one up to a maximum charge of £6.25, and goods are dispatched within 24 hours if in stock.

Chapter & Verse
www.chapterandverse.co.uk
This Christian resource centre sells videos with a Christian theme, including gospel concerts and children's morality tales. Order online or by phone or fax, and stock items will be sent within two days. Delivery charges start at £1 and are free on orders over £30.

FRIENDLY GUIDANCE

Building a film collection is a serious business. What you need is some friendly guidance, so check out these sites for a bit of film fan advice and insider gossip. There are also some great links to take you straight to film shopping sites.

----
www.aintitcoolnews.com
----
www.film.com
----
www.imdb.com
----
www.movies.go.com
----
www.mymovies.net

Doctor Who
http://members.tripod.co.uk/whovideos
Select a doctor to view an ample selection of cheap to reasonably-priced videos. And if you're not sure which episode you're missing, there's a search and find e-mail facility.

Science Fiction Continuum
www.sfcontinuum.com
Where else could you find *Dr Goldfoot And The Girl Bombs*? This site has a spectacular B-movies section alongside the more conventional sci-fi fare and UFO documentaries. It's a US operation, but overseas orders will be sent via registered airmail.

Sci-fi Net
www.sci-fi-net.com
Not exactly hard to find sci-fi videos, but you're unlikely to discover such a comprehensive catalogue at your local store. Listings include everything from *Star Trek* to *Blake's 7*. Prices are average at around £13, delivery a snip at £1.

Viaduc Video
www.viaducvideo.com
This European documentary video site sells films in English, German or French. Prices are shown in French francs and euros, but the site is secure so you can let your credit card do the maths.

Fishing

Angling may be a
low-tech sport but the
Net offers a surprising
variety of items, from a
bonefishing holiday in the Bahamas to a
"liquid smell attractant" for carp-chasers

Beekay International
www.beekay.force9.co.uk
The carp is king at Beekay International. You can buy carp books, carp
videos, carp T-shirts and bait from the Kevin Maddocks Carp Bait Range
(how about a "liquid smell" attractant? Choose from a big selection including
tangerine and double cream). Trout and pike do occasionally get a look-in,
but there's no mistaking the star fish here. Shipping costs £2 per item, up to
a maximum of £6, and delivery is promised within seven working days.

Bonefish Adventure
www.bonefishadventure.com
If you want to fly fish for bonefish, you can buy the equipment and even a
bonefishing holiday in the Bahamas here. Folding rods, reels, luggage and
tropical accessories are all available for dispatch within 24 hours. Delivery is
free for orders over £100, and there's a seven-day refund offer. Dorset-based
Carol and Graham Pepler are bonefishing enthusiasts, and there are plenty of
photos of them in action to browse through while you make your selection.

Flymail
www.flymail.com
If Mini Nobblers and Boobys are your thing, this is the place to head for.
Unadventurous but easy to navigate, this Aberystwyth-based site offers a
huge selection of fishing flies from 30p a pack, with UK delivery from just 60p.
There is just one minor downside: the dodgy, vari-blue colour scheme, no
doubt intended to remind customers of their favourite fish havens, but which
left this browser a tad seasick.

Harris Angling Company
www.harrisangling.co.uk
Hundreds of types of lures are on sale here, along with books, videos, hooks,
lines and collectibles (including pewter common carp lapel pins – though the

pike is the favoured fish here). You'll also find a section on fishing tips and techniques, a readers' photos page and a selection of half-price bargains of the day, from cut-price lures to a tackle organiser's cabinet. Ordering is straightforward, delivery is free in the UK, and your kit should be with you within 48 hours.

Sharpe's of Aberdeen
www.sharpes.net/sharpes/home.html
Founded in 1920, Sharpes sells high-class rods, reels, nets and accessories. This old-fashioned site features in-depth, if overblown, product descriptions and background info on everything from Stealth Rods to the Millennium Bug (a high-tech fly that emits subtle light and the "correct frequency of sound"). This is a site to browse at leisure, and you'll no doubt find the answer to your fishing prayers – provided you're armed with plenty of cash. Perhaps the prices are given in US dollars rather than sterling to soften the blow.

Summerlands Tackle
www.summerlands.co.uk
This large, crowded site is packed with fishing news and articles, pictures and products. On the downside, the thousands of items available are not arranged in any obvious order, so even if you know what you want, you'll have to search hard to find it. On the plus side, this is an endearingly non-corporate site, driven by obvious enthusiasm as well as a desire to spread the nets of this Devon-based store. Postage is from £3.95 for a rod.

Thos Turner & Sons
www.turners1838fly.demon.co.uk
Antique and secondhand fly-fishing tackle are on offer at this site. Flies, rods, centre pinwheels and more are graded from A ("pristine") to D ("well-used. Flaws as stated"). There are plenty of pictures and a lot to choose from, but the organisation is poor. You'll have to scroll through the goods to find what you want – product categories are evidently an alien concept at this site. Postage costs vary according to the weight and your insurance requirements, but worryingly, there's no evidence of a secure ordering system. If you really want to buy an antique gut-eyed salmon fly for a fiver online, we recommend that you telephone your details through to them.

Sharpe's caters to the platinum credit card-holding, and apparently mainly American, fishing enthusiast

Flowers & Gifts

You can say it with flowers, jetskis, or a pair of skull-shaped maracas. Call us fuddy-duddies, but we'd advise you to think hard before saying it with maracas

 Cards Digital sentiments for that special occasion

Clinton Cards

www.clintoncards.co.uk

You know the drill. Browse through the collection and either have the card sent directly to the recipient, or have it delivered to you to add your message.

Cyber Card

www.cybercard.co.uk

Search Cyber Cards' extensive range of images to create your own card for whatever occasion and have it posted to the recipient, all for £2.50.

Moonpig

www.moonpig.com

For £1.99 plus postage, your chosen card with message can be delivered anywhere in the UK by the following day. The Naughty Filter will help whittle your selection down to the cleanest or dirtiest cards according to your whim.

Occasions Observed

www.ocob.co.uk

Handmade cards with an average price of £4, with 60p added for postage. You can even have the message written in the handwriting most like yours.

Sharp Cards

www.sharpcards.com

Easy to shop and fun to browse. Prices vary but are generally under £2.

Roses, posies, sprays and bouquets

Daisy 2 Roses
www.daisys2roses.com
This site is perfect if you want to create your own bouquet. Select the flower, colour and amount and the store will do the rest, keeping you informed of how much you've spent so far. Delivery is free for orders over £15.

Expressions
www.expressions.co.uk
This easy-to-use flowers and gifts site can be a bit pricey for bouquets but the balloon in a box option is a cheaper and more original alternative. A dozen red roses will set you back a tidy £60. A balloon is more palatable at £16.

Floritel
www.floritel.co.uk
Floritel's worldwide service lets you specify how much you would like to spend, then makes the bouquet up accordingly. There are images and descriptions of existing arrangements so you can specify the type of arrangement and the colours. A bouquet of long-stem roses will set you back a reasonable £18, but delivery is charged on top of that at £10.

Flower Card
www.flowercard.com
Flower cards – cards sprouting fresh flowers – are an unusual alternative to your typical bouquet; it's only a pity that the range is limited to six cards. Prices range from around £7 to £15, including delivery from Guernsey, aka the Island of Flowers. You can specify the date that you would like the card to be delivered, which should suit the forward-thinking.

Flowers Say
www.flowerssay.co.uk
Flowers Say sells longer-lasting artificial arrangements alongside its natural bouquets, cut flowers and spring flowering bulb collections. It's sparse on details, so buyers need to put their faith in the arrangements shown. Whether artificial or the real thing, bouquet prices range from £10 to £20 with p&p an extra £3.50. Good value for money if the bouquets live up to their portraits.

Interflora
www.interflora.co.uk
Comprehensive site where you can search by occasion, price, type and colour. Prices range from £12.50 for a single red rose in a bottle, to £45 for the most expensive bouquet. As you would expect from Interflora, there's a concise description of each arrangement, along with an enlarged image.

Gifts From the trendy to the tasteless, presents to go

Cody's
www.codys.co.uk

The ultimate gift solution, Cody's offers gift advisors, vouchers, reminders and emergency remedies to get you out of a forgotten anniversary moment or to make up after a fight. It offers the usual chocolates and homewares along with so-called "Wow" gifts; a jetski for just under £7,000 for example, or a home waterfall for £60 – ideal for any friend who yearns to return to nature. Unique experiences include the Formula 1 scholarship for £304 and the luxury health break that will help rejuvenate any tired soul. The images are clear and you can search according to gender, occasion, personality or price. Worth visiting despite the complicated ordering form.

Emma Julia
www.emmajulia.co.uk

Men, pay attention. This is the perfect site for those of you, and that's easily more than half, that every year struggle to buy their girlfriend or wife a birthday or Christmas present more creative than gift vouchers or something useful for the kitchen. Your standard box of chocolates and sensual toiletries are of course included, alongside the more exciting spa retreats, rally car driving and a large selection of lingerie – exciting for the man, not the woman that is. With such a selection you'll definitely be able to find something to suit even the most high-maintenance woman.

Feng Shui Catalogue
www.thefengshuicatalogue.co.uk

If it's not yoga that your mother's decided to take up, it'll be the art of Feng Shui – and you should have no problem finding something to harmonise her spirits or just add to her New Age wardrobe at this comprehensive site. The catalogue has gifts both for those wishing to simply create a balanced Feng Shui feel to their home (see Shanti musical chimes and water features), to beginners' packs and courses for those wishing to truly take up the Feng Shui life. Navigation can be slow but it's worth the wait for the perfect gift.

A STAR BUY
www.starregistry.co.uk

If you're looking to impress someone with your originality, buying a star as a gift will definitely do the trick.

For £55 you receive a certificate, a map of the constellation that the star appears in an explanation booklet.

To ensure that you have a fighting chance of seeing your bit of the galaxy, the star is chosen in a constellation that the recipient will be able to see from where they live. If you really want, you can also choose a star in the same part of the sky as your favourite celebrity like Elton John or George Best. Easy to order and delivery is free within the UK.

Found

www.foundat.co.uk

Vastly improved over the last few months, this site now couldn't be easier to use. Lovely things you didn't know you needed but now have to have are clearly illustrated with useful descriptions like plate diameters. Many items are from Morocco and though not cheap, they are objects of beauty. There's a 'hot finds' and 'special offers' section. All items are wrapped and shipping is free on orders over £150.

Gift Delivery Company

www.giftdeliveryco.com

You can search by gender and age combined with price range here, or just browse the categories (His, Hers, Sports and Travel etc). Two flights to Brussels wrapped in a box of Belgian chocolates is a bargain at £65, although the balloon ride for £149 seems a little stratospheric. They do offer the typical chocolates and flowers, but they should stick to dealing in their more unusual items. Well worth a look for a special gift.

Gift Inspiration

www.giftinspiration.com

Selling both luxurious (see the Sari Photo Albums), and fun items (check out the Cat Napping Cushion & Pyjama Case), here's a shop that offers something a little more interesting than his 'n' her chrome pens. Prices generally range from £10 for a Hangover Cure, to £25 for the Oriental Lotus Ceramic Bowl, with free delivery. Gift Inspiration also sells stuff you may have seen in style magazines and coveted, such as those transparent PVC wall planners for £10.95, or a fine rose glass ball to fill with fragrant oil and hang in a window for £19.99. Search through his, hers, kids and friends categories or head straight for the Inspiration section for the best buys. Lots of original ideas and easy to use with free delivery out the same day if ordered by 3pm.

The Gift Store

www.giftstore.co.uk

If you can bear to ignore its pedestrian design, you will find this site quite useful. Categories include run-of-the-mill chocolates, flowers and balloons, alongside magic sets, juggling equipment and Majorcan Pearls. A Cornish clotted cream tea for £7.25 or a saffron cake for £9.50 have to be among the best gift items, although the personalised front page of a tabloid newspaper comes a pretty close second at £24.95. All the information is contained on one page so you don't need to spend time searching. Marks are for content, not design, and delivery charges can be steep – at £6.55 for a £9.50 cake, you might be better brushing up on your home baking skills.

Go Bazaar

www.gobazaar.co.uk

Baz the Cat and his friends at Go Bazaar see their wares as the perfect alternative gift. Kitsch in other words. What you'll find are the usual array of neon lights, UFO lamps, cigarette cases and board games, oh and how could we forget, "Babes of the Week" posters. The bright and wacky design complements the content well. Prices are good, £4 for posters and board games cheaper than you'll find on the high street. Not the most sophisticated of sites but should appeal to certain tastes.

Hugs & Cuddles
www.hugsandcuddles.co.uk
Hugs & Cuddles offers furry friends old-style, and has teddies galore to suit every pocket. None of your Forever Friends bears here. Each comes with a brief description and character reference, with prices ranging from Bearalia at £179.99 to Tennyson at £18.69. Ordering is easy and bears are dispatched free by first-class post, though you can opt for next-day delivery for £3.

Internet Gift Store
www.internetgiftstore.com
Beanie Babies, South Park inflatables, Austin Powers plush toys and World Wrestling Federation tankards and shot glasses are just a few of the sophisticated gifts on here. Ordering is easy, and prices are average for such branded merchandise with a £4 delivery charge.

Oxfam
http://oxfam.org.uk/shop
You're unlikely to find Ghanaian clay pots or Mankind Vases from El Salvador just anywhere. Divided into standard food, home and gift categories, the range is limited but not pricey. Peruvian Pan Pipes and Maracas for under a tenner each are just two of the more unusual presents on offer. Delivery is slow at £3.50 for 14-28 days or £8.50 for seven days, but it's worth the wait.

Bears to suit every budget are available from Hugs & Cuddles, but we like the ones that come with chocolate

Presents Direct
www.presentsdirect.com
A well-organised site, if lacking in inspiration. Search by category or personality through an adequate selection of both refined and fun gifts. Top items include pet robots, fish radios, weather stations, and for those a little less gadget-obsessed, floral photo albums and cufflinks. Whatever your price range you should have no trouble finding something to suit, with delivery charged at £4.

Flowers & gifts

Propagangsta
www.propagangsta.com
This bright and stylish site offers appealing and competitively priced gifts.
Help to deck your friend's new home out with a lava lamp for £20 or an
inflatable chair for £10. Descriptions are available so you can read
precisely what a mystic 8 ball is before you buy one. Postage and
packing is only £2.95.

Rennie Mackintosh
www.rennie-mackintosh.co.uk
This site offers a large range of jewellery and homewares inspired by the
artist. For those who want to recreate that Willow Tea Rooms ambience at
home, an Argyle chair will set you back £445, and a table lamp £39. If
you'd just like a little piece of Mackintosh, the jewellery range includes
rings for under £10 and bracelets for £50. Ordering is simple and the site
includes information about each product and design, with clear images.

Wheesh
www.wheesh.com
Advertised as Online Gifts in a Hurry, with Wheesh you don't need to
register, navigate through any flashy graphics or pay any delivery charge.
Standard categories include For Him, Her and Home, but it's hard to
determine the market Wheesh is aiming at. Gifts range from a bright,
rose-painted Pedestal Bowl for £15 that resembles something your granny
has stashed away in her pantry, to a trendy Mauve Bubble Clock, also for
£15. One that requires time to search, so not that fast after all.

 **Not to be given lightly**

City Morgue
www.citymorguegiftshop.com
"Welcome to the best place for gothic, mortuary, forensic and death-related
gifts" this site greets you cheerily. Guide your cursor past the flying skulls and
about halfway down the homepage you find a button for the gift shop. Click
here and you enter a strange world of skull maracas, model guillotines and
celebrity death certificates. You can order online, if you're that way inclined.

Forget Flowers
www.forgetflowers.com
It's definitely unusual, we'll give it that. What you find are gift boxes filled with
Swizzels Matlow sweet treats, everything from Drumsticks to Parma Violets.
Not everyone is likely to jump at the chance to ask their loved one to marry
them with a personalised Love Heart, but it's a good site for silly gifts. On the
downside the loading of each page takes forever, and we mean forever.

Food

Jamie, Delia et al have made us expect more from our meals these days. The Net can help you track down stunning eats for impressive dining, or just get a stack of baked beans delivered to your door

General So what do you want to cook?

Fabulous Foods
www.fabulousfoods.com
American gourmet site devoted to good food in all its forms. There are lots of different transatlantic recipes to try (it's not all hamburgers and hotdogs over there, you know), especially in the healthy eating and seasonal favourites sections. You can sign up for a newsletter tailored to your eating habits, like vegetarian or low fat, or just surf around with your mouth watering.

Taste
www.taste.co.uk
Huge portal site from Sainsbury's and the Carlton Food Network, packed with recipes, foodie competitions, restaurant reviews, cookery advice and links to food shopping or cooking sites. A great place to start when you're looking for culinary inspiration.

Eating out "Your usual table?"

Curry Pages
www.currypages.com
Don't know your paneer from your paratha? Then the Curry Pages dish glossary will put you straight on all intricacies of Indian cooking, as well as find you the nearest curry house in a hurry. That said, we keyed in half a dozen postcodes to test it (knowing that each area we tried had at least one

You tell them what sort of nosh you're after and how much you fancy spending, and they'll point you in an appropriate direction

good curry house) and it scored half marks and was certainly better on central London than out in the surburbs and regions. Some of the restaurant reviews, which come from real punters as far as we could glean, are worth reading and features include a review of readymade curries. And if you're really into the subject, check out the curry statistics where Kingfisher tops the beer poll.

Top Table

www.toptable.co.uk

This free service will book you into a restaurant in your area within your budget. Backed by Gary Rhodes and Sir Alex Ferguson, all the restaurants have been visited so you can trust the info. Sign up for the newsletter and they will keep you informed of special deals in your area.

 GM and pesticides not welcome

Cooks Delight

www.organiccooksdelight.co.uk

The online Berkhampsted-based organic and biodynamic food shop offers a worldwide service, so you can buy your fruit, veg and biscuits wherever you happen to be. Delivery charges are at Royal Mail cost price (get in touch if you want to know the exact costs for shipping abroad), but if you pay by card, for orders totalling less than £30 you will have to pay an additional 25p to cover bank charges.

The Fresh Food Company

www.freshfood.co.uk

This award-winning, online, organic supermarket has a good specific product or recipe search facility, or you can just browse the site to see the full range. Box descriptions are precise including quantities and country of origin. There are many organic items you may not easily find elsewhere. Delivery is on

Thursdays only – for which you'll have to have your order in by Monday lunchtime at the latest.

Greenwich Organic Foods

www.greenwichorganic.co.uk

This is the site of an organic supermarket in south-east London which will deliver locally. There's plenty of choice and the prices for the vegetable and fruit boxes are reasonable. If you're in need of organic meat and poultry, you can add a variety to your order by contacting Sparks Organic Butchers through the site. Different postcodes get deliveries on different days, so this site won't be able to help you in a last-minute organic emergency.

Iorganic

www.iorganic.com

Full-service organic supermarket site with all the usual food stuffs as well as news and recipes for organic food fans. It strives to keep the cost of quality food within reach of everyone, and certainly the prices compare very well with supermarket organics. Delivery to mainland UK is £5.00 for orders up to 15kg, with a 40p charge per kilogram over this weight. Any orders received before 10am on Mondays to Thursdays will be delivered before 4.30pm the following day, apart from the organic wines which may take two to three days to arrive.

Meat Direct

www.meatdirect.co.uk

If you're worried about how many heads the pig had before it became sausages, ease your concerns by ordering from the organic section of this company. There are hampers and bulk buys for those with hearty appetites or capacious freezers, but even the smaller packs are reasonably priced in comparison to supermarket organics. Delivery costs £4 for orders under 10kg and is guaranteed next day if you order before 11am. No deliveries on Mondays, but you can order a Saturday drop for a small extra charge.

Organic Delivery

www.organicdelivery.co.uk

Another London-only vegetable box scheme that has expanded to include more general organic groceries such as milk and bread. Different postcodes get their deliveries on specific days of the week, and you can order up until 5pm on the day before your delivery is due. When we visited they were offering a free bag of potatoes with your first order.

Organics Direct

www.organicsdirect.co.uk

Register your delivery address and instructions once and after that you only have to give your name, postcode and phone number. Weekly or fortnightly deliveries of super-fresh organic vegetables save you money in the long term, or choose from the excellent selection for a one-off delivery of organic

Hampers
If it comes in wicker, it's here

The Internet is groaning under the weight of sites that will send a basket of goodies to wherever you want it. The following sites have a wide selection of hampers in a range of prices and delivery costs are reasonable.

Clearwater Hampers
www.hamper.com
Innovative and reasonably priced with some good choices in the themed hampers section.

Gourmet Ireland
www.gourmetireland.com
Celtic food and drink based on natural products. Gorgeous presentation too.

All Occasions
www.alloccasions.co.uk
Everything from wine and chocolates to a full Christmas blowout. The hampers themselves are top quality too.

Worldwide Hampers
www.worldwide-hampers.com
Not the most elegant site but the hampers contain quality foods, many with a Scottish flavour. Prices include UK shipping, Saturday delivery is £10 extra.

800 Hampers
www.800hampers.com
Scottish hampers starting at £19.99 and stuffed with Highland goodies. They also ship all over the world.

French Hampers
www.frenchhampers.co.uk
Gourmet food from across the Channel. Le Gastronomique will set you back £650, but it will feed up to ten people. Not sure about the frog logo though.

York Gift Hampers
www.yorkgifthampers.com
Traditional Yorkshire foods great for gifts or picnics. Prices start from £15 for UK delivery – and they also deliver worldwide. Buying is by e-mail or phone.

Food of the Gods
www.food-of-the-gods.co.uk
Upmarket food gifts which you can customise if you wish.

groceries, from breakfast cereals to baby food. It may take a while to complete your order as you have to scroll down through every item rather than jumping quickly from category to category, but it's a good way to see the whole range. If you are ordering a vegetable box, delivery is free on orders under 20kg; otherwise it's £5.95.

Simply Organic Food Company

www.simplyorganic.net

Brilliantly easy-to-use site where the food is divided into aisles. It's a doddle to skip through and see what's there, and to find exactly what you need. There's everything you'd expect from a supermarket, including chilled meals, dairy products, baby food and even organic toiletries. You can choose which fruit and veg you want, or save money with one of the box offers. Orders placed before 8pm on a weekday will usually be delivered by 12pm two days later (except Sundays and Mondays). Delivery costs £5 per order, but if you're a regular customer spending more than £60, it's free anywhere in the UK.

Somerset Organics

www.somersetorganics.co.uk

A group of West Country farms have got together to provide an organic site where you can get a variety of quality meats, including duck, delivered anywhere in the country. You can order either individual cuts or boxes for you to freeze or share with a friend. Since you're buying direct prices are lower than buying organic in a supermarket (though you must order a minimum of £40-worth), and delivery is only £4.99, so on bulk orders the savings can be huge. The farms deliver on Tuesdays to Fridays and only need two days' notice to put your order together.

Swaddles Green Farm

www.swaddles.co.uk

Selling their own naturally raised meat as well as other organic groceries, Swaddles farm is devoted to promoting the cause of good food for all. There's a fabulous ready-prepared meal selection for dinner party cheats (pretend you've always known how to bone a chicken), as well as children's meals to satisfy both parent and offspring. Orders have to be over £25 and delivery is free in the south-east on Wednesdays to Fridays, with charges depending on the order value for the rest of the country.

 **Special diets** For the sick and the religious

Allergy Free

www.allergyfreedirect.co.uk

Not only does it refuse to stock GM food products, this site is helpfully aimed at the growing number of people who suffer from food intolerances. Common

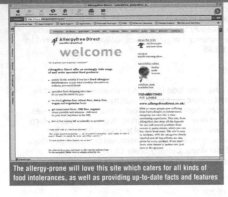

allergies like nuts, eggs, wheat and dairy products are all catered for, and the site also has a collection of articles and information pages to help people shopping and cooking for allergic eaters. It welcomes suggestions on new products. Ordering is currently only by phone or e-mail, fax or post, but they are working towards offering an online ordering service shortly. Delivery is

The allergy-prone will love this site which caters for all kinds of food intolerances, as well as providing up-to-date facts and features

£3.95 and your sugar/gluten/dairy-free foods will be with you in three days.

Clearspring
www.clearspring.co.uk

Lots here for folk following vegetarian, vegan or macrobiotic diets. It specialises in Japanese products, but there's far more than brown rice and soya milk, with exotic oils and seasonings also on offer. There are also plenty of tempting products for regular diets. Ordering is secure and if you get the order in before 2pm, it will be delivered the next working day.

Diabetic Emporium & Confectioner
www.diabeticemporium.com

US-based online catalogue with more than 1,000 speciality foods for diabetics, including normally forbidden items. There are nutritional facts for each product, a boon for those struggling with a sugar-free diet. There is an online order form but you have to e-mail for international shipping details.

Food 4 Thought
www.food4tht.com

This US site offers a wide variety of 100-per-cent kosher gift baskets of gourmet goodies for any occasion. They do ship internationally but you will have to e-mail them for shipping costs and delivery advice.

Lifestyle Healthcare
www.glutenfree.co.uk

An impressive range of gluten-free baked goods for people with coeliac disease. Prices are reasonable, but you have to buy all items in multiples of six so make sure there's room in your freezer. Delivery costs are calculated at the checkout. As all goods are baked to order you need to specify when you want them and the site will endeavour to deliver them when you require.

Lumen Foods
www.lumenfds.com
Selling "animal replacement products" may make this site sound a bit scary, but this is a good place to buy bulk soya-protein products. Prices are very competitive, although you will have to pay for shipping from the US.

Sugarless Shop
www.sugarlessshop.com
Suppliers of a wide range of sugar-free foods including candy, baking products, desserts, snacks and spreads. Overseas orders are shipped out within four days and shipping is calculated by weight.

Vegan Store
www.veganstore.co.uk
Online store for vegan products for delivery all over the UK and Europe. Vegan sausage and burger mix, vegan stock powder, chocolate-nut spread and more. Orders over £15 are sent via Parcelforce's two-day service.

 **Don't surf on an empty stomach**

Asia Foods.com
www.asiafoods.com
This international website offers everything from Chinese teas and drinks to grains, veg, beans, spices and of course, noodles. You can also pick up the cookware essentials and a couple of Japanese snacks, including some Hello Kitty Crunch Candy. Best to buy in bulk – shipping to the UK will set you back $30 (about £20).

Butler's Cheese Shop
www.butlerscheeses.co.uk
This site may be lacking in visual inspiration but it's easy to use, focusing on a small range of quality cheeses. You can read descriptions and strength levels for favourites like crumbly Lancashire down to more exotic vintage varieties. Each cheese is sold in 450g and 2.25kg weights, and the smallest wedge is around £3.65. Better to buy in bulk as shipping is charged at a hefty £6, with an extra £1 charged for next-day delivery.

Carmichael Meats
www.carmichael.co.uk
Click on Estate Farm Meats to visit this Scottish site selling traditionally

farmed meats, with beef and lamb products and also top quality venison on offer. Although not fully organic, Carmichael prides itself on humane farming methods. The site is quite basic but the order form is secure. Delivery costs £11.50 per 10kg – although if you spend more than £100 it's free.

Chandos Deli

www.chandosdeli.com

This Bristol deli offers delivery of its range of treat foods and store-cupboard essentials for keen cooks. The recipe section has links to suitable wines to enjoy with your meal, and some really quite obscure ingredients can be tracked down here, though you have to search by keyword rather than browse the site. Delivery within two days costs £4.99 for orders under £150 (it's free above that), although for Northern Ireland or the Highlands of Scotland you have to wait around seven days for it to arrive.

Delicious

www.delicious.uk.com

Moving into consumer Italy rather than traditional Italian produce, the catalogue is comprehensive if lacking innovation. You can pick up all the Italian delicacies you find on the high street, like Panettone cake, salami piccante, pancetta and fresh pasta, but the prices are high-street too.

Fifth Sense Trading Company

www.fifthsense.com

Delicious marinades, chutneys and sauces are among the large range of yummy foodstuffs this site imports from the US. The focus is on natural ingre-

dients and on being able to produce gourmet food at very short notice. Good sections on south-western food (some items have an almighty kick to them) and Asian specialities. Shipping is free on orders over £65, otherwise it's £4.50 and takes four to 10 days, although our test order arrived in only three days (and was all gone two days later).

Italian cooks will love this site packed full of delicacies – but nothing you can't get at your local deli and for about the same price too

Gourmet World

www.gourmet-world.com

If you're trying to avoid artificial flavours and colourings as well as genetically modified ingredients, but you still want outstanding quality and taste in your food, this site could be the answer to your prayers. With lots of tip-top foods from around the world, all made with natural ingredients, you can stock up your larder or put together a gift box for a hungry friend. Delivery is free on orders over £50; otherwise it's £5.95.

Le Gourmet Français

www.jayfruit.co.uk

You may not be impressed when the homepage reveals that this company is based in Rickmansworth, but it does import classic food goodies direct from French producers. The site is one for those with an adventurous palate, with categories including foie gras, terrine and truffles. It offers reasonable prices for such delicacies, with five dozen Burgundy snails selling for £12, and four stuffed quails marinated in cider for the same. Delivery is charged at £7.99 and the minimum order is £20 – although for orders over £100 the delivery is thrown in free.

Galloway Smokehouse

www.gallowaysmokehouse.co.uk

Smoked Scottish Salmon (as opposed to Scottish Smoked Salmon, the difference being that Smoked Scottish is fish caught in Scotland, rather than imported and just smoked there) is the main draw on this independent smokehouse site. Since you're buying direct the prices – especially if you're in the market for a whole side of salmon – are excellent at around £20 per kilo for the really good stuff, slightly more if you want it sliced. It also sells smoked trout, venison and duck. Standard delivery is steep at £6, so a bulk order might be more cost-effective.

Inverawe Smokehouses

www.smoked-salmon.co.uk

Inverawe Smokehouses offers over 80 different smoked products – covering Scottish fish and game, despite the web address – plus a recipe archive if you want ideas for what to do with your goodies. The product descriptions are mouthwatering, there's a reassuring amount of information about the family-run business and their traditional smokery, and the prices (which include delivery) are reasonable. For extra savings there's also a monthly offer on a few items too.

Martins Sea Fresh Local Fish
www.martins-seafresh.co.uk
Live lobster and crabs, along with other fish and shellfish from a Cornish fishmonger, delivered direct from the boats to your door. If it's freshness you're after, this is the service you're looking for, and it supports responsible practice to help the UK's beleaguered fish stocks. Availability on most items depends on the day's catch, so it's well worth checking back regularly if

Britgrub It's not all fish and chips

Waving the flag for much-maligned traditional British cooking, the following sites offer some tasty stuff for the patriotic foodie:

Grayson & Starts Sausages By Post
www.sausagesbypost.co.uk
Pork, beef, even venison sausages made by a family butcher and delivered to your door. Reasonable prices given some products' prizewinning status.

Harpers Food
www.harpersfood.co.uk
Tasty, solid British food without a hint of lemon grass or balsamic vinegar to be found. Meat pies, game, fruit puddings and a variety of Christmas staples will keep any gastro-Brit happy.

Jack Scaife Butchers
www.jackscaife.co.uk
Those people who have been wondering what bacon used to taste like before they started injecting it with saline and painting it pink, can find out by ordering from this Yorkshire butcher who offers traditional British cured meats, as well as sausages and black pudding.

Mrs Elizabeth King's Pork Pies
www.emnet.co.uk/kingporkpies
Top quality traditional pork pies supplied ready to bake at home, including a whopping five pounder if you're feeding the whole pub.

Proper Cornish
www.propercornish.co.uk
Cornish pasties made to an authentic recipe supplied either cooked or ready to cook.

you're after something specific. If you order by noon, your fish will be with you the next day.

The Oxey Herd

www.oxeybeef.co.uk

Desperate Dan wannabes can buy a whole cow (but not the pies) from this farm site based near Leicester. Reared naturally and butchered locally, the 50-70 pounds of beef arrives at your door frozen in packs made up of prime cuts, mince, stewing beef, sausages and burgers. It's not a delivery for the faint-hearted, but the savings are immense when compared with buying the same amount of quality beef from a supermarket. Depending on the size of the cow, the cost is between £130 and £185 (£2.65 per pound), with delivery extra unless you live within 30 miles of the farm.

Pepperama

www.pepperama.co.uk

You could be mistaken for thinking this is the site for the peculiar, processed meat Pepperami, especially when you see the comical cartoons, but this is actually the place to buy the hottest pepper sauces from around the globe. Macho eaters can choose from Mexican Iguana Mean Green Jalapeno, the "XXXHot" Mad Dog Inferno or the Caribbean Bee Sting. Each is priced around the £4 mark and delivery costs £2.99. The Chile Facts page will entertain any spice bores.

Porcini

www.porcini.co.uk

This vast selection of fine foods and drinks – from rare coffee and tea to chocolate-pecan brownies and smoked eel – compares well with high-street deli prices. Arranged in clear sections, the site is well laid-out and easy to use. Beautifully presented hampers and food gifts are also on offer and the magazine and recipe sections have plenty of inspirational food ideas for everyday or special occasions. Delivery costs £3.50.

Snackmix

www.snackmix.co.uk

If you're a bit of a snack monster, this site could save you a fortune. Bulk boxes of favourite nibbles and drinks such as Kettle Chips, flapjacks and Purdey's, are available here at cash-and-carry prices. You have to order at least £35 worth of goodies, but it's a fantastic site if you're having a party and need a tortilla chip mountain and a Red Bull lake. Or you can just munch your way through them on your own. Delivery costs £3.99 within the UK.

The Teddington Cheese

www.teddingtoncheese.co.uk

You can almost smell the goods on this beautiful site brimming with British and European farmhouse cheeses that make supermarket offerings look pathetic by comparison. You can buy a chunk of your favourite, or order an entire cheeseboard for a special event. It also runs a Cheese Club where you can sign up to receive a selection of their finest goods throughout the year. Get your order in before 12noon for next-day delivery which costs £5.95 for any size order.

Take It From Here

www.takeitfromhere.co.uk

This online deli stocks all the essentials you need to produce a traditional Italian meal – fresh pasta, pesto sauces and Amaretti biscuits for dessert. The range is a little limited, however, and it seems expensive (£3.20 for 250g of fettucine with spinach), although the quality should make up for that. There are some good special deals, but buy in bulk as delivery is £4.50 – though that does get you next-day delivery as long as you order by 2.30pm.

The Fish Society

www.thefishsociety.co.uk

With categories ranging from Everyday to Some Say Eccentric, searching this site can be great fun – if not very fast. There's also an emphasis on special offers and last-chance buys, while books, recipes and cooking accessories are also on offer. They currently only deliver one day a month (the last Friday). Delivery charges are £10 for orders under £50, £10 for those over, and free if you're spending more than £100.

Supermarkets Fresh pasta or Spam, it's all here

Asda

www.asda.co.uk

The Asda site is fairly basic with very few bells and whistles to distract you. Thankfully they've replaced the registering process, so now you can just enter your address details online, rather than having to send off for a CD-ROM or catalogue – but do a postcode check to ensure Asda delivers to your area.

Budgens

www.budgens.co.uk

Check this site to find out if Budgens delivers in your area (no search facility though unfortunately – you'll have to scan a full list of stores to find your nearest). If it does, you can phone or fax through your order any time between 10am and 6pm Monday to Saturday, with orders placed before 1pm being delivered the same day. Service was slightly restricted in coverage at the time of going to press, but if you do qualify, your groceries arrive quickly and service is very helpful. Delivery is also free on orders over £20, plus you can choose to pay the van driver by cheque if you're not keen to hand over your credit card details.

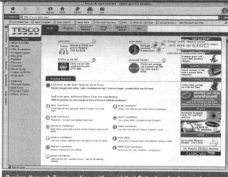

Buying through Tesco online will avoid that Saturday drudgery of aisles clogged up with screaming children and over-laden trolleys

The Food Ferry

www.foodferry.co.uk

Bespoke grocery delivery service only operating in central London when we visited, but offering a wide selection of brand-name foods, fresh fruit and vegetables, plus specialist items like coffee from Whittards or ready meals from The Pie Man. The site is user-friendly and promises next-day delivery or same-day delivery for the truly panic-stricken (place your order before 10.15am). Delivery charges vary between £2.30 and £8.80 depending on the time of day you select and the length of slot you will accept (a one-hour slot being more expensive than a four-hour one).

Iceland

www.iceland.co.uk

The freezer giant has spent wads of money convincing people that it sells more than frozen burgers and cheap ice cream, and this site will come as a pleasant surprise to those who still haven't got the message. There's an online shopping demo for newbies, highlighted special offers, and all items are marked if they can be microwaved. Iceland guarantees that its own-brand products are GM-free, and it has also banned artificial colours, flavours and, where possible, preservatives from its range. The minimum spend is £40 for delivery (which is free), and it claims to cover 97 per cent of the population.

Sainsbury's

www.sainsburys.co.uk

Fast and efficient with plenty of information on how to shop online, plus current special in-store offers. Unlike some sites, you can look around before

Perishables by post
How fresh is my lobster?

It's one thing buying your baked beans multipack, quite another making the mental leap to buy perishable goods like meat and fish. Will it be within its sell-by date when it reaches you? How will it be packed? Did the person who packed it wash their hands first? No-one can guarantee positive answers but specialist food retailers who are serious about developing their online trade, know that they'll stand or fall by upholding scrupulous standards.

We found this largely to be the case if you shop at stores who are proud of their reputation and of what they sell. We telephoned Lobster.co.uk (*www.lobster.co.uk*) to ask how fresh our crustacean would be if delivered the next day and they replied: "Well, it's still alive at the moment…" The lobsters arrive packed in ice inside a polystyrene container. We had a similar experience ordering from award-winning butcher Edwards of Conwy (*www.edwardsofconwy.co.uk*), with our range of meats and sausages well packed and in fine fettle after making the journey from the salt marshes of Wales.

With fresh food, the only real hurdle is delivery. Smaller outlets don't have the luxury of a fleet of refrigerated vans so can't offer flexible time slots like online supermarkets. Instead, they tend to rely mainly on traditional couriers, who inevitably arrive after you've left for work. Delivery to the office is an option, but don't make the mistake we did which was to have our bulging box of organic veg delivered on the one day of the year we'd decided to cycle in.

you register, which is a help if you're unsure about how the system actually works. Delivery costs £5, is available seven days a week, and our order arrived well within its two-hour time-slot, with only a couple of items substituted. If you lose your Internet connection halfway through shopping, Sainsbury's promises that what you have in your basket will be saved until you are able to log on again, avoiding any tedious refilling. You can now use a Mac to access the site but it has to be running Netscape Navigator 4.08 or above. Links to restaurant reviews when you just can't face the kitchen.

Tesco
www.tesco.com

The homepage can link you to all manner of deals on books, housewares, phones, financial products and computers as well as sorting out getting those all-important baked beans delivered to your door. The registration process can be temperamental (particularly if you're using Internet Explorer 5.0), though you don't now have to be a Clubcard holder – if you're not it will create a "virtual" Clubcard for you. Once in, the service is excellent, though the option of having a "substitute" product if they can't provide your particular item of choice can be a bit hit and miss. All special offers are brought to your attention so you don't miss out on in-store deals. Delivery costs £5, but do make sure that the service covers your postcode before you get going.

Food

Waitrose
www.waitrose.com
Waitrose has recently increased its delivery range, and now it includes most items available at the store. The organic boxes contain a good selection of either vegetables, salad or fruit or a mixture of each, and are delivered between Tuesday and Friday to ensure freshness. Waitrose strives to buy as much produce as possible from British farmers, and all organic boxes have to be ordered at least two days in advance. For wine delivery you must register with the site, after which you can keep notes on the wines you like, or set up a wish list for future purchases or gifts. Limited delivery area.

 **A moment on the lips...**

Cakes Direct
www.thin-end.co.uk
Browsing this site will test the will-power of even the most dedicated dieter. A virtual trip down memory lane, this store sells all the harvest-festival favourites: fruit, carrot, saffron and chocolate cakes. You can also get clotted cream teas by post if you're really not bothered about your weight. Unfortunately you have to memorise your choices as there are no direct links to the online order form. They are, though, modern enough to cater for those of the vegan and healthy persuasion, and prices are around £10 for small cakes or £15 for medium. Delivery is via courier and takes two to three days, although rush orders can be taken by phone.

Fudges
www.fudges.co.uk
With more than 70 years in the biscuit baking business, Fudges should know a thing or two about sweet delights. With online ordering you no longer need to be in Devon to discover the delights of the Cerne Abbas Giant embossed shortcake and cocktail florentines. You shouldn't have too much trouble making up the £10 minimum purchase price. Once you've placed your order, delivery is within five days.

Photo Toppings
www.intercake.co.uk
Make sure the birthday girl or boy is left in absolutely no doubt as to whose cake it is by plastering their ugly mug all over the top. There is a choice of designs, although pictures of the cakes are not as plentiful as you might hope, leaving you to simply fill in the order form, attach a picture file and send it through. You can also request a personalised chocolate bar as a special gift. Free delivery.

Food

The Village Bakery
www.village-bakery.com
Cakes and buns, shortbread and fruit slices – all organic to boot – can be delivered to your door from this Cumbrian bakery. There are codes to indicate which items are sugar- or gluten-free, and although there are no pictures of the goodies on the site, the descriptions will make your mouth water anyway. Many products, especially the breads, freeze well so why not buy in bulk? Orders under £100 cost £8.50 shipping, over that and it's free.

Take-Away No cooking, no washing up – perfect

Domino's
www.dominos.co.uk
First check to see whether this reputable pizza shop delivers in your area. If it does, register your contact details and away you go. The standard menu of

starters, pizzas and desserts is available with prices and pictures which, obviously, resemble nothing that will turn up on your doorstep. You can opt to collect or have them deliver (delivery payments are required in cash). A useful system if you're stuck at work and fancy a Mighty Meaty.

O'Briens Sandwich Bar
www.obriens.ie
If you're lucky enough to live in the right areas of Ireland, the UK or Singapore you can get lunch delivered from this chain of yummy sandwich shops that operates across the country. Choose your bread and fillings, with special items like Irish Whiskey Salami making it a delicious prospect, then click to buy and your food is on its way. You have to register before you can order, but it's definitely worth it.

The UK Takeaway
www.theuktakeaway.com
Details of more than 6,895 takeaway restaurants in the UK, including Chinese, Thai, Indian, Italian and good old chip shops. You can search by restaurant name or by location, and although there's no way of ordering online, many have their full menus displayed along with their telephone contact details.

Football

A Dukla Prague away kit, rare Norwich Hospital Cup programmes from 1989, even trophies, can all be found online if you give 110 per cent and cover every virtual blade of grass on the pitch

 General For kit, shinguards, goalposts etc

Go4soccer

www.go4soccer.com

Not the first site to describe itself as a one-stop shop and certainly not the last, this pretty much lives up to its billing with kit, equipment, software and coaching CDs. The kit selection isn't quite one-stop though if you support Walsall or anybody who doesn't play in a Nike kit.

JJB Sports

www.jjb.co.uk

General sports retailer with a small range of replica kits for international sides and Wigan Athletic – which may just be related to the fact that JJB owns the club. So Latics fans, at least, are spoilt for choice. Otherwise, you can peruse the trainers.

Kitbag

www.kitbag.com

The usual selection of replica kits plus Bolton Wanderers and Derry City. Too much stuff with the wrong shaped ball but the range of extras is impressive especially if you're willing and able to splash out £19.95 on a paint-it-yourself model of White Hart Lane. (Bizarrely it's only £16.98 if you're outside the EC.)

Kitman

www.kitman.co.uk/aboutus.stm

Worth visiting if you like nauseating shades of green and seeing self-raising footballs. The online catalogue is rather clumsily presented and actually consists entirely of Jako kit, which doesn't do the site any favours because if you're persistent you can find other products elsewhere.

When Saturday Comes

www.wsc.co.uk/shop/index.html
Lurking on the *When Saturday Comes* website, a small but perfectly formed selection of *WSC* T-shirts plus a handful of books very much reflecting the independent magazine's take on the beautiful game. No online ordering facility but you can e-mail an order form and they'll call back for your credit card details.

You may also find these general sports retail sites of use:
http://sportselite.com
www.firstsport.co.uk
www.sweatband.com/sweatband/default.asp

Memorabilia Buy now, sell at a vast profit later

Christie's

www.christies.com
The auction house doesn't just sell Fabergé eggs, the international gavel banger also puts a hell of a lot of football memorabilia under the hammer, including the shirt in which Sir Geoff Hurst scored that hat-trick in 1966. Company policy has changed to allow you to bid for stuff online, but only as an absentee bidder in that you name a figure and the auction company will bid for you, but only up to that limit. If money's no object you'd better turn up in person or get on the blower.

Football Directory

www.footballdirectory.co.uk
You cannot bypass this site if you want to know where on the Web you can find someone to sell you (in no particular order) floodlights, club ties, footballing figurines... This site even tells you where to buy a trophy (calm down, Plymouth Argyle fans) as well as pointing you to the usual stuff like replica kits.

Ray Taylor's Football Souvenirs

www.footballsouvenirs.co.uk
Whether it's a team-specific lunchbox or a bath towel bearing the colours of the club that's closest to your heart, Ray Taylor could fill that yawning gap in your life. The site looks a bit thrown together but there's a secure server for those online buys and it promises that the goods will be dispatched "without delay" (whatever that means) at a cost of anything from £2.50 upwards depending on the cost of your order.

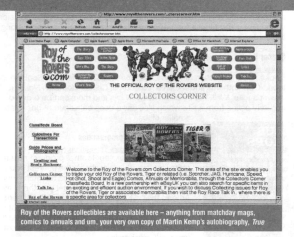

Roy of the Rovers collectibles are available here – anything from matchday mags, comics to annuals and um, your very own copy of Martin Kemp's autobiography, *True*

Jon Learmouth
www.learmouth.com/football_mem/index.htm
You can't actually buy anything from this site at all but Jon Learmouth's private cyber-realm is full of advice on how to collect everything from football programmes to the cards you used to swap as kids. Or not.

Philosophy Football
www.netline.co.uk/philosophy
The thinking person's replica shirt store or, if you're not a fan, the place where football first became deeply pretentious. Philosophy Football's eclectic range of shirts enables the buyer to pretend they are anybody from Albert Camus to Lev Yashin to Cain (to name just three keepers). And secure ordering online to boot! Postage and packing for the first shirt is £1.65 in the UK.

Roy of the Rovers
www.royoftherovers.com
You can get £2 off *Roy of the Rovers: The Playing Years* and buy last Christmas's Roy annual for £3.50. That's as long as you're not blinded by the luminous yellow in which this site is so inconsiderately bathed.

Signs of the times
http://members.aol.com/ianphipps
This virtual extravaganza of celebritous autographs has a very good football

section marred only by the inclusion of Jim Rosenthal and by the decision to define Gaby Yorath as a footballing celeb. Probably worth perusing along with the confusing, but packed, www.autograph-hunter.com.

Soccer Books

www.soccer-books.co.uk
Books, great collection of videos, that immortal CD of famous Scottish World Cup anthems and the little red book of Chinese football. No, that wasn't a joke. Well, not by us anyway. All this and more can be ordered securely online from a site which also has a deep catalogue of books about smaller clubs.

CLUB SHOPS

These club sites are among those which sell the usual panoply of kits, books, videos, toilet seat covers, underwear etc

----

http://shop.manutd.com

----

www.arsenal.co.uk

----

www.astonvilla-fc.co.uk

----

www.barnsleyfc.co.uk

----

www.celticfc.co.uk

----

www.evertonfc.com

----

www.hartlepoolunited.co.uk

----

www.itfcshop.co.uk

----

www.montrosefc.co.uk

----

www.rangers.co.uk

----

www.seagulls.co.uk

----

www.whufc.co.uk

Steve Earl football programmes

www.footballprogs.freeserve.co.uk
You'll never find another football programme site quite like this. This is probably the nearest equivalent on the Internet to a garage stuffed full of the kind of stuff mum was always trying to get you throw away. Among the "big match" programmes listed here is the 1989 Norwich Hospital Cup showdown between Norwich and Ipswich. Yours for just £1 but you'll have to print the list out and send it to him in the post as you can't order online.

Toffs

www.toffs.com
Toffs doesn't stand for snobs but for The Old Fashioned Football Shirts company. This is a treat for those who remember the game before clubs changed strips more often than some fans changed socks. You can order online on a secure server but you have to know which Dukla Prague away kit you want because the full catalogue of 600 kits isn't online yet.

Yahoo auctions soccer

http://list.auctions.yahoo.com/21864-category-leaf.html?alocale=1us
Some of the items on display in this auction category are so cheap you feel like making a ludicrously high bid to make sure you get that *FA Book For Boys*. Amid all the gems you do get some real drivel like, er, the kitsch classic *Legs Eleven: Zoë Ball's Football Dream Team*. If you're trying to build up your collection you will also find football memorabilia regularly auctioned off on www.amazon.co.uk.

Free stuff

Yes, there really is free stuff on the
Net (even if it doesn't yet extend
to lunch). Whether it's worth
having is another matter
and, like the real world,
there's always a catch...

General   Gateways to the giveaways

British free stuff

www.britishfreestuff.co.uk/default.asp

Americans, forming at least 50 per cent of the world's online population as
they do, are constantly bombarded with invitations to get something for
nothing. Bargain-hunting Brits generally find cyberspace a less generous
place although, in the last year, companies like this have sprung up. This site,
which directs visitors to myriad offers, also illustrates some of the drawbacks
of this sector of the Net. Some of the products allegedly available here for the
princely sum of nothing are only free when you sign up, say, to a phone
service or enter a competition. It does tell you whether you will have to mail
the company. Overall, a good launch pad.

Freebies

www.jfreebies.com/main.php3

Among the free categories listed here is, slightly confusingly, "toys and
babies". On closer inspection this turns out not to be part of a government
drive to speed up adoption, but a link to a site which will announce junior's
arrival online for free. A lot of the freebies pointed to here are hi-tech and
there are the usual competitions for the lucky – and gullible – to enter.

Free cash for you!

http://freecashforyou.co.uk

When people start offering you money for nothing there's always a snag. In
this case the catch involves being paid to do things like read e-mails (imagine
how boring they must be if people have to be paid to read them) or surf the
Internet. Anybody who follows some of the advice on this site will probably
find themselves shunned by their virtual friends, colleagues and pets.

Free Channel

www.freechannel.net

A fairly comprehensive directory of links to all the stuff to be had for free on the Net. Why do companies give all this stuff away? Because they want you to fill in the form and become part of their database. And a healthy database equals advertising revenue. So you'll find that you have to register to get your mitts on that free baby formula or colouring book, and then tolerate tons of junk e-mail. Your choice.

Free online

www.nothingisfor.free-online.co.uk

The web address is an exercise in post-modern Internet irony, as this site goes on to prove that you can indeed get quite a lot of IT-related stuff for free. There still seems to be no such thing as a free lunch.

POETRY FOR NOTHING!

Sounds too good to be true? Well, as always there's a catch, and the catch in this instance is that the poet in question happens to be William McGonagall.

Infamous, inimitable and, so critics have said, poetically illiterate, the Dundee-born, Victorian clerk-cum-poet wrote these immortal words: "A chicken is a noble beast/The cow is much forlorner/Standing in the pouring rain/With a leg at every corner."

If you're feeling robust, for more in the same vein (but different arm) log on to www.dundee22.freeserve.co.uk – where you'll also find a great portrait of the man himself looking uncannily like Quentin Crisp.

Free Stuff Junction

www.freestuffjunction.co.uk

Some of the stuff here is just cheap, and a lot is just advice, like how not to waste your time trying to get useless free stuff. The Food and Drink category has one free item (but you have to pay postage) and a lot of coupons. You do get a free gift when you subscribe to the site's newsletter.

Free stuff UK

www.freeukstuff.co.uk

An essential gateway for the aspiring British free-loader. Of course the reality of what you can get free over the Net isn't always as glamorous as the idea, as the invitations to get a free Kiss FM car sticker or University of Glasgow engineering department poster clearly show. The pick of this crop is probably the free software and free webspace.

Free UK Stuff

www.free-uk-shares.co.uk/free-uk-stuff.html

Not to be confused with the above, here you get a financial twist. Filling in a form will get you a "free" share-dealing guide, and there is the usual software and coupons. The 250 free business cards from Vistaprint does sound like a decent offer, however; you just have to pay for postage.

Mouse mats

www.hotmat.com/index.htm

Still not quite as good as a free lunch, this site offers

you a free mousemat in exchange for your address. In fact, if you're really keen, they'll give you a mousemat every year for free wherever you're living in the world or solar system. Desperate or charitable? It's your call.

Shaving gel
www.shave.com

The people from King of Shaves are so convinced that you'll like their gel, they'll send you a free sample. The only trouble is, you can't ask for your money back if you don't like it.

The Ultimate
www.adsenger.co.uk

Thankfully broken down into categories, from competitions to freebies and offers. The clothing section had free gloves, a "free" fleece once you got nine others to sign up, a free T-shirt for joining. The adult section had lots of free (plain and flavoured) condoms and lubricants. Yum.

 Charity It starts at home, on your computer

Charity Café
www.CharityCafe.com

Go to your favourite search engine via this link and money will be donated to charity every time – it even tells you how much. Add it to your favourites and you could be feeding that family in Somalia in no time – but do check out the Donations Total page; though the site promises at least 80 per cent goes to charity, this amounts to some pretty paltry figures, so tell your friends and make those figures more respectable! Impossible to find out which charities actually receive the loot.

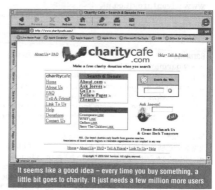

It seems like a good idea – every time you buy something, a little bit goes to charity. It just needs a few million more users

The Hunger Site
www.thehungersite.com/cgi-bin/WebObjects/CTDSites

Free food for the hungry! Sounds too good to be true but for once it isn't. Just visit the site, make a couple of clicks and someone in need gets a 1/4 cup of rice.

Gadgets

Online shopping is never
more fun than when you're
looking for something utterly
ephemeral – like chopsticks, a
truth machine or an Alien
Voice Change Recorder

General Ain't you got fun...

21 Store
www.21store.com
Not so much gadgets but new electrical products. A few
devices feature on the main part of the page with other categories listed on a
sidebar and clicking through brings up all the technical specification you could ever
need. A phone and fax ordering option counters any last-minute security jitters.

Adventure Kit
www.adventurekit.co.uk
The homepage offers an exciting looking range of products and purchasing is
simple – so simple in fact it's easy to miss the specially featured products at
the bottom of the scroll bar. The lack of security info is disappointing though.

Barmans
www.barmans.co.uk
Fancy a pint? Then get yourself down here. Whatever your chosen tipple,
Barmans has gadgets, games and accessories to keep you amused from
flocked wallpaper to match that in your local to authentic pub signs to create
a home from home. Drinking tools include a half a yard of ale glass for £4.75,
professional bar measures and pourers, and shot belts priced at £230.

Boy's Stuff
www.boysstuff.co.uk
An attractive homepage leads to a list of categories which is pretty easy to
follow. The most remarkable feature of this site is its unashamed targeting of
men. When you click to confirm an order the phrase "Don't listen to her"
appears. On the plus side the site is clearly secure and ordering is simple.

EFX Design
www.efx.co.uk

Sadly the gadgets at EFX don't quite live up to the promise made on the sophisticated homepage. 'Lifestyle' gadgets range from a mini cooler to the less-than-enthralling fly swatter and drinks coaster pack. Admittedly you're unlikely to discover finer chopsticks elsewhere but a little less time on the design and more on the product catalogue wouldn't go amiss. Gadgets for people with everything – except a Titanic salt and pepper set.

Gadget Shop
www.gadgetshop.com

Strong high-street brands don't always translate into good online services but the Gadget Shop site is excellent. Products are listed in alphabetical order rather than by category, a useful gift selector service has products above and below £20, and the registration process is logical if lengthy.

Gadgets UK
www.gadgetsuk.com

A speedy way to determine whether a gadget site is any good is to check out any 'Cool Stuff' category. You'll soon know if their cool is your dull. Gadgets UK came up trumps with this test: their cool stuff included novelty items like the Stress Shooter, the Cheering Basketball Basket and the Truth Machine. Pictures, descriptions and prices are all good, there are plenty of ingenious gadgets for under a tenner and delivery is free.

Have it Tomorrow
www.have-it-tomorrow.co.uk

This store sells all the usual MP3, handheld and general techie wonders but as the name suggests, these gadgets can be with you practically as soon as you've switched off your machine. Okay, not quite, but if you order by 3.30pm one day, your chosen parcels should hit your doorstep the following day. All prices include postage and packaging and special offers are available – but they do highlight the fact that products available one day may not be in stock the following day, so a site for the decisive shopper only.

Initial Ideas
www.initialideas.co.uk

This site is simple and uncluttered but isn't that easy-to-navigate. Categories could be clearer and product descriptions and photos are not obvious. Also the range is pretty limited. Getting to the checkout when you have decided to buy could be more logical and there are plenty of details to fill in, but a link on the homepage does at least give details about security.

Innovations
www.innovations.co.uk

This is the website from the people who make the catalogue that you love to

Gadgets

receive. Fortunately the well-defined categories mean you don't have to read all about "walking your way to a healthy lawn". Unless you want to. There is a dedicated Sony shop and an optional registration service for repeat shoppers.

I Want One of Those
www.iwantoneofthose.com
A great name and loads of desirable gadgets but that apart it could do better. Links are not clearly marked (though a sidebar helps navigation) and the site is targeted at men – a busty female e-host talks you through. The ordering process takes too much scrolling and there is a raft of useless technical info.

Obsessions
www.obsessions.co.uk
A featured product dominates the homepage with categories listed on a sidebar. Finding what you want is easy and there are plenty of suggestions. A bonus is the gift wrapping service but even Austin Powers would shy away from the choice of paper. Probably the simplest buying process of any of the sites here with e-mail confirmation for every product.

Pinball Heaven
www.pinballheaven.co.uk
In the 1980s, alongside movie heavyweights *Wall Street* and *Platoon*, Tom Hanks made the comedy *Big*, which in turn made its own mark in cinematic history. Although we didn't necessarily want to go back in time for more teenage kicks, we did want a loft apartment with our own pinball machine. And Pinball Heaven can now fulfil that dream. The site itself is rudimentary but there are enough images and additional information for you to convince your partner that this oversized toy is an absolute necessity.

Premier Direct
www.premierdirect.co.uk
Not fantastic graphically but readily available info on security, delivery and payment. Some of the products are a little bit dodgy and would be more at home on the back pages of your local paper. There is no direct link from the product picture to the purchase screen, but a colour-coded order form makes things easier.

Sharper Image
www.sharperimage.com
A good selection of featured products here for gift

ideas but the main category link is too small. Buying is easy though. Customers from outside the US must fill in a separate address box, which leaves room for error.

Propagangsta

www.propagangsta.com

Contrary to the images conjured up by the name of the site you can't buy meat hooks and trench coats here. Useful features include a select by price option and a top ten chart. A brief log-in and registration screen speeds up the buying process.

Obsessions is so pleased when you order something it will send you an e-mail to mark the occasion

Simply Sports

www.simplysports.co.uk

Gadgets with a sporting theme but you need to do masses of scrolling to find anything. Photos and descriptions are not consistent for all products and although the range is very large, it can be difficult to actually buy a product.

Via Gifts

www.viagiftsdirect.com

Via is a total mishmash of gifts and gadgets, but deserves a mention simply for a mobile disco as an essential gadget must-have. For £90 you too could have your very own Dave's Disco. Failing that, how about an Alien voice change recorder. Postage is included but could take up to 14 days.

 Conspicuous consumption at its most flagrant

QLink

www.qlinkworld.com

A site dedicated to QLink ("a modern day antidote to the modern day world") has only two products and the info about how they work is more than dubious. Ordering is simple but couldn't be completed when we tried.

Kitsch

www.kitsch.co.uk

The homepage of this award-winning site has clear category headings making it easy to find what you want. And there is so much brilliant tack that you can't fail to be impressed. The buying process is secure but also simple and fast so you won't have to wait too long for your WonderWoman mouse mat.

Games

Looking for the perfect antidote to Nintendo? You can try a game of Burmese billiards, shove ha'penny or Flibble, all of which are merely a hyperlink away

Big Game Hunters

www.gardengames.co.uk

Traditional garden games like croquet and skittles are joined here by oversize lawn chess and Snakes and Ladders sets. The stand out is the Hi-Tower, a large-scale version of the table game Jenga, which comes in various smartly presented in its own wooden box. All items are durable and beautifully made. Delivery is free within the UK and your order should arrive within a few days.

The Chess Shop

www.chess-shop.co.uk

It's chess and chess accessories only from this Scottish site. They range from wood and stone carved sets to an expensive novelty set depicting characters from the battle of the Alamo. Delivery is by regular post or Parcelforce.

David Naylor

www.backgammon-boards.co.uk

Make your opponents feel inferior with one of these gorgeous handmade leather backgammon boards. There are even custom-made dice rollers to make sure every throw is as random as possible. They come in various colours and a choice of sizes, but with prices starting at £495 it's not a game to shove under the sofa when you're not using it. There's an online order form which you can either e-mail or print and send with a cheque.

Discount Games

www.discountgames.com

If you're after the unusual at outstanding prices, the extra shipping might be worth it from this US-based site. Their vast catalogue of games, from traditional to video (including 28 different kinds of Monopoly) will keep even the most fanatical competitor quiet, although the site would have been even better fun with more pictures of the games. International shipping is via courier (plus $4 handling fee), so it won't be cheap, but hey, if you want to get your hands on a Spanish edition of Scrabble it's waiting for you here.

Dominoes
www.dominoes-highstreet.co.uk
In the traditional games section of this traditional toys shop, there are several odd games for sale. Carroms (Burmese billiards) might be just the ticket as a gift for the person who has everything. Delivery costs £2.50 within the UK.

Fleming Bridge Supplies
www.bridgesupplies.com
Bridge addicts need look no further for Contract and Duplicate bridge kit. Playing cards, scorecards, boards, wallets and even tables are available here at extremely competitive prices. You can e-mail them the online order form and then they recommend you phone or fax your credit card details through.

Gibsons Games
www.gibsonsgames.com
A site stuffed full of fabulous Nintendo antidotes. Mini-croquet and table top pinball are here, as well as stacks of old board games (Escape From Colditz, anyone?) and newer family games like Pass the Bomb. Not a full shopping site but there's a fast link to their mail order branch where you can make a secure order that will be delivered within four days for £2.99 p&p.

Masters Traditional Games Shop
www.mastersgames.com
If you can play it in a pub, you can buy it here. Loads of traditional table-top games like Shove Ha'penny (the set includes a set of old halfpenny pieces), outdoor games, chequers, and table bowls. They're all made to a very high standard and likely to last a lifetime. Shipping costs vary but are calculated for you online before you pay, and delivery is within three to four days for the UK.

Kevingston Boardgames
www.kgames.demon.co.uk
Very basic site with only a few items but worth mentioning because of a brave effort to support small independent games manufacturers who make the kind of board games your gran used to have. The vastly underrated Flibble, for example. Orders are by cheque only, prices include shipping.

R Somerville (Playing Cards)
www.playing-cards.co.uk
There are some 2,000 different packs of cards to choose from at this site, being renovated when last visited, with traditional and novelty shapes and designs like characters from Dickens. Online ordering is in its early stages and the site is not secure so you can phone through credit card details or send a cheque. Delivery costs £1 for the first pack and 50p for every pack after that.

Gardens

Whether your personal Eden is a
few geraniums in a windowbox
or a designer job complete
with uplighters and
the obligatory water
feature, it's time to get
those green fingers clicking

Birstall Garden & Leisure
www.birstall.co.uk
Everything you would expect to find at a large garden centre, plus a garden
diary and links to furniture and garden-feature websites. There are project
instructions for things like installing a pond, and you can buy all the
equipment you need online. Delivery prices vary, depending on your order –
seeds are rather cheaper to post than stone fountains.

Capital Gardens
www.capital-gardens.co.uk
Online store for a south-east chain has equipment including fencing, mowers,
and composters – everything, in fact, except the plants. There are also tips on
cultivation and on gardening problems. Delivery costs are calculated online at
the end of the ordering process, but are sometimes free within the M25.

CMS Gardens
www.cmsgardens.co.uk
Everything for the serious gardener, from propagators and watering systems
to greenhouses, with excellent savings to be made in the 'Specials' section.
Order online or print out the order form to send with a cheque. You will be
e-mailed an order confirmation and delivery date, as some items come from
the manufacturers. All goods can be returned within 14 days for a refund.

Crocus
www.crocus.co.uk
The big attraction with Crocus is that it has its own vans, driven by trained
gardeners, who will plant out your purchases for you. This service currently
covers 65 per cent of the UK with evening and weekend delivery possible;
otherwise your order will be sent via courier. It's a huge site, devoted to

gardeners at every level. Plants are clearly photographed and come with care notes. There are also plenty of quality garden accessories and equipment, plus a discount and sale section. Delivery costs depend on the order value and start at £3.95.

Dig It

www.dig-it.co.uk

If you're staring at an empty flowerbed and wondering what to put in it, one of Dig It's border kits – plants, food and instructions – could be just what you need. There are lots of other garden products here, mainly chosen with an eye for design and satisfying results. The postage charge is £3.95 (double that for Saturday delivery) and if you order before midnight on Wednesday you'll get your plants the same week; otherwise you'll catch the next week's delivery.

Direct Garden Supplies

www.directgardensupplies.co.uk

Very basic, no-visuals site offering a good selection of plants, shrubs and bulbs at prices far below those of your local DIY store. There's no online shop at the moment but if you know what you're looking for you could well save some money and find some quality plant varieties. And if you're not happy with your order when you receive it, you can have a full refund.

E-Garden

www.e-garden.co.uk

Bright and cheery site with a huge catalogue of plants and accessories whether it's a 10-acre estate or a simple window box that needs sorting out. Select a category, with everything from bulbs and shrubs to furniture and even water-misting machines. If you're not quite sure what to do with your bulbs (never mind water features), there's a handy hints section. Professional to search and buy from, delivery at £3.50 per order takes between three and ten days.

E-seeds

www.eseeds.com

There are plants to buy here too, but since this site is based in Canada you're more likely to have a few packets of their unusual seeds delivered to your door. There are excellent photos of most plants and seed packs, plus comprehensive links to information on plant care. International delivery has to be arranged via e-mail.

Dig-it won't actually get out a spade on your behalf but order a border kit and life should get an awful lot easier

Exhibition Seeds

www.exhibition-seeds.co.uk

North Yorkshire company specialising in vegetable and herb seeds via mail order. Lots of lovely ideas like a seed mixture for a wild flower meadow, but since the quantities they sell can be fairly large, you either have to have a large garden or be sharing with a friend. Some products are not priced on the site, but most can be ordered online using the encrypted order form.

Garden Buildings Direct

www.gardenbuildingsdirect.co.uk

Sheds, sheds and more sheds (with a few greenhouses, summerhouses and log cabins thrown in). Prices are advertised from as little as £80, but £200 upwards is a better figure to go on. You can customise your chosen haven with window features and sizing in some cases – but don't make it too complicated as the finished product depends on your own DIY skills.

Gardening 365

www.oxalis.co.uk

Horticultural portal with speedy and impressive links to loads of plant and garden shopping sites as well as gardening articles and know-how. For specialist plant varieties or propagation equipment, this is the place to come.

Greenfingers

www.greenfingers.com

The Ground Force of the Internet world is probably the best way to describe this busy, yet well-organised site. If you're looking to shop you can buy everything from plants and trees to decking and garden sheds, and benefit from hundreds of discounts. Beyond this you'll find step-by-step workshops, from how to plant a bulb correctly to how to plant a tree, and ideas for giving your garden a particular look or feel. A good all-round gardening resource.

GroGro

www.grogro.com

Official shopping site from the Royal Horticultural Society, selling a wide range of garden supplies, decorations and tools, as well as books, gardening-themed gifts and tickets to RHS events. Delivery time and costs vary but all larger items have this information included in their description.

Hortus Ornamenti

www.hortusornamenti.co.uk

Boost your garden's self-esteem with a few purchases from this glorious selection of handmade tools, planters and other garden accessories, all made from the finest materials to the highest specifications. Most items are available to buy online, and there are also gift wrapping and engraving services if you're feeling extra generous. Delivery depends on the weight of your order and will be calculated when you go to the checkout.

Indian Ocean Trading Company

www.indian-ocean.co.uk

This London-based site offers the ultimate in garden furniture, at a price. Chairs, benches, lounges, tables and parasols, all individual designs, made from quality teak. Such finery of course comes at a price: a single, simple armchair is around £300. Delivery is free, though, taking anywhere between seven and 15 days depending on your distance from the M25.

Mower World

www.mowerworld.co.uk

You probably didn't think choosing a new lawnmower would be so complicated, but there's electric, petrol and best of all, ride-on machines to choose from. Electric models come in at the cheapest, from £60 to £200. Descriptions are brief but adequate and they offer a 48-hour express delivery service for only £3.95.

Plantland

www.Plantland.com

Great source for mail order plants. The site looks hectic but most plants are clearly pictured and prices are fantastically low. Delivery is £4.95 anywhere in the UK, whatever you order (there's a minimum order of eight plants).

Stone & Water

www.stoneandwater.co.uk

Worth visiting for those novel garden accessories that Ms Dimmock might include in her own garden. You'll find plenty of information, images and pricing guides for each piece of furniture, pot, chimenea and granite feature listed. Prices are reasonable and while there's no online ordering, enquiries can be taken via e-mail or phone.

The Garden Shop

www.thegardenshop.co.uk

Turn your patio into an additional room with some fancy seating, outdoor heaters and lanterns. This beautifully designed site sells quality garden furnishings at outstanding prices – it offers a folding hardwood table that can seat 12 for only £249. There's an online order form to e-mail; once they have received it, someone from the site will contact you for your credit card details.

WATER FEATURES
The Charlie Dimmock Effect

Thanks to the recent rash of gardening programmes, no bit of outdoor space, no matter how miniscule, can now hold its head up without a fountain or pond. Water features come in all shapes and sizes, so take a look at some of these sites for inspiration:

Groundforce
www.bbc.co.uk/groundforce

Garden Guides
www.gardenguides.com

Chorney Studios
www.chorney-studios.com.au

Pool Products
www.poolproducts.com

Golf

From links to hyperlinks, the Net is the obvious place to buy that club, jumper or get advice on improving your swing. But can it make you into the new Tiger Woods? Sadly, for that you need his dad, Earl

Easygolf.co.uk

www.easygolf.co.uk
The site is orange and the name has Easy in it, but this isn't yet another EasyJet offshoot. There's an auction section where you can search through classified ads as well as an extensive online catalogue of new equipment but the information section could really do with more information in it. And if Easygolf really is Britain's "most established online golf retailer" it should be able to discuss shipping and delivery on site rather than in an e-mail.

Fade Fashion
www.fade-fashion.com
Thankfully you don't have to wear embarrassing combinations of plaid and stripes to tee off these days, and Fade offers an ample collection of more snazzy ensembles for men and women. Styles are modern, which isn't always easy to tell from the poor quality images used, and prices are good, with shipping at £3.50. The Lee Westwood of golfing sites rather than Sandy Lyle.

Golf Bidder
www.golfbidder.co.uk
Tidy site dedicated to auctioning off golf-related merchandise, including clubs, balls, holidays, tickets and collectibles. Descriptions and images are useful; less so is the snazzy graph that accompanies the bid history of each lot. Hottest item when we visited? A Tiger Woods autograph for £106.

Golf in a Day
www.golfinaday.co.uk
Current players will no doubt scoff at the idea that you can learn the revered game in a single day, but Martin Brockley is confident that after a day, nine holes and £95 you'll be able to hold your own. Booking for this, and the intermediate and advanced courses, can be done via a call centre or through the e-voucher gift service. We don't guarantee playing will be as simple.

Golf4less.co.uk
www.golf4less.co.uk
Fight your way past the homepage's red and green text and you'll find what looks like an electronic version of a mail order catalogue. The site's structure is not ideal for beginners (a lot of clicks are needed to get any product information) and ordering can take a while, but one excellent feature is the detailed online golf tutorial, "Ask the Pro." Golf4less is also a *Which?* Web Trader.

Nevada Bob
www.nevadabob.co.uk
Nevada Bob is a huge brand in the US and its UK site loads up with some cartoon graphics which set the theme for a site which is really easy to navigate – except, bizarrely, the product list. But the range is vast and you can search by item or brand. Ordering is simple and safe but delivery details are elusive.

PGA Tour
www.pgatour.com
The official site for the tour attracts zillions of hits from golf fans so it needs to be good. You access the online store by clicking on a toolbar icon. The range of merchandise is huge but it's still easy to find the item you want. There's a price match guarantee but for delivery to "4,000 cities in the UK" in two working days you will have to shell out $40-60. You might also pay another 20 per cent on top in tax.

Proshop.co.uk
www.proshop.co.uk
Proshop is the UK's biggest online retailer and this site has all the obvious signs of quality that savvy online shoppers look for: a *Which?* Web Trader guarantee, clear statements on privacy and shipping costs flagged on the homepage, a massive online catalogue to inspect, and free delivery within the UK.

St Andrews Golf
www.standrewsgolf.co.uk
The 'home of golf' on the Net doesn't let the game or the club down. There is a useful golf clinic and plenty to buy, from branded apparel to books. If you click to buy equipment you're referred to International Golf Outlet Inc. The site is secure so there are no worries from that point of view – though you do worry about the shortbread tartan on the homepage.

TEE OFF WITH YOU!

Golfserv.com is the definitive online resource for golfers. It's more of a portal than a simple site. Once you have signed up to become a member, which is free, you can get advice on your swing, book a round on a north American golf course or get the site to suggest a golfing holiday.

If you must win at all costs then there is a multimedia golf trainer where you can watch lessons online to refine your technique.

The store comes from chipshot.com and is well-stocked and easy-to-use. It would be fair to say that once you sign on here you might never use another golfing website again – especially if, as promised, it extends course booking to the rest of the world.

www.golfserv.com

Health & fitness

The quest for the perfect body, on the inside and on the outside, continues online. Whether you're after sleek muscles, clear skin or regular bowels, you'll find something here to cure whatever ails you. Or so it's claimed...

Alternative Therapies Find information

Association of Reflexologists

www.reflexology.org
Take the link from this US site to learn about reflexology in the UK and how your natural healing process can be stimulated by specialist foot massage.

British Acupuncture Council

www.acupuncture.org.uk
Get details of accredited training courses or find a registered acupuncturist for this ancient healing method. And needle-phobes don't fret: it doesn't hurt.

British Homeopathic Journal

www.homeopathyhome.com
Read cutting-edge articles like 'Homeopathic E-Mail: Can the "memory" of molecules be transmitted via the Internet?' Links to online suppliers too.

Foundation for Traditional Chinese Medicine

www.ftcm.org.uk
Plenty of articles and news about specific research projects undertaken to strengthen the position of Chinese Medicine alongside conventional practice.

International Federation of Aromatherapists

www.int-fed-aromatherapy.co.uk
Smell your way to good health with essential oils and soothing massage. This

site has details of courses and accredited aromatherapists throughout the UK.

The National Institute of Medical Herbalists
www.btinternet.com/~nimh/frameacc.html
Website for the oldest association of practising herbalists in the world, with
information on members, campaigns, herbal suppliers and training.

Osteopathy in the United Kingdom
www.osteopathy.org.uk
If someone's going to manipulate your back and neck, you want to be sure
they know what they're doing. Find a properly trained osteopath through the
search facility, and learn about how they can help more than just bad backs.

The Society of Teachers of the Alexander Technique
www.stat.org.uk
Learn about how FM Alexander's methods can improve your posture and your
health. The site offers guidelines for choosing a teacher, how much you
should pay and information on courses in your local area.

Tai Chi – Qigong Health Centre
www.taichi-qigong.net
Brief introduction to the art of Qigong, so you too can attain natural health
and harmony in body, mind and soul. Step-by-step videos can also be
bought online.

 Go for the burn

Dieting, Weight Loss and Nutritional Supplements UK
www.weightloss-supplements.co.uk
Busy and in-your-face, this site offers a limited range of herbal and mineral
concoctions which are meant to aid weight loss by either burning up fat or
stopping carbohydrates being deposited as fat. There is little scientific
evidence supporting their use – even though the site lists many glowing
testimonials from supposedly satisfied (and slim) customers. Each
supplement costs £19.95 for a one-month supply and there are some
discounts on offer if you buy three or more products. Postage is £1.50 for
one item within the UK.

Fitness Options
www.fitnessoptions.co.uk
Gung-ho home fitness equipment for the serious trainer. Treadmills, rowing
machines and multi-gyms, demonstrated by depressingly sleek-bodied
models, are all selected for reasons of quality as well as possessing the
power to make you feel guilty every time you look at them. For the

unreconstructed slob, there's also a comfy-looking electronic massage chair. You can't buy directly through the site, but you can e-mail for prices and further details, or ask them to send a catalogue.

Newitts
www.newitts.com

This large sports site has an excellent Health-Related Fitness section where you can buy heart-rate monitors, body fat scales and all sorts of hi-tech equipment to measure muscular strength and cardio-vascular fitness. It also sells home gym equipment and free weights to help you improve your scores and buff up your bod. Delivery appears to be free on UK orders, although check if you're buying a large item as you have to get a long way through the buying process before it tells you about shipping.

Health stores Full of vitamins and minerals

Bomiso
www.bomiso.com

This site is beautifully laid out and a pleasure to use, with a welcoming wish for a "healthy body, mind and soul". The natural health section offers vitamins and minerals, flower remedies, herbs, homeopathy and aromatherapy – the range of oils in the latter is particularly extensive. Most prices seem to be below the RRP and the accompanying Health Guide is helpful for deciding what remedies to try for different conditions. Bomiso sells to the UK and Eire only and will ship your order within 48 hours. Postage and packing costs £2.15 for first-class delivery.

No shortage of products from Goodness Direct, and no shortage of info either, to guarantee that there are no nasty surprises when your purchase arrives

E-med

www.e-med.co.uk

Despite the disturbing thought that a doctor's bedside manner could well soon be a thing of the past as it is superseded by good e-mail etiquette, you can't deny the appealing nature of never having to set foot in a doctor's surgery again – particularly with all those sick people around. E-med is just one of the many online surgeries emerging. A £20 annual membership charge will get you immediate access to Dr Julian Eden, a prescription service, consultations, diagnosis and general advice. Additional charges are of course made for each service, £15 for a consultation, but your time is your own and you'll no longer feel the pressure to explain your most intimate problems in a 10-minute time slot.

EMC Health

www.emchealth.co.uk

This is a homey, natural health shop, offering vitamins, minerals and herbal supplements. The range is limited to just a few brands and the choice of supplements on offer is far from comprehensive, but there are very good product descriptions and a number to call to check on suitability for children. Prices seem competitive and EMC offers free delivery, within the UK, on your first order and for all orders over £30. It also promises to get your order out within 48 hours.

Embarrassing Problems

www.embarrassingproblems.co.uk

Considering this site is meant to represent an unthreatening source to discuss health issues that people may have trouble revealing in a face-to-face consultation, the bright orange site and Embarrassing Problems banner doesn't make for a particularly inconspicuous introduction. Otherwise Dr Margaret Stearn has hit onto a great idea. Simply select the A-Z directory to view facts, guidance, including diagrams, and remedies (where possible), for a host of embarrassing ailments – everything from hairy backs and sweat patches to condom selections and impotence.

Frank Roberts

www.herbal-medicine.com

This pretty site is the online version of a herbalist's shop established in 1946. Frank Roberts makes its own remedies, 30 of which are licensed by the UK's

TIME TO QUIT?

www.quitnet.org

No instant cures for that disgusting habit, but Quit Net is a handy support site from the US. You can chat online with others struggling to cope without those little white sticks, but if that sounds too much like therapy or the smoker's equivalent of an AA meeting, the site also contains less hands-on advice.

The quitting tools aim to psychoanalyse what drives you to smoke in the first place and offer alternatives.

If this sounds more like psychobabble than real help, the Q Gadget takes the more shallow but no doubt more successful approach of pointing out how much money you'll be saving day by day if you give up. Either way, help much appreciated.

Health & fitness

WORK OUT ONLINE

www.beinnocent.co.uk

The Be Innocent site is actually an elaborate marketing tool to advertise it's range of healthy smoothie drinks, but it's also likely to be the most fun you'll have in any gym.

Pulling no punches, click on the 'I'm fat let me in' slogan to enter the virtual gym. Then off you go, navigating through all the different sections.

Online games can be found in the gym, aerobics suite, and even the toilets and shower areas. For genuine health tips, you can work out your BMI by simply answering a few simple questions, and if it proves what you already knew deep down, that you're an overweight, unhealthy lump, there's advice, including recipes and how to avoid unnecessary hangovers – drinking a smoothie, not too surprisingly, being top of the list.

Admittedly only your fingers have any chance of being toned following this experience but at least you'll truthfully be able to say that you've been to the gym.

Medicines Control Agency. Nearly 200 different formulae are on sale, and the site claims prices are lower than both high-street and online competitors. All orders are dispatched by return of post and there is a range of postage and packing charges – from 95p for orders up to £14 and no charge for UK orders over £50.

Garden Pharmacy

www.garden.co.uk

The online store of London's Garden Pharmacy, this site offers a comprehensive range of products, but no prescription medicines. You can, however, buy hair-loss treatments, contraceptives and anti-smoking aids, as well as a wide variety of cosmetics and toiletries. Complementary treatments include vitamins, minerals, homeopathy, Bach flower remedies and herbs. The price for Rogaine, for example, is similar to other online pharmacies at £60 for three months' supply. Ordering is easy and delivery (available worldwide) costs £2.95, first-class post, to UK addresses.

Goodness Direct

www.goodnessdirect.co.uk

Online shop for Leicester-based healthfood store, selling a standard range of vitamins and minerals at high-street prices, with regular special offers. The site's strength is in classifying its products to show which are safe for diabetics, or are kosher, gluten-free or dairy-free. It also has a good selection of sports drinks and supplements for athletes. Delivery is free on orders over £20 which will be dispatched overnight if received before 11am.

Healthfoodstore

www.healthfoodstore.co.uk

Lanes Modern Herbals may sound like a contradiction but it's the sort of thing that appears on the virtual shelves of this online health store. The section specifically devoted to back remedies had a grand total of just two products but you get much more choice if it's vitamins, minerals and food supplements you're after. There's not a huge amount of product info, though, so you'll need to know what you want. If you manage to spend more than £30, post and packing is free; if not it's the cost of first-class post.

Not sure what you want? Check out the Nutravida lifestyle formulas to see how areas of your life could be improved

HerbalNet

www.herbalnet.co.uk

Aromatherapy oils and herbal remedies are available here. Despite being seriously text-heavy the site is easy enough to get around but the range is rather limited. To counter that, the quality looks very good. There are also books, some interesting gift ideas, plus prize draws and competitions, free gifts, health tips, and a 10 per cent discount scheme for regular shoppers. Postage and packing in the UK costs £1.50 and shipping of the order is within four to five days of receipt.

Magnetic Therapy

www.magnetictherapy.co.uk

Magnetic Therapy is credited on this site with the ability to help any number of health-related conditions from arthritis to seasickness. There are impressive testimonials in many of the product descriptions, but the site could benefit from more information about exactly what it is each item is designed to achieve. If you're interested, there's a range of books about magnets and even a section on therapeutic products for your pets. Delivery is free within the UK on orders over £15 (otherwise it's £2) and your goods should reach you in two to three days.

Medicine Cabinet

www.medicinecabinet.co.uk

Elegantly laid out, this site automatically inspires confidence. The range on offer includes vitamins, minerals, homeopathic remedies, aromatherapy oils, diet/weight loss and sports nutrition supplements and other natural health products, many of them at discounted prices. Information is hazy on each product, though the selections are comprehensive. To complete the service there is also a health e-zine, a news section and an excellent encyclopedia to look at. Shipping is by first class or special delivery within the UK only.

mynutrition
www.mynutrition.co.uk
Mynutrition claims to be the only UK website to offer users a free personal consultation and to then provide nutritional advice tailored to their needs. You can either fill in a detailed questionnaire and an eating plan will be designed for you, or choose from a range of more than 1,000 specially selected supplements, such as vitamins, minerals and diet aids, searchable by brand or medical condition. There are also lots of health-related articles on the site. Mynutrition delivers anywhere in the world, with orders sent out within 48 hours of receipt. For the UK, postage and packing is a reasonable £1.50.

Nutravida
www.nutravida.co.uk
This is a lively site with a wide range of vitamins, aromatherapy oils and other health products on offer. You can also search special categories such as women's health, green foods and lifestyle formulas. Nutravida has some good offers, such as a number of 'buy one, get one free' items, and claims that many prices are below the RRP. You do have to go through a few pages to get to the products, and illustrations are small, but you can pick up some interesting health tips along the way. Orders are dispatched on the same day and postage and packing are free within the UK. According to customer comments, this is an excellent online store.

Planet Botanic
www.planetbotanic.com
This site is heavy on green – both the colour and the ethos behind what it does. Planet Botanic sells a wide range of herbal remedies, backed up by well-written and comprehensive fact sheets. There are also a number of appealing environmental and spa products on sale here, such as de-stressing bath-oil concoctions. Loads of information on each product can make buying a long process, but it is reassuring. Online chat with the company's founder, herbalist Douglas Schar, is available, together with a library of herbal information for those who want to research their products in more depth. Planet Botanic ships by first-class post to the UK, with postage and packing charges depending on the cost of your order.

Simmonds Herbal Supplies
www.herbalsupplies.com
Simmonds has been busy making its own herbal formulae since way back in 1982 and a very good range of them is on offer here. The site also goes out of its way to provide heaps of sensible advice and information on natural health, using those remedies, and other lifestyle tips. The testimonials page is impressive, with praise for many of Simmonds' formulae. This site is very easy

to use, but heavy on text and clashing colours – its design could use a little streamlining. Most orders are shipped the same day to UK addresses by first-class post.

ThinkNatural.com
www.thinknatural.com

ThinkNatural scores highly as an attractive, easy-to-use online store which offers thousands of natural health products. The shop is backed by an excellent Health File, packed with information from expert contributors. Reassuring to some, hypochondria-inducing to others. Savings are only a few pence compared with the high street, but new products are highlighted and there are regular special offers. Delivery is promised within two days, and charged at £2.50 for UK orders under £15; after that it's free. Worldwide delivery is available, though obviously it costs a bit more.

Vitamin Shoppe
www.vitaminshoppe.com

Vitamin junkies can save a fortune on all their supplements with this comprehensive US site. All the usual health-helpers are here, along with some you won't have heard of yet, at prices far lower than you'll find anywhere in the UK. The site also provides a newsletter and health articles if you're really interested in keeping in tip-top shape. International delivery is via DHL which takes around seven days, or United States Parcel Service which takes up to six weeks, and charges will be calculated at the checkout. Remember, this will bump up the costs, so you'll need to buy in bulk if you're going to make any real savings.

Web Direct Condoms
www.condoms.co.uk

Top of the list of modern health and safety products has to be the humble condom, but keeping stocked up can be pricey. Then, of course, there's the girl-in-the-chemist or slot-machine trauma of buying them. Solve your problems in one go with this straightforward site. Prices are excellent, delivery is speedy (often overnight) and free, and your order arrives in a plain brown package. As if it was anything to be ashamed of.

QUACK WATCH
www.quackwatch.com

Questionable marketing, fraudulent claims, dubious side-effects and general health scams are all topics which are investigated by this US site run by alternative health scourge, Stephen Barrett, MD.

Dr Barrett sides firmly with Western conventional medicine (that is where he gets his income from, after all) and the site would be improved by a slightly more open mind, but there are some very good investigations here, along with excellent advice on what should ring warning bells in a practitioner or product.

Coming in for particular criticism from Dr Barrett are badly trained chiropractors and some of the cancer therapies.

Hi-fi

Whether
you want a
steam-powered
radio, the latest in
MP3 technology or
the racks of silver boxes so
beloved of hi-fi 'enthusiasts', the Net is ready
to separate you from your money

 Separates, personals and portables

Barclay Square

http://catalogue.barclaycard.co.uk/cgi-bin/audio.storefront

Not a great look – a dull, silver-grey design and vast expanses of plain white space – but you can choose from complete systems, separates, personals and portables, and wade through top brands including Panasonic and Sharp. Descriptions and images are poor but competitive prices make up for it.

Electrical Discount UK

www.electricaldiscountuk.co.uk

This looks like a discount bargain basement site but there's no indication that the prices are world-beaters on the hi-fi systems, separates and MP3 players. Normal delivery is free; the Saturday service costs an astronomical £30.

Empire Direct

www.empiredirect.co.uk

A comprehensive range of sound equipment, from your average high street hi-fi system to state-of-the-art separates and in-car stereos. Additional info is limited and images are poor, but prices are excellent so it's ideal if you know what you want. Become a member and get even more benefits.

Hi-fi Bitz

www.hifibitz.co.uk

Another nondescript site with a tiny sidebar indicating the sub-categories, mostly comprising hardcore hi-fi items: amplifiers, receivers, turntables and subwoofers – definitely one for those already babbling audio facts and stats. The level of information provided varies according to the price, with a few lines for a £100 CD player and full pages for £5,000 AV Processors.

Link Online
www.linkonline.co.uk
Not the most startling of sites but it does its job and does it well. You initially get only DVD players but search harder and you should find a large selection of hi-fi systems, separates and speakers from top brands such as Teac, Sony and Panasonic. There are full specs, additional warranty options and delivery details for each individual item. Good for more advanced products.

Richer Sounds
www.richersounds.com
Select a section on this warehouse site and scroll through. Many items are either not in stock or are only available in store but every pocket is covered – £50 for a standard Ariston CD player to the Alto, said to be the sexiest stereo system, for £500. Best of all, the price reductions come thick and fast.

Teac
www.teac.co.uk
Nothing to buy but tons of info about one of the trendiest brands going.

Unbeatable
www.unbeatable.co.uk
Unbeatable is possibly an exaggeration but there is everything from simple

Enough is enough It's the music that counts

While we'd all like megamoney systems, drawing on electronics and speakers with five-figure price-tags, the whole purpose of buying a system is to listen to music. Isn't it? If you're constantly worrying whether a new amplifier or that piece of black sponge you put under a CD player would make all the difference, you're not enjoying the music – just indulging in electronic masochism. So what's the answer? A large part of it is to buy right in the first place: when you're auditioning a system or a component, only buy something that blows your socks off with the improvement it makes to the music. We're often asked what is the best single upgrade anyone can make to their system, and the answer is invariably more music. Music is relatively cheap – especially if you buy online – and the thrill of discovering something new via that system on which you spent all that money is hard to explain. But one thing's for sure: it beats hearing a CD player just a tad better than your current one any day.
Source: www.whathifi.com

You may or may not get a best buy; you will certainly get a good choice of products and competitive prices

clock radios to the very latest mini disc systems. Handy descriptions and comparison charts compensate for a distinct lack of images. Prices are competitive, with delivery charges tallied once you add products to your basket.

Value for Less

www.valueforless.co.uk

Bargains galore to be found here. The promise of big names at low prices is true for once. Pick up a Panasonic portable CD player, or ghetto-blaster as they used to be known, for £50, a Sony CD Walkman for £30 and a complete Sharp mini-hi-fi system for less than £90. The pictures are poor quality and descriptions are limited but then that's perhaps no surprise with a discount warehouse.

The following sites are also worth checking out:

www.bestbuyappliances.co.uk

Everything mini and midi from top names including Sony, Philips and Samsung, all at high-street prices.

www.comet.co.uk

Just like your high-street store.

www.dixons.co.uk

Find of the day! A space-age Matsui CD ghetto-blaster, yours for just £30.

In-car systems Cassette players and CD systems

Blue Spot

www.bluespot.co.uk

In-car cassette players rub shoulders with Blaupunkt CD systems here. The range is limited yet covers most brands and prices. Plenty of explanations for those confused by the technical info; if you're still struggling, head for the specification comparison chart. Most stereos are reduced by 25 per cent.

Car Audio Direct

www.caraudiodirect.com

Let's face it, if you've seen one car stereo you've seen them all. Most of us distinguish one from another using the fine art of counting the number of dials on a model. Car Audio not only offers a huge store, but also a useful, simple advice section where you can generally become more informed. Once you know what Bass Engine Plus and Rotary Control mean and do, you can browse the offering of top brands including Pioneer, Maystar, Blaupunkt and Alpine. Ordering is simple and delivery is free.

 The brave new world of music on the Internet

MP3 Players

www.mp3players.co.uk

Who would have thought there were so many MP3 players? Begin with the news, reviews and beginner's guide to get you started, then move on to the online shop. Latest models displayed include Sony, Jaz Piper, Hango and the Diamond Rio, each with reviews, spec sheets and images. Prices range from £100 to £600, including free next-day delivery, insurance and parcel tracker. An excellent all-round MP3 universe.

Premier Direct

www.premierdirect.co.uk

Scroll past the health and automotive sections and head straight for the future of portable music. Although limited to a choice of five brands (including top dog Diamond at £209 and the less familiar Yelo, £115), there are prices to suit all pockets. If you're an MP3 novice, the additional information at the beginning should answer all your queries, such as what 32Mb or 64Mb actually means, and encourage you to move on from that free portable cassette player you received when you joined the Britannia Music Club.

 Still alive and kicking, despite the video star

Roberts Radios Direct

www.wesellradios.co.uk

You can't buy online but the radios are funky enough (Ferrari-yellow, leather-bound, 1950s-style model for £130 anyone?) to get a mention. Roberts has been producing its kitsch radios since the 1930s (they have a royal warrant, you know) but have now at least embraced e-mail. Make your selection, either e-mail them or phone, and your chic radio will be with you within 48 hours.

Simply Radios

www.simplyradios.com

The older it looks, the more expensive it probably is. Search by brand – Roberts, Grundig, Freeplay – or select by design and function. A 1950s revival, claret-coloured model will set you back £130, personal or pocket compact designs are around £25. Standard ordering and free UK delivery.

Hobbies

There is no better proof that you can buy almost anything on the Net than the sites listed here. Whether you want to buy a meteorite, pick a lock or go birdwatching, read on...

Birdwatching

www.birdwatchers.com

For those to whom 'attracting birds' has different connotations, this online store from Michigan covers most bases, from suet feed to houses and even a curiously-named jazz water sprinkler. The selection of bird seed is slightly disappointing as it doesn't include any architectural experiments with our feathered friends' food. You have to e-mail for international shipping costs.

Boccerball

www.boccerball.com

Table football with marbles (but no players) hasn't caught on yet here and this site is strictly US-only. The inventors claim it's like table football, table tennis and billiards all rolled into one. Others might say someone's lost their marbles.

Boxes

www.worldofboxes.com/

Whoever decided to call this site "the enchanting world of boxes" has never worked in a warehouse. These boxes are made in the Tatra mountains of Poland and are, if not quite enchanting, certainly tasteful. The alchemist's box seems the pick of the bunch at $56, even if it does look slightly sinister.

Juggling

www.jugglingstore.com

"We're glad you're here" announces this site in such a cheery fashion that you feel you ought to reach out and shake its hand. The Dube Squosh bean bag kit is billed as "the best bean bag kit on the market", and other delights include a book on the art of juggling, three hard juggling balls (not for beginners) for $20 and, for the master or the foolhardy, juggling knives. The company does deliver overseas but can't tell you how much this will cost until the items are weighed.

Kites

www.kiteshop.co.uk/cgi-bin/kiteshop

Shopping here is 100 per cent safe, says the homepage, which makes it several per cent safer than actually flying a kite. The selection varies from beginners' kites for less than £20, all the way up to the "easy to assemble and virtually indestructible" Flexifoil range of power kites. Free delivery in the UK.

Lock-picking

http://lock-picks.com

If lock-picking is one of your hobbies it suggests, at best, you are congenitally forgetful. But if picking locks is important to you, this is the place to be. A 'pick set' could cost as little as $25 plus $7.50 shipping, but if you're ordering bona fide locksmith's tools you have to sign a declaration that you are either in the business, a cop or a car dealer. Wary of having its own software picked, Lock-Picks.com asks you to print out the online ordering form and fax it over.

Magic

www.magic.co.uk

For wired wizards everywhere, this online magic merchant offers such mouthwatering tricks as the 'bewildering floating bank note' and the 'Easter Island mystery'. The Amazon-associated site offers secure shopping and promises to deliver goods ASAP, although it does add the caveat "we are occasionally flooded with orders so please allow 28 days for any eventuality".

Metal Detecting

http://ukdetectornet.co.uk/

It's a fascinating world, metal detecting, at least so this site claims, which helps you enter its world with a link to a selection of shops that can help you get kitted out and set you on the path to buried treasure. Plenty of other info for the wannabe detector too.

Meteorites

www.geocities.com/~meteorite/catchafallingstar.html

This is the place to come to if the obscure object of your desire just happens to be a Sikhote-Alin meteorite from the eponymous mountains of eastern Siberia. You can buy just five grams for $50 (plus shipping outside the US) or spend $25,000 on a rock which is good enough to be on show in a museum.

Model Rockets

www.suborbital.com

Airfix schmairfix – the people at Suborbital have much loftier ambitions. But if you like the idea of launching your own high-powered rocket, heed the site's reminder that "You are now flying really big, potentially dangerous aircraft loaded with large amounts of propellant!" Strangely, such a high-tech organisation doesn't take credit cards. For those who prefer to do their rocketry over sea or pond, www.nerdsinc.com is worth a peek.

Home

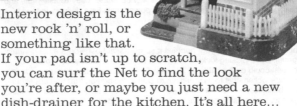

Interior design is the
new rock 'n' roll, or
something like that.
If your pad isn't up to scratch,
you can surf the Net to find the look
you're after, or maybe you just need a new
dish-drainer for the kitchen. It's all here…

General Liven up your living space

Gilatimur

www.gilatimur.co.uk

Select from Indian, Mexican and Indonesian inspired furniture and
accessories, everything from dining suites to mirrors are available. Images,
descriptions and dimensions are all listed for confident shopping and the
choice is larger than that found on many more professional outfits. The only
drawback is the rudimentary order form which you have to fill in yourself.

Grimesco

www.grimesco.ie

Stylish furniture and accessories site selling modern and original wares.
Select a category, kitchen, bathroom, bedroom and so on to view clear
images and ample descriptions of items. Price-wise items vary from a very
reasonable, under £30 for a tasteful shower curtains, to extravagant, £35 for a
single, plain, dinner plate. Delivery chances are handily listed next to each
item and there is the option to use alternative billing and shipping addresses.

Accessories From Czech chandeliers to Greek rugs

Chandeliers

www.chandeliers.co.uk

Glamorous chandeliers at reasonable prices, delivered direct from the Czech
Republic. All the designs are fairly traditional and they will also supply wall

sconces and lamps to match if you want the complete bordello look. The site is secure for credit cards, but delivery takes up to 28 days.

Chiasmus

www.chiasmus.co.uk

Don't be put off by the wordy homepage: this site is full of funky housewares and gifts to add a little originality to your home. The site is easy-to-navigate once you get past the opening blurb and you don't have to register to order, which will be a winner with those concerned with privacy issues. Funky items include Mr & Mrs Salt & Pepper pots which resemble baby space-hoppers, and inflatable table lamps (a snip at £26). No one will ever mistake you for an Ikea shopper with that on your side table. Can be temperamental.

Clickdeco

www.clickdeco.co.uk

The site is quite random in its layout and you don't get a list of categories until you've already looked at one item up close, but there's lots of fun and groovy stuff here for every room in the house. Prices are reasonable and there's a bumper section for lovers of all things kitsch, including day-glo nodding doggies and Indian sun-god candle-holders. Delivery takes around 14 days and all items come with a money-back guarantee.

Fig

www.fig.co.uk

Despite the dubious, not to say pitiful, boast that goods found here can't be found on every high street, Fig manages to successfully combine stylish ideas and design with the practicality that every consumer craves. Before you even hit the online store you can browse through a handy directory to discover where precisely you can find yourself a Swedish-style mirror or a piece of abstract art, or if you're more of an antique hunter the events calendar and guide should keep you up to date. The shop itself offers a wide selection of furniture and home accessories, obviously pricier than your average Ikea but far more interesting. Delivery is free, and goods should be with you within three to four days.

The Feng Shui Shop

www.feng-shui-shop.co.uk

This site offers all the kit you need to balance and harmonise your home according to ancient Eastern principles. Books on feng shui, as well as such accessories as three-legged frogs (very important) and windchimes, are available, although if you're a beginner, you might want to start with one of the kits they have thoughtfully compiled with you in mind. Despite championing pared-down simplicity in the home, the site is a hectic mish-mash, but you should be able to find your way through it as long as you read all the instructions carefully. Delivery is £3.95 in the UK, but they don't specify how long orders will take to arrive.

Handles Direct
www.handlesdirect.com
Sleek and stylish door and cabinet handles to give your house that just-had-the-architect-round ambience. You won't find these at your local DIY store and prices start at a reasonable level before heading off into the realms of interior design fantasy. A range of light switches and plug sockets is also on the launch schedule. Delivery costs £5 plus VAT and as long as the handles are in stock, you'll get them in seven days.

Holding Company
www.theholdingcompany.co.uk
Although small, the Holding Company offers a vast collection of products with mesh, bamboo and chrome featuring prominently. It prides itself on being able to mould any fabric into anything you desire, but may have gone a little OTT with the denim shoeboxes and Perspex tissue-dispensers. They do offer more practical items, however – £60 for a woven-grass folding screen is cheap compared to what you're likely to pay in John Lewis – and they only charge £4 for delivery. Stylish yet practical and easy to manage.

Inhabit
www.inhabit.co.uk
Yet another site offering wacky novelties. This one is easier to navigate than Chiasmus but it lacks that site's variety, with many products listed under multiple headings. Particular favourites were Harry Mobile Holder and the Bubblo placemats, both of which can be bought with Beenz points. On the downside, however, they ask you to register before they'll tell you about any discounts, and postage and packing more than doubled the original cost of an aqua door-mouse doorstop to £8.98.

Nice Irmas
www.niceirmas.net
A luxurious site with an equally lavish purple homepage, held together by the products themselves. The home accessories include cushions in tactile velvet and beaded fabrics from £16, with beaded napkin rings and tea-light holders from £2.50. Unfortunately not enough thought has been put into the buying process, with poor images and a faulty link to the checkout letting the site down. Persistence is needed here but the products are worth the wait.

Nubold
www.nubold.com
Hot contemporary designers like Nic Wood and Bodo Sperlein sell their accessories through an excellent site that does them full justice. The lighting department is particularly irresistible, and there's even a wedding list service for brides with seriously good taste. There's 10 per cent off your first order, although many of the prices are surprisingly reasonable anyway. Delivery is calculated at the checkout and your order should arrive within seven days.

Out Of Afrika

www.outof
afrika.co.uk

Truly lovely wood, ceramic, metal and glass accessories for people who want a touch of Africa. The site is beautifully laid out with easy-to-view photos, and all products are bought at a fair price from small co-operatives (five per cent of each order is donated to a children's home in South Africa). Orders over £150 are carriage-free (otherwise it's £3.50 for delivery), arriving within three to five working days.

The Roman Blind Company

www.roman-blind.co.uk

A simple and straightforward site offering roman blinds, with full measuring guidelines and examples of previous commissions. All blinds are made to order with fabric that you supply, and you can pretty much cover any window. E-mail the site for further details and prices.

Taste By Mail

www.tastebymail.com

If it's a juicer it's chrome-plated, if it's a toilet brush holder it's stainless steel and if it's a set of chopsticks they're silver-plated. Think you get the picture. Aptly titled, this site offers an adequate range of home accessories for every room, shiny metal being the general theme of the site. Prices are as you would expect for such fine items, but the site is so well designed you feel encouraged to pay that little extra for a new toilet brush holder.

The Forge

www.eshopone.co.uk/OnlineShopping-TheForge.html

Wrought-iron accessories for the home, handmade in Derbyshire. There's a good selection of curtain poles and some very funky candlesticks, although the pictures are a little small. If you don't see anything you like, you can commission a piece to your own design, Buying direct makes the prices a bargain, and as a bonus, delivery is free. Goods are usually dispatched within two days.

Urban Icons

www.urbanicons.com

If you thought the Qube was already pushing the furniture design boundaries, the range of drum furniture found here could come as quite a shock to your chic sensibilities. If you weren't aware of unique design qualities of the instrument which is generally given, and immediately taken away from, small children, the homepage should prove an informative read. The store collection comprises table units for home and garden as well as storage facilities, with prices starting at an unbelievable £300. Gob-smacked will be your immediate reaction we're sure.

Voodoo Blue
www.voodooblue.co.uk

Despite being based in Brentwood, Voodoo Blue specialises in traditional, natural wares from Kenya. Storage is generally the name of the game, with products in a variety of natural materials: soapstone, earthenware, wood and basket weaves. Prices are good, £12 for a set of three baskets is less than half what you'd pay on the high street, with a £3.95 delivery charge.

WebRugs
www.webrugs.co.uk

Huge selection of floor coverings to choose from here, including oriental and modern styles, natural rugs or cartoon ones for children's rooms. Prices are competitive, particularly since they include delivery, and the availability of each design is specified with its description. All household sites should be this informative and easy to follow.

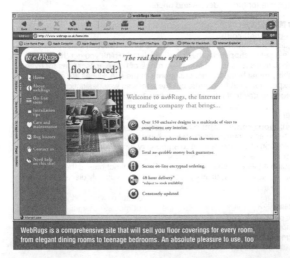

WebRugs is a comprehensive site that will sell you floor coverings for every room, from elegant dining rooms to teenage bedrooms. An absolute pleasure to use, too

 **Designs for living**

The Cotswold Company
www.cotswoldco.com

Not everything sold at this site is as twee as the name suggests. Wood and luxurious ethnic patterned fabrics do feature strongly, but you will find more than a hint of chrome lurking along the way. Design is middle-of-the-road. Browse by room or product, but if you're looking for something in particular you can narrow your search down by product, material, price and the look you're aiming for. Prices are good with a set delivery charge of £1.95, although you may have to wait 28 days before you get your new bamboo storage trunk. An excellent site.

Ikea
www.ikea.com

It's not immediately obvious that Ikea as yet doesn't sell online as the shopping cart is in full view and the store is fully functional to the point where you can browse and add items to a list for future reference. If this seems like a waste of energy, you can at least take inspiration – if not an actual Iggesund cabinet or a set of Bang mugs – away with you. Entire rooms are whittled down to individual pieces showing you how to create that Ikea experience in your own home. You then need to head for your nearest industrial estate to buy the things.

Lakeland
www.lakeland.co.uk

This Lake District family business publishes a range of hugely successful catalogues featuring high-quality, great value-for-money household basics and accessories. You many find some designs a little on the twee side, but there are many things here, especially in the storage section, that will warm the heart of even the most minimalist interior decorator. This easy-to-use website is a recent launch and continues the business's emphasis on excellent customer service. Post and packing is free on orders over £35 and deliveries usually arrive within a few days.

Manners
www.mannersmailorder.co.uk

The fact that this site is laid out like a tour of a country manor, complete with a library and a lily pond, should give you an indication of what kind of items are for sale here. There's not much in the way of modern design, but there are plenty of decorative and well-made accessories, including lead statues for the traditional look, as well as some excellent gift ideas. Delivery costs £3.95 (more for heavier items) and that trellis gazebo will be ready to install in your garden within 14 days.

McCord

www.mccord.uk.com

This site offers well-made products for all over the house, selected with an eye for contemporary design. There are several useful services available, such as a fabric swatch request service. Postage costs are £2.95 per order, but they do ask that you allow 28 days for delivery, which seems excessive these days, although apparently most deliveries arrive earlier.

Ocean

www.oceancatalogue.co.uk

Delicious but pricey furniture and accessories for the modern home. If chrome, frosted glass and pale wood appeal to you, you'll love this stuff. Delivery costs £5.95 for a three-day service or £6.95 for next-day, although our next-day order turned up two days late and with half the items missing, so it's probably not worth the extra pound.

Contemporary Design It's the new retro

Blue Deco

www.bluedeco.com

Lovely homewares, many of them handmade, from a selection of modern designers. The oak furniture is particularly attractive, but even if you're only after placemats there's something here for you too. Delivery costs depend on the size of your order and are calculated on site, but there doesn't seem to be any information on how long your items will take to reach you.

Desaster

www.desaster.com

Whether it's an inflatable UFO for your playroom or a set of glass scales for your bathroom, we defy you not to find something quirky and hugely desirable on this fun and easy-to-use site. There are larger items of furniture as well as accessories for all over the house, all of which have good photos and descriptions so you know what you're getting before you click to buy. The site offers a giftwrap service and all items come with a 14-day refund guarantee. Delivery is promised within two days.

Groovy Style

www.groovystyle.com

The funky Sunny Delight-coloured backdrop and an entire category devoted to toilet seats should make it plain that the bathroom, kitchen and general accessories to be found here aren't exactly on a par with Conran pieces. If you're looking to brighten up the minimalist look of your flat, the sunflower, butterfly, spider and barbed wire toilet seat designs should do the trick if the wave-effect lighting and mosaic tables don't. Prices are good for such unusual items – you can pick up a folding stick chair for only £20. The England flag mosaic table is a touch more costly at £225, but for a bit of originality it's worth it.

Ochre

www.ochre.net

There's some fabulously pretentious language on this site which invites you, for example, to "get beyond the initial stage of the

The perpex toilet seats featured here, at below retail prices, are sure to give you a jolt when visiting the loo in the middle of the night

identification of an object". But the site is saved from being ridiculous by the fact that its collections of furniture, accessories and especially lighting, are truly outstanding. The prices vary from reasonable to jaw-dropping, but you're unlikely to come across any of this stuff in the high street. Delivery costs vary (you have to e-mail them for details) and goods can take up to six weeks – six weeks! – to arrive.

Pepper Mint

www.pepper-mint.com

If you're not interested in the Qube then it's pointless going any further, but who wouldn't be interested in a £50 piece of plastic furniture that will remind you of the building blocks from your childhood. Stir up those memories by using the Qube as shelving, seating, a display unit, a table, even a hostess trolley. And you thought the sofabed was a work of genius. Orders are via e-mail or phone only but all you need to know is on hand here.

White Company

www.thewhiteco.com

A minimalist's dream, the White Company not only offers you a tasteful store selling simply designed housewares, but also items for you and your family to match. Now you too can have bathrobes which will match exactly with your towels, and pure white napkins to match your pure white china. Such somewhat eccentric needs for colour co-ordination do come at a price however, but special offers are available and, let's face it, one white duvet cover looks the same as any other so why not just wait for the bargains. A good, if slightly plain site.

Decoration & DIY From strimmers to seagrass

B&Q

www.diy.com

The online version of the DIY giant has multiple sub-categories, which offer everything from flooring and tools to gravel and the proverbial kitchen sink. Added information and images are available but not for all products. Delivery is free if you go wild and spend over £250; otherwise it's charged at between £10 and £20 depending on the distance from your local store.

Cooksons

www.cooksons.com

Hand tools, power tools, engineering tools and even tools for the ironmonger. Top brands include Black & Decker, Stanley and Dewalt. Head for Special Offers first with most sale items half-price. Free delivery on orders over £45.

Interior Connections

www.interiorconnections.net

This is a New England-based company selling wallpaper and stencils for the home decorator. The designs veer towards a country style, but there are some simple and unusual ones too. Prices are very reasonable, although you have to allow for international shipping which they can arrange by special request.

The Original Seagrass Company

www.original-seagrass.co.uk

If you can't decide between wooden floors or carpet, this stuff provides a good compromise. Natural matting, sometimes blended with wool to make

it easier on the feet, is featured in a range of styles at very reasonable prices. You can order samples through the site, or ask for someone to get in touch about giving you a full quotation.

No longer just a trend – seagrass is now recognised as a good alternative to wool and a much better option than nylon

Stencil Library
www.stencil-library.com
Who needs wallpaper when you can go stencil crazy for a fraction of the price. Themes include art deco, flower garden, Celtic and children's designs. Prices range from £10-200, although uncut stencils are cheaper.

Walking On Wood
www.designerwoodfloors.com
Straightforward site offering photos and technical specifications for quality hardwood floors, ranging from traditional parquet to more modern styles. There's an online enquiry form if you want further details of any of this London-based firm's products and services.

Wallpaper Direct
www.wallpaperdirect.co.uk
A wide online selection of wall coverings. If you're an expert you can search by designer; alternatively browse according to the look of your home. Thumbnail images of papers and borders can be enlarged and you can order samples free of charge. Free delivery on orders over £50.

Wallpaper Online
www.wallpaperonline.co.uk
Bored with plain walls? This easy-to-use site can search through its database of 20,000 papers and borders to find exactly the right one for you. You can ask for samples to be sent, or buy the whole lot using their useful calculator to make sure you get the right amount. Delivery is free within the UK.

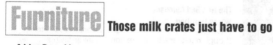

Furniture Those milk crates just have to go

Adrian Reynolds
www.adrianreynolds.com
This beautifully laid-out site represents a bespoke wrought-iron furniture-maker in Shropshire. Details of his standard designs for dining tables, chairs, beds and other accessories are all available to view, and you can contact Reynolds through the site if you have a commission in mind. By shopping direct you can save a fortune over the retail prices of his designs.

Conran
www.conran.co.uk
You need to take your time to get into this site as it takes several clicks through over-designed pages to get to view some actual products – and then there aren't a hell of a lot of them. Only six items in the tabletop category, for example. Still, it gives you a taste, but you're much better off trekking down to the offline shop.

Furniture Web Store

www.furniturewebstore.co.uk

Basic ranges of traditional furniture, delivered direct to your door. There are some good designs in the bed section, and all the prices are very competitive compared to many furniture superstores. Delivery is free on all items unless you've requested the 'express bed service' (same-day delivery if ordered before noon – cost £14.99) for people who have nothing to sleep on.

Futons Direct

www.futons-direct.co.uk

This Oxford-based company offers futon sofabeds and mattresses. The information accompanying each futon isn't particularly detailed but then there's only so much you can say. A three-seater will set you back about £250, and delivery is charged at a flat rate of £20 for a mattress and £30 for the whole package. An amateurish-looking site but it does the job.

VINTAGE VENDING

www.vintage vending.com

This US site is in the business of selling restored 1950s furniture, juke boxes and vending machines. The diner sets are particularly glorious and if you're looking for a touch of bad-boy glamour, what about a Harley Davidson barstool for $129?

For your garden why not check out the range of classic gas pumps – beats those plastic flamingoes any day.

The site can arrange shipping to the UK, but you have to e-mail or call for full details and delivery could take as long as ten weeks. Worth it though.

Habitat

www.habitat.co.uk

This is a disappointing site from the high-street furniture giant. First, you can't access some areas of the site without Shockwave. Then, when you do get into it, they quite often only have a photo of one item from each range with line-drawings of the rest. All very chic, but no use to shoppers. The site doesn't say if full online shopping is planned, so for now you'll just have to keep visiting the shops.

The Iron Bed Company

www.ironbed.co.uk

Excellent sales site from a made-to-order bed retailer, though not all the beds are iron – Shaker-style wooden beds are also available. (Their future plans also include bedding and accessories.) Beautiful photos, size details and careful descriptions make this a happy shopping experience. Beds are delivered in around four weeks by the company's own vans.

Sofas And Sofa Beds

www.sofabeds.co.uk

As the URL suggests, this site sells a wide range of sofas, all of which are also available as sofabeds. Choose your base, then the fabric, and order online with a minimum of fuss. Alternatively you can request further information or fabric swatches. All sofas are made to order, so getting your sofa can take a while, but the site will contact you to arrange delivery.

Sträad

www.straad.co.uk

A Birmingham-based online department store, Straad offers art prints, lighting and executive gifts along with furniture and home accessories. A simple system of clicking on a small image produces a larger version along with the usual information. Unfortunately the blurred and tiny images can make it hard to recognise what you're clicking on in the first place. There's a large selection of items on offer but not everyone will race to order the glass Homo Sapiens Valet, also known as a clothes horse, for £858. Pricey but unusual.

Viva Sofa

www.vivasofa.co.uk

Despite the level of sophistication shown in the design of the site and the sofas themselves, ordering is a fairly rudimentary process. Once you've decided what takes your fancy you have to go through the selection process again to place your order, so just make sure you know your Lindo from your Lindo Padova or you may get a bit of a shock on delivery. Images are clear, with each sofa available in a choice of colours, although we suggest you take advantage of the fabric sample service for complete piece of mind.

 **Ideas for improvements**

Improveline

www.improveline.com

This site's main service is to hook you up with professionals in your area, whether they're architects or plumbers, who are interested in quoting for your home improvement project. There are lots of inspirational pictures and ideas in the design gallery, as well as articles on how to get the best out of your home and any improvement you want to make to it.

Interior Internet

www.interiorinternet.co.uk

An impressive design portal with links to lots of interior sites. There are sales sites as well as web pages representing designers and their work. Well worth a visit, especially if you're planning a real household overhaul.

Wood for Good

www.woodforgood.com

The homepage comes across as a public service announcement on how wood is one of the wonders of the world, but beyond the promotional campaign you'll find a useful resource if you are already considering wood flooring, decking or you're just going for fancy beams throughout your house for that pub deco look. The site offers information on building and living with wood, as well as a directory of suppliers in your area.

Kitchens & Bathrooms
Pots and pans

Bathroom Express
www.bathroomexpress.co.uk

Investing in a new bathroom suite isn't something that every online shopper, no matter how savvy they may be, can possibly contemplate, hence a distinct lack of vendors around. If you're feeling particularly bold, Bathroom Express offers a large range of bathroom suites, shower units and general bathroom accessories. Detailed descriptions and dimensions, alongside clear images, aid the process somewhat and you can customise your suite. Next-day delivery is also available for those with cleaning issues.

The Cook's Kitchen
www.kitchenware.co.uk

Competitive prices on a vast range of kitchen equipment from specialist utensils (such as crème brulée torches) to picnic hampers. The site is easy to use, if a little dull, and it's a good pace to look for gifts for keen cooks. UK delivery costs £2.95 and orders should arrive within 14 days.

Culliners
www.culliners.co.uk

If you're following the trend for all things industrial, this site will help you kit out your kitchen with a range of professional catering equipment, whether it's oversize baking sheets or indestructible knives. Note that prices do not include VAT – which is calculated at the checkout – and delivery costs £2.95 unless your order is over £80 in which case it's free.

Doors Direct
www.doorsdirect.co.uk

Overhaul your old kitchen for far less than the cost of getting a new one by simply changing the cabinet doors. This site has a selection of both rustic and modern styles – choose from standard sizes or their made-to-measure service. There's also a good choice of handles. For a deposit of £20 you can order a sample door so you can check that it's definitely what you want, or just take the plunge and order the whole lot with a detailed e-mail, to which they will respond with a firm quote and delivery time.

Pots & Pans
www.pots-and-pans.co.uk

After taking so much care to highlight their Scottish heritage with a beautiful tartan banner, it's a shame they didn't concentrate more on the product visuals. Using silhouette images to encourage you to buy a single pan for £35 is not helpful for shoppers. We were also confused to find a Seahorse bathroom radio on the Special Offers page while searching for a bargain wok.

Scott and Sargeant, The Internet Cookshop
www.scottsargeant.co.uk
High-quality branded kitchenware such as Portmeirion, Global and Le Creuset at extremely good prices. You would be hard pushed to find this amount of choice in any high-street store and there are usually some good special offers to be had, along with wedding gift ideas. Useful for all those who want to emulate Nigella and have a gadget for every job. A recent addition is the recipe section so you can try out all your new kit, though at the moment it's a bit short on actual recipes. There's a 30-day, money-back guarantee on all items and delivery costs £3.95 on orders under £100 (it's free over that). Goods should be received within seven to 10 days, often sooner.

Thomas Crapper & Co
www.thomas-crapper.co.uk
We couldn't leave this one out, could we? Traditional Victorian and Edwardian-style toilets and sinks from the sanitary-ware supplier to Edward VII and George V. Crapper's ranges of toiletries, bathroom towels and accessories are available for secure ordering through the site; alternatively you can place a provisional order for any of their toilets or sinks and someone from the company will get in touch with a full quote and delivery details.

Kitchen Design From budget to bespoke

All the designer tableware in the world is not going to help you if your kitchen has seen far better days. Kitchens are where everyone hangs out these days, so it's only polite to make it as cool and user-friendly as possible. Of course, few people have the serious cash it takes to completely remodel the whole thing, but with a few ideas nicked from the professionals, even the saddest of cabinets and mouldiest of fridges can be persuaded to have a new lease of life. The following kitchen design sites, ranging from the cheap and cheerful to the eye-crossingly pricey, might provide some inspiration for your own kitchen ambitions.

www.chantrykitchens.co.uk
Bespoke units at factory prices.
www.magnet.co.uk
Affordable prices with a surprisingly stylish choice of designs.
www.mfi.co.uk
Low prices and special offers on a wide range of kitchen cabinetry.
www.moreland-classic-kitchens.co.uk
Family firm doing kitchen design and installation.
www.ps4kitchens.co.uk
Delicious contemporary and traditional designs.

Jewellery & Watches

Easier than trudging the streets, but can any computer screen stir the soul like a jeweller's window?

Jewellery — From catalogue to contemporary

Abooga
www.abooga.com
A huge selection of jewellery, watches and body jewellery. Style-wise most items are relatively traditional, with the addition of a contemporary range from Jeff Banks. Prices are good (watches from £30 to £70) and shipping is free.

Argenteus
http://argenteus.co.uk
Contemporary and modern designer jewellery at high-street prices. Silver dominates, and among the more unusual items is a wavy, square ring set with gemstones from the Ming Collection for less than £100.

Bijoo
www.bijoo.com
French company Bijoo sells a limited selection of fine gold, white gold and gem-set jewellery. Contemporary ring, necklace and earring designs set this apart from its competitors, but the prices are steep – £200 to £350 for rings and £75 for gem-set pendant necklaces. Shipping to the UK is £11 via FedEx.

Gem for Joy
www.gemforjoy.com
Simple and stylish jewellery and site. And prices are good for the quality – 18-carat white gold and diamond cross pendants for around £350.

Great British Jewels
www.gbj.co.uk
Offering fine art and sculpture alongside an ample selection of jewellery items,

the pieces here range between more contemporary and regal designs. Search by item or designer, but scroll through each range as prices vary widely from £50 to £500. Delivery is £10.

Higuchi Inc

www.higuchi-inc.com

In the battle of the watches, Higuchi could help restore your reputation as the king of style. The timepieces here are generally currently only worn by the Japanese, but this simple site lets you buy them light years before they reach these shores. All the top brands and a secure, if rudimentary, order form.

Ice Cool

www.icecool.co.uk

Yes, you read it correctly: beneath the usual offerings are eyelashes. Click through to buy one of only 10 pairs of diamond-encrusted eyelashes (created by Eylure and designer to the stars, Julian MacDonald) to be found in the UK. Ice Cool also offers a comprehensive catalogue of your more traditional diamond accessories at excellent prices.

Icon

www.icon-jewellery.com/st

Each item here is handcrafted and you can regulate the expense according to which carat of gold or gem you choose. The price depends on the designer and a ring will set you back anywhere from £30 to £400. A good choice if you're looking for something a bit different that won't break the bank.

Inspirals

www.inspirals.co.uk

On the plus side Inspirals offers a varied selection of funky silver and gem-set jewellery pieces, all moderately priced, but the site can be a nightmare to use if you're actually in the mood to buy as the designs pop up for you to browse one at a time. Still, worth a look.

Jewellers

www.jewellers.net

This busy catalogue-style site offers gold, silver and luxury items, along with cheap and cheerful fashion novelties. Multiple sub-categories allow you to narrow your search but you can't search by price.

Silver Chilli

www.silverchilli.com

A limited selection of South American-inspired jewellery. Select a category to view clear images. Prices are moderate and shipping is only $5 to the UK.

Tateossian

www.tateossian.com

This stylish site sells unusual and contemporary jewellery items. There's only a small range of fibre-optic glass jewellery and silver and zircon designs, and £40 for a pebble design necklace seems quite steep, but these are one-offs.

The Jeweller

http://the-jeweller.com

Not an inspiring look but a huge range of standard Ernest Jones/H Samuel items. At half the RRP it's advisable to make your search as specific as possible, but this is easily done by choosing a style and price range to suit.

 **Watches** **From club-style to computer buff**

Apple Watch

www.applewatch.co.uk

Apple's dedicated watch site has only a few offerings, but there's an iWatch available in iMac colours for £42, and a counter-clockwise watch for £29.95. Details of shock resistance and waterproof capabilities are provided.

Storm

www.storm-watches.com.au/index.html

The site seems to comprise the entire Storm range, but prices are in dollars (they do offer a link to a currency converter, however). At $100-200, there are few bargains, but you may find something unusual. Check delivery prices.

Traser Watches

www.traser-uk.com

No run-of-the-mill timepieces, but watches guaranteed to glow in the dark for up to 10 years, useful if you're into all those dark, gloomy and frankly scary sports, like caving or deep sea diving. You pay for such technology, around £130, but it means you'll be able to read under the covers.

Watch Heaven

www.topbrands.net

Pages and pages of Swatch watches (better than the problematic official site), with brands including Seiko, Casio and Baby G at prices anywhere between £20 and £150. A separate bargain section and free delivery make this an excellent site.

Magazines

Whether you're looking
for a publication about
carp or something more
obscure, you'll find it on the Net

British Magazines Direct

www.britishmagazines.com

"The UK's largest online magazine store" is the boast here, although
WHSmith might dispute that. Still, extensive interrogation did suggest that the
catalogue is pretty vast (the site says it has 3,500 titles in stock). A good
swift-to-download site with a fast search mechanism and secure ordering of
either one issue or a full subscription. Database includes seven magazines
about carp.

English Magazines

www.englishmagazines.com

This site claims to offer over more than 3,000 titles. The homepage is not that
appealing and the search mechanism can be laborious at its worst. But there
is a very good range of magazines and an e-mail form for when you can't find
what you want. Database includes six magazines about carp.

Magazine Café

www.magazinecafe.co.uk

You can search this site by title or browse by category, although the selection
is not exactly huge. Database doesn't include any magazines about carp –
possibly because the titles here are all international magazines and the rest of
the world doesn't find this particular fish quite as fascinating as the British
evidently do. This site does, however, stock the tattooist's bible, *Skin & Ink*.

Magazine Shop

www.magazineshop.co.uk

Database includes only one magazine about carp, aimed at anglers who
consider themselves "advanced". That lapse apart, this is a decent site,
sensibly structured to make it as easy as possible to find the title that
interests you. You need to subscribe to order but there are some good offers.

WHSmith

www.whsmith.co.uk

Apparently driven by a compulsive need to offer online customers 50 per cent

All the magazines here are international so just imagine our disappointment when we found none featured carp

discounts, this site is well worth checking out. Customers can order a single issue of a favourite magazine or subscribe to it. Plenty of specials and there's even a 'magazine of the week'. Database only contains one title about carp but it does also link to www.DrMag.com, an international (ie American-based) magazine store which, while not having any magazines about carp, did stock one title about marlin and another about fur fish, whatever they are. If Dr Mag doesn't list the international oddity you're after, you can e-mail them to find out if they have information on it.

Yahoo Auctions
http://search.auctions.yahoo.com/search/
auctions?p=magazines&alocale=1us&acc=us
Thousands of magazines are on auction here at any one time which makes it a must for collectors, whether they're after a copy of a gay magazine starring a nude Sylvester Stallone or a 1951 edition of *National Geographic*. Among the items on sale were four magazines about fish.

The Net also plays host to countless e-zines – magazines that don't exist in printed form. Here are some of the best:

The best of the general e-zines is probably **Salon** (www.salon.com) which, although it has fallen on harder times of late, is still the nearest thing to an online *Vanity Fair*. Its range is astonishing – from the minutiae of technology and health to a report on American marketeers who hypnotise consumers to find out what they really think about products.
The Onion (www.onion.com) is justly famous for the sharpness of its wit, although it hasn't been as funny since the Clinton impeachment hearings ended.
Modern Humorist (www.modernhumorist.com) is the latest launch by a Salon writer who outed Tinky Winky as a joke – a joke which the American Moral Majority took seriously. This site's 'downloading MP3 equals communism' poster is truly wonderful. No e-zines about carp yet, but it's only a matter of time.

MAGAZINES ON THE NET

Some magazines make all or some of their content available online. Others generate new material. Just try keying in www. and then the magazine title, and finally .co.uk or .com. Among the more unusual titles in cyberspace are www.ctmmag.com for "correction management" and www.pitandquarry.com serving the non-metallic mining industry.

Motorbikes

Head out on the information superhighway and you can do everything from buy a bike to book a holiday on the open road

Accessories   Helmets, leather and spare parts

Aftermarket Motorcycle Parts

www.oem-uk.com

Not the most imaginative of sites but it does its job. Organised by manufacturer, select your bike model from top names, then scroll through an adequate list of accessories including footpegs, oil caps and end weights.

Go Faster Goodies

www.gofaster-goodies.com

A simple site with a huge catalogue of accessories to help turn your bike from the butt of your mate's jokes into a demon machine. Brands include Yamaha, Ducati and Triumph. One-line descriptions with no images. Free delivery.

Motorcycle City

www.motorcycle-city.co.uk

No bikes here, just leathers, waterproofs, accessories and helmets. Huge discounts make up for lack of stock; reductions can be as much as £300.

Rainbow

www.rainbow.co.uk

BMW-mad site with bikes for hire, used bikes, spare parts, leathers, boots and helmets. You need to know your bike to ensure you get what you need, but it does offer a sizing guide when you buy a helmet. Clothing-wise there's everything from all-in-one leathers (from £350), to kidney protectors (£48).

Urban Bikes

www.urbanbikes.co.uk

Standard clothing and accessory categories, plus multiple visor tints, tyre sizes and boot colours. Top brands include OGK and Caberg helmets, Sidi boots and PowerBronze screens, with something for all budgets.

Motorbikes

 Before you empty your wallet...

Abbey Cross Scooters
www.abbeycross.co.uk
E-mail them about the scooter you're interested in, price needs and whether you need finance options. A sales rep will then contact you. Prices from £999.

Bike Trader
www.biketrader.co.uk
This online relation of *AutoTrader* provides the same information. Make a basic search stating your preferred price, model and the distance you are prepared to travel, and it will list the matches.

Scooter Zone
www.scooterzone.co.uk
Peugeot, Italjet and Malaguli scooters, with prices ranging from £1,400 to £2,000 for 50cc and 100cc. You can only order by e-mail, however.

 Bikes with attitude (and without)

TPC Motorcycles
www.tpc.motorcycle.hire.mcmail.com
This Southampton-based, family-run business hires motorcycles for business or pleasure. Despite its limited range of six models, there are bikes to suit all needs, from a bike with attitude – the Retro GSX750 – to the racing TL1000R. Daily rates are from £55 to £90 or weekly from £310 to £400. You can't finalise the deal online, but you can make provisional bookings.

 **On and off the road**

Grass Routes
www.grassroutes.freeserve.co.uk
Holidays and weekend breaks to suit both the experienced biker and those just wanting something a bit different. Choose from on- and off-road tours of Britain, Ireland and shortly, America and Canada. The site is easy to navigate with all the info on one page. Make enquiries and you'll be contacted.

INSURANCE

You must make Bennetts a priority stop when looking for bike insurance.

Aside from the instant quotes you can get online by answering a few simple questions, this Coventry-based company provides a veritable mine of essential biker info. The maps, weather reports and guides to essential drinking stops will get you thirsting to get out on the open road.

If you've just received your biker wings and are ready to take the plunge with your very own 100cc metal whirlwind, Bennetts can also guide you in the right direction, from whether a Honda or a Buell suits you best, to whether full cover or just third-party will cover your needs. A great all round site.

www.bennetts.co.uk

Museum shops

Desperately seeking a (model) Battle of Britain fighter? A Freud-styled Brainy Beanie Baby? Or maybe a gold-plated pocket watch (a snip at £700)? What luck! You just happen to have come to the right place...

Armagh Planetarium

www.armagh-planetarium.co.uk

All the problems we had with this site last year – secure shopping that had expired; no customer service section with delivery details and return policies; no pricing until the checkout – have all been addressed and now this site is much improved, though far from perfect: if you are going to buy a poster, you want to see what it looks like first – surely not too much to ask. And some of the illustrations are very poor, not exactly inspiring confidence that it will look any better on your own walls. If none of this puts you off, they do sell some interesting items at reasonable prices.

British Museum

www.thebritishmuseum.ac.uk

Britain's premier museum hosts an equally interesting shopping site, with replica jewellery and collectibles alongside standard hieroglyphic-printed tea towels and the inevitable mugs for the tourists. Some of the more interesting items include replicas of historical jewellery, with prices starting at around £40 for a gold-plated snake-ring, traditionally used to ward off evil and to ensure fertility. For the kids, wean them off Pokémon toys with Egyptian Prince and Princess dolls or the Mancala counting game which dates back to the time of the Pharaohs. Novel gifts with a real history.

Freud Museum

www.freud.org.uk

Freud would probably have his own interpretation of why this website is so dull and unsophisticated but it sells gifts for every taste and age. Replica statues of those which adorned Freud's own hallway can be bought for £34, although it's unlikely the Freud picture mugs (£9.50) mirror his own kitchen collection, and one can only guess what he'd read into the Freud-styled Brainy Beanie Babies for £17. Most annoyingly there are no direct links to the order form. No straight answers from the genius even in death.

National Maritime Museum

www.nmm.ac.uk

In terms of price this is far from your average museum gift shop. Only the extravagant will be tempted (or able) to afford a gold-plated pocket watch costing anywhere between £300 and £700, or a Hoggett crystal decanter for £200. Even the cheapest globe comes in at £100. With no indication of delivery charges until the final tally, it probably assumes you're not bothered about a few more pounds' extra expense if you can afford such treats. Otherwise it has info on the museum and events – just keep that wallet away.

National Portrait Gallery

www.npg.org.uk/portprt.htm

More than 7,500 portraits from this museum are available to order online on paper or printed onto canvas. Or so they say. Searching the database is simple enough, but there's not much point if there is no image available. Say you know the painting well and are willing to buy blind – well, prices are right there, shipping costs are displayed, but when you fill in the form all you get is a confirmation that it has been sent to the shop. You then have to wait for them to contact you for payment. Typical English (in)efficiency.

Victoria & Albert Museum

www.vam.ac.uk

An attractive, well-designed site in imperial purple, offering jewellery, books and art nouveau gifts. All the information you need is contained on one page, with enlarged images, descriptions, history, costs and delivery times. Pewter, William Morris, decoupage and tulips feature strongly and you should be able to pick up a delicate decoration for under £20. Search the V&A Gifts section rather than a sub-category to appreciate the full range.

Westair Reproductions

www.westair-reproductions.com

Westair produces gifts for museums around the world, but it also sells from its

own online store. Another dull grey site, it sells mostly miniature models of planes, cannons and soldiers. A Battle of Britain fighter complete with box and historical account will set you back £7.50; American Union and Confederate soldiers can be yours for £3 or, if you prefer, there are cannons for £1.

Truly one for the boys – keep them happy in the football off-season with these toys

Music

From acoustic guitars to zithers,
from JS Bach to Beatles on the
organ, it's all there in cyberspace

Instruments If you were born to play the noseflute

Dawsons Music Store

www.dawsons.co.uk

This impressive store sells a wide range of instruments ranging from tenor saxophones to Fender guitars, all through its secure server. You can apply for store finance online if you're looking to get the band back together and buy the instruments at the same time, and delivery costs will be calculated at the checkout. There's also a monthly competition with some very cool prizes, or if you're fed up with the life of a struggling musician, you can offload your old kit in the classifieds section.

Guitar Base

www.guitar-base.com

Despite the flashing graphics this is a fairly amateur enterprise, the flashing lights being about as high tech as it gets. But of course looks aren't everything and this Nottingham-based company offers a comprehensive selection of acoustic, electric and guitar accessories at competitive prices. Descriptions are brief, but the catalogue images are adequate enough, with prices to suit every pocket, from £150 to over £1,000. Online ordering is available, but you will have to ring for a chat to book any tuition time.

Harmonicas Direct

www.harmonicas-direct.com

Let's face it, Bob, Neil and even the Boss himself wouldn't be nearly as popular if they hadn't added the woeful harmonies of this simple piece of metal to their blue-collar worker songs. This Bradford-based store offers a comprehensive catalogue of both harmonicas and video tuition packages to get you started. The catalogue itself can be daunting particularly if you were expecting to simply choose the shiniest model and click to buy. Additional information about how to decide on an Echo 28 or 30, and which key to choose would help, but everything is well organised with prices to suit all pockets (although between £20 and £40 is a good average guide).

House of Musical Traditions

www.hmtrad.com

Lovely online store offering a great selection of unusual musical instruments from around the world. Decorated mandolins, ukuleles and zithers rub shoulders with such esoterica as noseflutes and panpipes. There's a secure ordering system, but since the company is based in the US, you will have to e-mail for full shipping costs. These will vary greatly, depending on whether you're after a set of bagpipes or a harmonica.

Newcastle Drum Centre

www.newcastledrum.co.uk

Indispensable for those who really hate their neighbours, this site offers a full range of percussion instruments from a beginner's drum kit to samba band bongos. There's a good selection of sale items and a special service for schools. Online shopping is not available yet, but if you e-mail the store through the site they'll do their best to get you what you want.

Phuture Sounds

www.phuture.co.uk

Small online store for analogue synthesizers and drum machines. There's not much information about each model on the site but if you're in the market for such things, it's odds-on you know what you're looking for anyway.

Piano Man

www.pianoplus.co.uk

Offering new pianos at discounted prices as well as secondhand ones – especially unusual and decorative instruments. The Piano Man also buys old pianos and will quote for restoration, repair and removal work if you e-mail them. There's not a lot of stock to look at online, but a detailed enquiry form is provided for you to describe what you're after.

Poole Percussion

www.poole-percussion.co.uk/

It's only a guess but we think this self-advertised 'Drummer's Drum Store' is based in Poole – although we weren't aware Poole was famed for its drumming fraternity. Kits and accessories are all neatly laid out with brief descriptions and clear images for each item. Shipping is free, no matter how far away from this drumming Mecca you live, and ordering follows a standard Yahoo style system.

Wesson Accordion Company

www.crosswinds.net/~zydeco/

Serving as a sales page for Castagnari Melodeons as well as the homepage for the Joe le Taxi Zydeco Dance Band, this site offers a range of traditional squeeze boxes at varying prices. You can e-mail Rees Wesson for an up-to-date stock list and he accepts credit cards and cheques in payment.

Sheet Music For downloading too

G&S Works Inc.
www.gsworks.com
If you yearn to be a pirate of Penzance but lack the resources of the D'Oyly Carte Opera Company, this site can provide scaled-down scores of Gilbert and Sullivan classics for production by small theatre companies and bands. You can attempt HMS Pinafore with just seven musicians (and presumably even fewer sailors), and there's a list of companies who have successfully used the scores.

Look Music
www.lookmusic.com
There's no excuse for murdering the same show tune over and over again when there are so many pieces to chose from, no matter what the instrument. The site aims for user-friendliness, and even has a clever 'sounds like' search facility – though it came up with a Dire Straits track when we asked for the *Concierto de Aranjuez*. You should receive your order in three days.

Sheet Music Now
www.sheetmusicnow.com
If you have Adobe Acrobat you can use this site to buy and download sheet music direct to your computer. Search by composer or instrument, then follow the instructions and you'll have your music in a jiffy.

Music For A Song
www.musicforasong.co.uk
Learn new tunes and save a packet by buying used sheet music and music books. It won't always have what you're after but it's worth a look. Search by composer or instrument, e-mail to reserve your choice, then ring through credit card details or send a cheque.

Music Room
www.musicroom.com
Whether they're after the Bach Lute Suites or a book of Beatles hits rearranged for the home organist, budding musicians can surf this easy-to-navigate site for hours. All orders are sent out by first-class mail.

PIANOLA ROLLS

Once again proving our assertion that you can get *anything* over the Internet, what about some new music rolls for your pianola?

If you're lucky enough to own such a treasure, check out The Keystone Music Roll Company at *www.keystonemusicroll. com* in Bethlehem, Pennsylvania where player pianos can find tunes from Beethoven to Irving Berlin.

If this whets your appetite further, you can always surf over to *www.leedyrolls.com* where there are links to The Automated Musical Instrument Collectors' Association and The Pianola Institute in London. Other sites are:

Bam Bam Player Piano Rolls
http://members.aol. com/BamRolls

Meliora Music Rolls
http://members.aol. com/meliorarol

New England Music Rolls
http://members.aol. com/NEMRoll/home. html

QRS Music
www.qrsmusic.com

Net stuff

Thousands of websites say
they can make your surfing
more productive and enjoyable.
But only a few actually deliver

E-greetings Save trees, handwriting and pandas

Blue Mountain Arts
www.bluemountain.com
Missed someone's birthday? Quick, send an e-card as though that's what you
intended to do all along. Blue Mountain offers a huge range of cartoon cards
to personalise and send, from the silly to the soppy. They even have cards for
events you never knew you had to celebrate, like Kiss and Make Up Day.

E-Cards
www.e-cards.com
This site, run by three Netheads in San Francisco, generates revenue for a
variety of wildlife and ethical charities and many of the cards feature stunning
photos of the natural world, including endangered species and rare flowers.
You can also send video cards if you're feeling really ambitious.

E-greetings
egreetings.indiatimes.com
Send an animated(ish) card through this site, which as you would expect,
has a leaning towards Indian holidays. Vast selection for every occasion.

Screen Decorate your desktop

Celebrity Desktop
www.celebritydesktop.com
Customise your screen with a favourite star of the screen or sports field.
Loads of celebs to choose from as either wallpaper or full screensaver, as well
as links to many other celebrity sites. It should make coming to work just that
bit more bearable.

Screen Savers Bonanza

www.bonanzas.com

When you get bored of the selection of screensavers that came with your computer, this site can help you out with over 450 different screensavers for Macs and PCs, all arranged depending on your operating system. Anything you might possibly want, from a tribute to Frank Sinatra to an Egyptian mummies cube to bounce around your screen, is here, and you can also download a free version of WinZip to open the files.

 **Try, buy or download it**

Dave Central Shareware Archive

www.davecentral.com

This may sound like someone's dodgy homepage, but it's actually a brilliant portal for finding software downloads for Windows or Linux platforms. Whether you need conferencing software or a graphics package, you'll find something to link to here, with many downloads reviewed by techies.

DemoNet

www.demonet.com

Try before you buy. Many of the 47,000 items of software available here have demonstration versions for you to play with before you take the plunge. The site also contains updates on the NASA Mission to Mars, and they are planning a new venture, DemoNet TV, which will broadcast information and instructions for all kinds of software.

Training Downloads

www.trainingdownloads.com

This isn't software for you to download, but useful downloadable manuals on how to use all the software you have. Mostly in course format for $19.95.

ZD Net Downloads

www.zdnet.com

You can find software downloads for Mac, PC and even Palm from here. There are free downloads, as well as costlier programs to make surfing more fun or just provide you with some new games.

Office supplies

Let the Internet be your very own personal digital assistant even if all you really need are some new pages for your Filofax, a rubber stamp and some more business forms

Action Office Supplies
www1.action.com
Specialising in computer supplies, hardware, software and peripherals, Action's online store is a boon for busy offices. Customer service is outstanding. Prices are always low and delivery is next day for most of the UK with a same-day service for panicking customers in central London.

Avon Business Centre
www.avonbc.co.uk
Bypass all other links and head straight for the stationery and office supplies section to view Avon's entire catalogue including general supplies, office furniture, computer equipment and even janitorial supplies. Searching is easy with idiot-proof descriptions and images and prices are competitive with discounts galore. Credit applications can be made online.

City Organiser
www.cityorg-pdq.co.uk
For those Luddites refusing to get on the PDA bandwagon, this is where to come for accessories and inserts for your trusty Filofax. Some complete binder systems are available for one-hour delivery in central London, or you can choose your delivery method and cost, starting at £2 for first-class post.

Euro Office
www.euroffice.co.uk
Bet you never thought office supplies could be so glamorous. OK, slight exaggeration, but Euro Office has a stylish site with everything from fire extinguishers and storage solutions to copier paper and rubber bands. Browse or make a search using catalogue references and if you go to the small trouble of registering you can benefit from customised lists and reward schemes.

NEBS Business Forms

www.nebs.co.uk

You can buy from their stock of standard forms such as invoices or purchase orders, including some compatible with software packages like Sage, or e-mail the company for a more personalised job. They'll also print things (T-shirts, mugs etc) to order.

Polka Dot

www.polka.co.uk

All the top brand names are here, from Avery to Xerox. This site is best for large, expensive orders as there is a fixed £7.50 delivery charge. And don't worry, the yellow dots vanish after the homepage.

Rubber Stamps

www.rubber-stamps.co.uk

Rubber, pre-inked, date, animal and heavy-duty stamps are all on hand for any stamp emergencies. Prices are good, with the added bonus of free shipping, and a free gift for any orders over £20 – that being the chance to select a phrase and have it embossed on one of your new stamps. Riveting stuff.

Toners.Co.UK

www.toners.co.uk

Toner and copier supplies for new and not-so-new machines. If yours is not listed, e-mail the company and it will try and track it down. Delivery costs depend on the item and VAT is not included until you reach the checkout. Orders received before 3pm will be dispatched the same day.

Viking Direct

www.viking-direct.co.uk

Stock up on Post-its and paper clips at this online warehouse. New users are offered a free gift with their first order and the site is simple to use. Prices exclude VAT, but delivery is free on orders over £30 and most goods will be with you by the next day – at the latest.

Willett

www.willett.co.uk

Give your control freak side full rein with Willett's range of label-making printers. You have to register with this site in order to look at many of the products, but there are solutions here to labelling everything from hanging files to large shipments – including printers, software, labels and other accessories.

SORT OUT YOUR HOME OFFICE

Time to move on from that rickety table in the corner of your lounge...

Space 2
Groovy and well-made desks and computer workstations for the most design-conscious.

Posture Point
Ergonomic chairs and seating that are as easy on your back as they are on the eye.

President Office Furniture
Impressively versatile desk and storage systems for companies.

Interior Motives
Glamorous desks and chairs for any location.

www.space2.com

www.posture.co.uk

www.president.co.uk

www.int-motives.co.uk

243

Outdoors

Face masks, 'frequency pants' and men with beards – you'll find them all in the great outdoors which, confusingly, you can access from the less-than-great indoors thanks to the Internet

Climb Limited

www.rockrun.com

Although it's billed as Climb Limited on some search engines, the homepage bears the brand name Rockrun which spins off the company's two Rock and Run shops. A member of the *Which?* Trader scheme, the online shop can take a while to load. Depending on the time of year, the Clearance Sale section can have some decent deals. Any minor flaws in speed and navigation are more than compensated for by some of the discounts on offer on the rest of the site – 50 per cent marked off some sleeping bags – the secure ordering, and the range of products from Black Diamond gaiters to Terminator crampons. There's also a telephone helpline from 9am to 5pm on weekdays to answer any questions.

Complete Outdoors

www.complete-outdoors.co.uk

A large range of big-brand trekking, rambling and camping gear, including a separate kids' section, and accessories and gizmos (pedometers, cooking equipment, Leatherman tools and much more) make for a packed and useful outdoor site. There's a distinctly above average online magazine to inspire your choice and a few special offers to tempt you. Delivery is guaranteed within 48 hours and costs £3.95, but VAT is added only after you arrive at the checkout. The tents look like a particularly good deal.

Ellis Brigham

www.ellis-brigham.com

Plenty of photos of bearded men dangling off cliff faces and smiling couples barely breaking into a sweat as they hike through the wilderness are the order of the day at Ellis Brigham's striking site. Having been improved since last year, the site now has a much better navigation system. You can opt to search by brand and you will find a great selection of outdoor clothing, footwear, rucksacks, camping and ski equipment – even a Snowboard Asylum. There are loads of clearance bargains available, some with very intriguing names like 'frequency pants'. You can also hire equipment by phone or fax. Delivery depends on value and weight – bigger items like skis are shipped via TNT for a very reasonable £10.

Hugh Lewis

www.outdoor-leisure.com

Despite failing to break the mould in the design stakes, Mr Lewis (and that's Hugh not Huey and his news following) offers an extensive catalogue of outdoor equipment with something for everything from a weekend in the Lakes to a polar ice cap survival expedition. Select a category to view images and descriptions of products for sale. Prices are good, with delivery starting at £3. Hugh has also included a handy tips section for those more of a Ralph than a Ranulph Fiennes. Worth a look just for the answer to what all those rucksack pockets are supposed to be filled with.

Jacksons Outdoor Leisure Supplies

www.jacksons-camping.co.uk

Out hiking in the wilderness but want to keep up with the latest *EastEnders* tragedy? Then get the battery-operated TV from Jacksons and never miss an episode. Oh and there's also a portable DVD player so you can entertain yourself at night by watching those blockbusters you missed. In fact, why not bring along a gas-operated freezer to keep your beer cold? And why do without hot food when you can just pop it into a battery-operated microwave? All the comforts of home away from home are available, mostly geared to caravan enthusiasts, but plenty for campers and even just for the back garden. Good line of above ground pools – useful when global warming really kicks in. You can buy online or call to check availability first. Shipping depends on the item ordered.

Oswald Bailey

www.outdoorgear.co.uk

This is a great outdoors site absolutely packed with products – everything from tents and boots to mosquito head nets and waist wallets. You'll find decent product descriptions, very reasonable prices and an order tracking facility. But, though prices supposedly include mainland UK delivery, a £1 'carriage' charge will be tacked on to your

PRACTICE, PRACTICE

If you want to go climbing, you don't have to head for the country. If you're in London, you can find a castle wall to climb on a Grade II-listed folly in Stoke Newington. Find Stoke Newington's finest residence on *www.castle-climbing.co.uk*.

The Castle Climbing Centre has a counterpart in Glasgow called Cliffhanger which you can find on *www.glasgowclimbingcentre.co.uk*.

If you need to brush up on your kayak skills, try the Vive La Montagne consultancy on *www.vlmadventureconsultants.co.uk/*. See, even in the wild you can't escape consultants.

final total. What makes this seem unforgivably underhand is that it's done only after you've entered your credit card details. Pity really because the rest of the site seems to support the homepage boast about how well loved this outdoor shop is.

Outdoor Megastore

www.outdoormegastore.co.uk

It claims to have more than 7,000 lines of outdoor gear at discounted prices so you are bound to find just what you are looking for – if not, the site says it will track down your item and quote a "rock-bottom" price. You do have to do quite a bit of mouse action to get to the goods, but once there, the illustrations and descriptions are excellent and the sizing advice is useful. Shipping is free on orders over £25. A friendly site with excellent choices; a bit of clean-up on the navigation and this would be first class.

Pennine Outdoor

www.pennineoutdoor.co.uk

Do you have some sewing skills and don't fancy the latest Berghaus fleece? Think you could improve on Patagonia's shorts? Then this site is for you. Pennine Outdoor sells a staggering range of specialist outdoor fabrics – everything from fleeces and breathable waterproofs to heavy duty neoprene-coated fabric (perfect for running up your own bivi bag). You can also buy patterns for outdoor gear, including one for a not very natty but no doubt functional Mountain Jacket, and even a child's hooded ski jacket. Freezing-temperature zips? No problem. Seam waterproofing? You can buy it here. Ordering is fairly straightforward (it's the choice that will be hard) and low-cost delivery takes 72 hours to most of the UK. A couple of complaints: there's simply too much information running down the left-hand side of the homepage, and the illustrations could be better.

Everything to plan that ultimate camping experience. Now, if they could only sell rain-free weather

Pro-Line Sports

http://shop.proline-sports.co.uk

If the mind's willing but your flesh is weak, this is the place to come. Pro-Line Sports specialises in shoulder braces, knee supports, calf protectors, kidney belts, toe warmers, face masks... in fact, a whole range of outdoor body aids that will keep you safe from all manor of scrapes and injuries. Ordering is easy, delivery is free and there's a 30-day refund. Internet shopping should always be like this.

Simply Scuba

www.simplyscuba.co.uk

Billed as the UK's biggest online dive store, this site has everything the scuba diver or snorkeller could need. This excellent site has a phone-back facility, order tracking, and a highly detailed chart matching dozens of body measurements to equipment size. Secondhand kits are for sale – details are on the message board and you can add your own if you have something to sell.

Snow and Rock

www.snowandrock.co.uk

It isn't too hard to guess this site's speciality. Big-brand skiing and climbing gear is arranged into categories (including a section for kids), but frustratingly, you can't cross-brand browse for a particular item. Delivery depends on cost, but though orders up to £100 supposedly incur a £2.50 charge, you may well find £4.50 added at the checkout. Rather unhelpfully goods are dispatched only "as they become available". Plenty of pictures make the site pleasant to browse, and you'll find the usual range of clothing, tents, backpacks, etc, but you may prefer to buy from a site with delivery guarantees.

Stif Mountain Bikes

www.stif.co.uk

If you're into mountain biking, you'll find this site truly indispensable. There's a big selection of bikes on offer, plus associated "software" – bags, Oakley glasses, drinking systems (just so you know they're serious), jerseys, helmets... even replacement bike parts. Well designed, the site also features plenty of biking news and views to soften the sales edge.

Wild Spirit

www.wildspirit.co.uk

It might not have the most sophisticated website in the world, but this Northumberland-based store does offer a reasonable selection of outdoor clothing and equipment for everything from trekking to camping and mountain biking, and web customers get 10 per cent off every order over £200. Downsides? You'll find your clicking finger aching by the time you actually access the shop, delivery can take up to 28 days, and there is no secure ordering system. You'll have to e-mail those credit card details if you're keen.

Parties

Let the Internet sort it all out for you: personal security paraphernalia, a home supply of helium or a Jane Asher cake are only a few clicks away

General All you need for big kids and little ones

A Big Smile
www.abigsmile.com
Suppliers of party goods for children's parties and other celebrations, with some great time-saving theme packs containing items like banners, table cloths and napkins, based on kids' favourite characters or movies. There are also dress-up items like masks, or you can e-mail for details of full costumes.

Dr Party
www.drparty.com
Fabulous site that will get you in the mood to party as soon as you reach the homepage. Whether it's a raucous bash or a kiddies' tea party, there's plenty of advice and help here to make it all run smoothly so *you* can enjoy the event too. There are loads of links to party sites in the usual categories, plus a few you won't have thought of. Don't get on down without it.

Fox Magic
www.foxmagic.co.uk
Unusual amateur site offering the services for Magical Mac and friends for children's and even adult parties. The opening homepage song is a little unnecessary, but everything beyond here is simple. Click on adult or children to view brief descriptions of how your party will run. They also list helpful, if sometimes obvious, advice such as ensure the little ones go to the bathroom before the show begins. No prices are listed, but information requests and bookings can be made online.

Happy Party
www.happyparty.co.uk
If your idea of fun isn't organising a kids' birthday party, the Happy Party site

with its bright yellow homepage, can take the pain out of arranging treats for the little darlings. With tableware, decorations and party bags, all the bases are covered. You can buy pre-filled party bags for £2.50, or create your own from a wide selection of toys and novelties. They also sell a selection of party food boxes in pirate ship, Safari jeep and Cinderella coach designs – more interesting for the kids and safer than having them eat off your best china.

Just For Fun
www.justforfun.co.uk
Loads of fancy dress here for kids and grown-ups alike, along with decorations and joke items. Need the biggest afro you've ever seen? There's one here for just £9.99. The site is user-friendly and well designed with a good help section if you get lost among the bunting. Delivery within two days.

Party Time
www.partytime.co.uk
This is a helpful planning site to remind you of all the things you need to really make a party swing. There are links and contact details for party suppliers, entertainers and caterers, plus ideas for games.

The Party Store
www.thepartystore.co.uk
Huge selection of party goods with almost any theme you can think of, including pirates or the Roaring Twenties. The best novelty items include pinatas for kids' parties and inflatable guitars for a rock 'n' roll themed event. There are helpful suggestions of co-ordinating products plus lots of planning tip and ideas for harassed hosts. Delivery time is three to four days.

 **Get your perfect patisserie here**

Entertainment
www.mmssoft.force9.co.uk
For a touch of the kitsch you can always hire an entertainment act to liven up your evening. Acts from stand-up comedians to puppeteers and from after-dinner speakers to The Fraud Monty are profiled on this site; you can e-mail or phone their agents for further details and prices.

Jane Asher Party Cakes
www.jane-asher.co.uk
Impress the socks off your birthday boy or girl (well, their parents anyway) with a flash cake from Jane Asher's shop in Chelsea. You can chose from fruit cake or sponge cake, and there are a number of fancy designs including one in the shape of a Game Boy. The speed at which this reviewer's cake disappeared is a glowing testimonial to how good they are. Use the online

order form to send them your request and then phone your credit card details through – but they do need seven days' notice.

Security

www.idcband.co.uk

For those who are into party organising in a big way and are concerned about security, this site can supply ID wrist bands, hand stamps and stewards' vests to guard against gatecrashers and other trouble. They can also supply a range of table-top party bombs which can be themed for your event.

 From fireworks to restaurant tours

Balloons

www.webshops.co.uk/shops/The_Balloon_StoreD

This simple, easy-to navigate site offers a range of party balloons from adorable heart shapes to balloons for modelling, along with more standard shapes and colours. If you're after a lot of balloon décor for your bash, you should save money here. There's speedy, secure online ordering and the goods are promised to reach you within five working days.

Balloons

www.kentballoon.co.uk

Secure online ordering was not yet up and running when we visited but the hassle of ordering by phone or e-mail is worth it if you're after personalised balloons for a special celebration. All styles can be printed with a message of up to five words and you can even rent helium gas equipment through the site so your guests can giggle in Mickey Mouse voices.

Kent Balloons allows you to personalise your message for any occasion – so go ahead and embarrass your loved ones

Fireworks

http://208.185.197.122/fantfire.html

You can request a display to be created for you at this outstanding (and very noisy) fireworks site, or simply buy one of their ready packs to use at home. There's info on each kit which tells you how much space you need to be safe and how noisy each of the rocket packs will be.

Pets & pet supplies

Evening primrose vitamins for
cats, pizzas for dogs – amazing
what you can find on the Net

Animail

www.animail.co.uk

With quick and simple registration and a bright, inviting cartoon homepage,
you can't help but be swayed into spoiling your pet. Luxuries range from the
extravagant pine cat bed (£129.99) to a pizza specially created for your pooch.

Burns Pet Nutrition

www.burns-pet-nutrition.co.uk

The Burns in the title of this site has an awful lot of letters following his name
so you can be certain the health of your pet is in safe hands. Ingredients and
nutritional info and guidance is on hand, and prices are good for such
specialised products. Shipping is free on orders over £24.

Edkins Aquatics

www.edkins.com

You probably imagined a fish would be the perfect low-maintenance pet, but
this amateurish site proves even a goldfish can live in style. Everything from
pond pumps and filters, to simple fish foods, whether for coldwater or tropical
varieties. Prices are good with many items discounted. Delivery an added £4.

Gillrugs

www.gillrugs.com

Some people can go over the top when it comes to pet clothing but Gillrugs
is about providing your dog with extra warmth, waterproof protection and
even safety clothing. This family-run business offers a selection of jackets and
matching extras; you just have to supply the measurements. Free delivery.

Pet Emporium

www.petemporium.co.uk

An obvious range of cat baskets, scratching posts and dog homes, but quite

Pets & pet supplies

If you're concerned that your dog may be teased by the neighbourhood hounds about the size of his hefty pot belly, why not head for Interplanetary Pet Products and put him on a nutritional, tasty diet.

No prizes for guessing this is an US site, selling food formulated by a team of vets, bio-chemists and scientists. Low-fat treats include chicken, beef or peanut butter Zukes Power Bones, high in protein and low in satu-rated fats ($30 for a box of 20), and low-fat dog wafers for $7.95.

http://shop.store.
yahoo.com/ippi/
natpetnut.html

a variety of colours and materials. The most unusual item is a zebra-print duvet cover for £26.75.

Pet Mad
www.petmad.com
If you can get past the chaotic homepage this site is easy to use with pet food (some brand-name foods are available at around half supermarket prices), beds, toys and ailment remedies. Search by animal, product or category. Pet Mad will also send you and your pet a free gift, no purchase necessary.

Pet Mobil
www.petmobil.com
A variety of contraptions to transport your pet anywhere you wish without the little blighter. They double up as shopping trolleys, but make sure you remove the cat before you dump your groceries in. Prices vary depending on whether you opt for the basic or deluxe options; shipping is a flat £5.

Pet Planet
www.petplanet.co.uk
This site offers info on pet services, particular breeds, vets and pet passport information, the usual dog, cat and bird items, plus more innovative ideas such as a thermal bed or grooming mitten. Order before noon and they'll deliver that day if the product is in stock.

Pets on the Brain
www.petsonthebrain.com
Food, toys and equipment for your animal, whether it's a cat or common garden-variety lizard. It's worth joining their club for discounts – though you have to give them your credit card details to be eligible.

Pets Park
www.petspark.com
Pets Park offers the natural way to pamper your pet with organic catnip toys and Evening Primrose vitamins, features on the pros of acupuncture treatment, and even food for hedgehogs and rats.

Pets Pyjamas
www.pets-pyjamas.co.uk
A revamped site but still one that makes the user work too hard. It offers hundreds of items of pet paraphernalia but the type is too small to read, the category links don't always work and the keyword search is too non-specific.

Phones

Whether you're after a fashion accessory, something you can use to access the Internet or just a tasteless novelty to appal the neighbours with, the Net can help

 The hippest way to say you're on the train

Alcatel

www.alcatel.com/consumer

Alcatel's bubblegum design mobiles are distributed through French company Walkyries, and are therefore governed by French, not English, law. Prices start at around £120 but you will need to sort out line rental elsewhere.

Motorola

www.motorola.co.uk

If the Motorola 'look' appeals, head here to buy online. Plenty – possibly too much – technical bumph to sink your teeth into.

Siemens

www.ic.siemens.com/mySiemens?world=MW

Tiny compact phones, but only four models to buy online, including the latest M35I and the C35i. And linking to the checkout seemed almost impossible.

 **You've got the hardware, now hook up**

BT Cellnet

www.btcellnet.co.uk

BT manages to demonstrate once again why it is top of the class with its simplistic yet comprehensive shopping site. Choose from the very latest mobile models from top brands Ericsson, Nokia and Siemens, and select either Pay As You Go or monthly tariffs to suit your budget. Unlike a number of outlets you can choose your own combination to suit your needs, and if you're not sure what these are, simply answer a few questions and it will come up with the best for you.

Phones

Orange

www.orange.co.uk

This quick-stop shop is useful with a simple layout. Orange offers four different tariffs and a choice of the latest phones. Blissfully uncluttered and clear.

Worth a look:

www.one2one.co.uk

www.vodafone-retail.co.uk

One 2 One
Vodafone

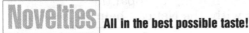 **All in the best possible taste!**

North Coast Phone Center

www.phonecenter.net

If you fancy a phone which really makes a statement, why not have one styled to look like R2D2, a bag of golf clubs or even a pair of red pouting lips? A surefire winner has got to be Marilyn Monroe poised above a grate; when the phone rings, up goes her skirt and she belts out *I Wanna Be Loved By You*. All these and more are here – but you may not find instant e-gratification, as it was impossible to confirm whether they delivered to the UK.

 **Hot deals from your friendly salesman**

Carphone Warehouse

www.carphonewarehouse.com

Far easier than waiting for one of its store representatives to serve you, Carphone Warehouse has developed an excellent site to suit all. If you're an old hand opt for the express service, simply choose a tariff and a phone, and buy. If you're a mobile virgin opt for the interactive service. Said to take around 30 minutes, it only took me 15 and by the end I had a network, tariff and phone tailored to my individual needs.

Direct Phones

www.directphones.co.uk

Busy and text laden, once you move past the initially confusing homepage the site is easy to navigate and purchase from. It's simply a case of choosing three of the five networks, with several tariffs available and popular mobile models from Siemens, Panasonic and Ericsson. Standard yet comprehensive.

Just Phones

www.justphones.co.uk

Alongside the usual selection of new contract and pre-pay mobiles, this busy

A WAP rap WAP 0 GRIMSBY 0

Life's full of disappointments and, up until now, one of them has been getting a WAP (Wireless Application Protocol) phone. "I've only really ever used mine for the football results and rail times," said one WAP user, whose experience must have been doubly disappointing since he supported Grimsby.

Despite the fact that some networks claim that WAP usage has rocketed, it's still not where it's at when it comes to shopping. We've found a few offerings below but, as reported last year, it's probably still faster to use your phone in the traditional way to order a pizza than try to ask them to hold the anchovies and olives across WAP.

As ever, a lack of agreement between the big players over which delivery platform to use held things back, and while GPRS (General Packet Radio System) has made WAP life more practical because it offers an always open line and you only pay for the data you download, it does mean buying a new phone to take advantage of it. Not that the average mobile phone junkie is usually averse to a stylish new handset, and little numbers like the Motorola Timeport T260 have already proved irresistible. At the time of writing, Orange was the latest to sign up to GPRS and there was talk of the said Timeport being part of an inviting £4-a-month for three months' trial.

3G (third generation) phones remain the mobile Internet user's nirvana because they will offer a far superior browsing experience being able to handle multimedia content at browsing speeds more commonly associated with the desktop. There was talk that 3G would start to appear worldwide in 2002 but that may be optimistic. However new technologies are emerging that could bring fully-featured web content to phone browsers a lot sooner. Bitstream (www.bitstream.com) a company previously better known in the graphic arts market for its fonts expertise, has developed a way to shrink content down so it fits in the screen of a mobile phone or a Portable Digital Assistant (PDA). If manufacturers decide to run with its ThunderHawk technology, proper web content could be on phones before 3G. Pogo Technology (www.pogo-tech.com) meanwhile, has developed a mobile device which looks like a PDA and incorporates a mobile phone, that claims to offer fully featured web content over the standard GSM network.

If we're lucky, we may not have to hang around for 3G at all to get more compelling content on our phone browsers, but if the mêlée that is the mobile phone market has its way it'll probably be all change again next year. Meantime, if you're desperate to get a piece of the action, try these:

www.amazon.com/phone
www.wapoffice.co.uk/bookit.wml
http://wap.ebay.co.uk
http://flowerwap.co.uk
http://wap.dealtime.co.uk

and happy site lets you choose a secondhand model, with prices ranging from £15 to £250 for the latest Panasonic GD92. Alternatively place a bid in the auction section and pick up a Motorola V3688 for less than £100. If you already have a phone going spare, sell it online or buy a Sim card package from the usual networks.

Small Talk

www.smalltalk.co.uk

Has no one managed to find a simple and stress-free method of selling mobile phones? Small Talk is a comprehensive site, offering some of the best deals on Orange mobile phones. Pick up the latest Nokia 8210 for just 99p with 50p a day line rental. However in order to leave the store safe in the knowledge that you've read all the small print and know exactly what you're getting for your money, you'll need a pen and paper handy ready to take notes. Persistence needed.

Talking Shop

www.talkingshop.co.uk

Working as a supplier for every network, tariff and phone manufacturer, it's easy to see how things have become a little complicated. The site itself is comprehensive and easy to navigate, but with so much choice you do feel the need for more guidance. But if you can work it out, there is lots of choice and most questions seem to be addressed – even if you have to hunt around a bit. Not for the colour-blind.

If you're certain that your mobile telecoms future is Orange, Smalltalk is a good online source of low-priced phones

IN THE RING

Forget WAP, a trendy ring and a funky screen graphic are the crucial factors where your mobile is concerned.

Choose from your favourite pop tunes – like 2Unlimited's *No Limits* or Michael Jackson's *Bad* – your fave TV anthems such as *Fame*, or make your own request. Prices vary from £3.49 to £4.99.

Customise your screen with funky images or brand yourself with a cartoon appearance. Alas, Nokia owners only need apply.

Mobile Rings – *www. mobilerings.co.uk*

Mobile Tones – *www. mobiletones.com*

Phunky Phones – *www. phunkyphones.com*

Property

Finding your home
sweet home can be a
doddle (well, almost) if
you take a look online

Buy & sell Track down the home of your dreams

Asserta Home

www.asserta.co.uk

You'll find 100,000 or so properties listed here, from estate agents
throughout the country. Each entry comes with a handy, if sometimes
depressing, estimate of how much a mortgage would cost on that property.
Other excellent features include directories of local tradesmen in each area.

Easier

www.easier.co.uk

The search engine can be temperamental but this site does have a huge
database of private and commercial properties up for private sale and rent.
If you're looking for anything from an ex-council flat near Harrods to a barn
conversion in Herefordshire, or even a *pied à terre* in Paris, there are online
brochures to be viewed and printed out, plus plenty of instructions and tips
for both sellers and buyers.

08004Homes

www.08004homes.com

Property portal with excellent choice of channels, including one for interiors
and another for the experts' view of what's happening to the housing market.
Properties for sale are registered by estate agents: buyers can search through
the thousands listed and link to the agents' pages for more info. There is a
nifty service finder that will locate anything from a local doctor to builder.

Home Check

www.homecheck.co.uk

Not a sales site but definitely one to check before you buy. Enter your
postcode and it gives local information on potential problems like pollution,
subsidence, flood risk, landfill sites and air quality. Some of these might come

Property

DOING IT YOURSELF

Dreaming of a self-built mock-Tudor dream, or a gleaming homage to Le Corbusier? ebuild (www.ebuild.co.uk) is low on visuals but is well designed, as you'd expect, and is a gold-mine of architects, legal help, and products and services directories.

If the story of the *Three Little Pigs* never struck home, try *www.mayabooks. ndirect.co.uk/selfbuild. html* for how to build your very own straw house. More practical souls might want to take a trip to *www. mwscaffolding.demon. co.uk/SelfBuild*.

up in your local authority search or your survey. No Northern Ireland, Scotland or Isle of Man coverage yet, but it's coming, along with local information about flight paths, train service performances, unemployment, crime and traffic levels.

House Net
www.housenet.co.uk
Dealing with both private sellers and estate agents, this site has a vast number of properties on view, from seafront flats in Hove to a traditional farmhouse with stables and barns in Warwickshire. On this site, however, small classified listings are free. This means very few people have gone for the option of paying £17.63 to have a photo added to their page, and almost no one has gone for the full-details option for £29.95, so the browsing process is incredibly frustrating. Links to regional estate agents are more useful, as are the insurance, removals and environmental check links.

Houseweb
www.houseweb.com
Launched in 1996, this site really is user-friendly, with 150,000 properties and features like auto-notify to let you know when a property matching your criteria comes up. Specify either a wide search, with hundreds of properties to browse, or narrow it right down if you know you won't be happy without a fireplace, Aga and a 60ft garden.

London Home Net
www.londonhomenet.com
London-only site aimed at private sellers and landlords, with a special section for flatshare listings. There's a one-off sales payment of £45 (£29 for lettings, free for flatshares) for which you get a full web page that will stay on the site until you sell your house, plus a photographer to snap the property if you live in Zones 1-4. All sellers and landlords who register a property are sent an information pack with tips on stumbling blocks like price negotiation and legal aspects of the sale or let, placing this service a cut above the rest.

Property Broker
www.propertybroker.co.uk
A site aimed at private sellers within the M25 looking to sidestep the estate agent's fees. For a flat £78, the site will send a photographer to take quality digital pictures of your home, list your property details and photos on the website, and they'll put up a sale board if you want one. Buyers can search or browse, then e-mail or phone sellers to make an appointment.

Property Finder
www.propertyfinder.co.uk
Search engine for sorting through the thousands of properties on estate agents' books. Using your specified postcodes, bedroom requirements and whether you want a flat or house, the site will come up with all matching properties plus easy links to contact the agents they are selling through. Fast and efficient with distractions kept to the minimum, plus a handy map locator.

Really Moving
www.reallymoving.com
Practical, well-designed and fun-to-surf portal that guides you through the whole house-moving process with skill and reassurance. There are just 20,000-ish properties to look at, but the real benefits of this site are things like the e-mail service to remind you of all the things you must do when moving house, from commissioning a survey to forwarding your mail. There are also online quotes on services like removals and spring-cleaning your new home.

This is London
www.thisislondon.co.uk
Stylish site which not only has property listings but a London lifestyle guide. Listings include information on new developments as well as estate agent-registered homes, with some fancy extras like a quick mortgage calculator and 3D tours of some properties.The whole house-buying process is gone through step by step, with the role of the solicitor and surveyor explained, and links to services along the way. This takes the worry out of any property decision. Fun articles about celebrity moves will keep you entertained.

Up My Street
www.upmystreet.com
The ultimate information site, containing demographic details for the area you are considering moving to, often in graph form. The data is usually incredibly detailed, offering insights on everything from average house prices, school performance and contact details for local tradesmen, to which newspapers your new neighbours read. Vital for those relocating over any distance, but interesting if you're thinking of buying a house. A fascinating browse.

 Don't forget to read the small print...

John Charcol
www.charcolonline.co.uk
The Mortgage Wizard search engine scans the products from 45 different mortgage lenders to find the right products for you – some of which are exclusive deals done with high-street names and which can be amazing value bargains for those who qualify. It can also offer you a mortgage if you're one

of those people many banks won't touch – the self-employed, those with a poor credit history, or people wanting to buy to let.

Ashley Page and Veingard
www.consultant-insurance.co.uk
Buying insurance direct can seem like the way to save money but sometimes, especially if you have some high-end kit you need extra cover for, using an insurance broker is better as you get a more individual approach, plus support if you need to make a claim. This site outlines the services the broker will offer you, and you can e-mail queries, after which you will be contacted to discuss your requirements further.

Direct Line
www.directline.com
Online arm of the TV-advertised insurance giant. Plenty of information here about Direct Line Household Buildings and Contents Insurance (including the whole policy document to download if you're really keen on small print). The basic outline of cover, including legal protection, leads you to a tailored quotation which you can accept and purchase, all online.

Ecology Building Society
www.ecology.co.uk
This mortgage lender is dedicated to promoting sustainable housing, and is the place to go if you are buying an energy-efficient house, restoring a dilapidated or derelict property or are involved in some ecological enterprise, private or commercial. Not the best rates, but you may get a loan on a project other lenders would run a mile from.

Easy Quote
www.easy-quote.co.uk
If you're concerned that requesting an insurance quotation online will bring a never-ending stream of sales calls, then this site is probably your best bet as Easy Quote promises no one will hassle you once it has provided a quote from one of the company's respected insurance partners – these include Northern Rock, CGU and Norwich Union.

Grove Insurance Services
www.grove-is.co.uk
Straightforward independent site offering quotations on policies from over 60 different insurance companies, along with advice on which one is likely to be the best for you. Fill in the detailed online form for a free initial quotation and you will be e-mailed information within a couple of days.

Northern Insurance Direct
www.northern-direct.co.uk
A fast service, designed to get you a quote based on information that you

provide to them. It then lets you learn more about the policies and find one tailored to your needs.

Wise Money

www.wisemoney.com

Here you'll find quotes offered on household insurance, mortgages and other financial products. You have to register in order to get a full quotation but the site is easy to navigate and quick to respond, so if you're serious about looking for a mortgage lender or insurer, this is a good place to start.

Unusual homes Psst! Wanna buy a pyramid?

Pavilions of Splendour

www.heritage.co.uk

If you're longing to find a home that isn't a three-bedroom semi in a greenfield development on the outskirts of a major city, then Pavilions of Splendour may be able to help. This company specialises in unusual and historic properties, often listed and even more often in need of a great deal of TLC. Since many properties have had preservation orders slapped on them, you have to be prepared to fork out vast wads of cash and spend weekends raking through architectural supply yards just to repair a window (no self-styled Handy Andys need apply) but a look through their portfolio may convince you it's worth it.

Ken Lund's Islands for Sale

www.islandsforsale.com

Always dreamed of doing a Richard Branson and buying your very own island? Ken Lund's your man with plenty of dreams to choose from. He specialises in the stunning islands off the coast of British Columbia, but if

Pick up a private paradise at Islands for Sale. Some are surprisingly affordable...

you're after a slice of Caribbean or Pacific heaven, he can help you there too. When last visited there was only one small island for sale in Michigan, but it does have seven lakes, all for a bargain $140,000.

Greek Property

www.parosweb.gr/house

Included as a warning because it's a good (bad) example of the kind of site you'll have to trawl through if you're looking for that dream Mediterranean home. The homepage unfolds to reveal a picture of a property on the Greek island of Paros. A cheesy Mediterranean rock theme blares out and you're told to click on the picture to view the property from different angles. This proves, eventually, to be true. But your only means of getting hold of such trivia as, er, how much it costs, is to e-mail the webmaster. It's a miracle this site attracted even 6,207 visitors in its first nine months.

Tropical Islands

www.tropical-islands.com

The Internet address which would most appeal to 21st-century Robinson Crusoes. Don't worry if you haven't got the £6.7m in your current account to buy an island off the Bahamas; you can lease yourself 1.2 acres of tropical paradise for a year for a £6,000 deposit and £6,200 in rent. Mind you, Lord knows where you're going to live while the local builders knock up a quick eco-lodge. But after all, as the homepage says, you are getting "your own kingdom in today's developed world".

Snake Island

www.webwave.com/snakeisland

The owners of this 53-acre island (less an island, more an "experience" according to the site) off the coast of California will listen to any offers. So even if you haven't got the $2.5m recommended retail price, it's worth e-mailing them as they have been trying to sell this island for some time. The picture of Rattle Snake Island seems to indicate that you'll have your own private jetty, but the valuation does appear to be based on the idea that if you buy it you'd want to build a casino, golf course, and health spa on your isle. Which seems to defeat the whole 'getting away from it all' thing.

World of Private Islands

www.vladi-private-islands.de/home_e.html

While some sites offer you the island equivalent of a package holiday in Marbella, Vladi Private Islands has something for the more independently minded, like the 62-acre Holm of Huip in the Orkney Islands for just £110,000, which features its own pre-historic Cairn. Millionaires of a sunnier disposition might prefer to lash out £7.5m on the eight islands that make up the Bock Cay Archipelago in the Bahamas. If islands really aren't your thing, you can also find a palace near Cologne, or express an interest in viewing billionaire Malcolm Forbes' old estate in Morocco.

Records, CDs etc

Music on the Net is a vast virtual treasure trove where you can find anything from The Farmer's Boys to the raw early recordings of Winston Churchill

General Sites where you can find (almost) anything

101cd.com

www.101cd.com

This store boasts that it has over 1.6m titles online. It's easy to be cynical about such claims. After all, who actually bothered to count them? But there's enough stock on display to convince you that, for once in commercial cyberspace, they're probably not exaggerating. Probably the only criticism that you could lob at them is that although you can browse music by price and search by artist, it's not easy to browse by category.

Action Records

www.action-records.co.uk

The online arm of one of the UK's largest independent record stores covers most of the bases from country/folk through rock to ambient, dance and indie. You can download the catalogue which is probably easier than trying to find your title on the site. You have to know what you want because the description begins and ends with the artist, title, format and price. The homepage, however, says it is updating the site to make it more user friendly.

Amazon

www.amazon.co.uk

Best known for books, Amazon's online music store is definitely worth perusing because you can find some good value on offer here. For example, in the site's exotica section, David Byrne and Brian Eno's acclaimed collaboration *My Life In The Bush Of Ghosts* is available for just £7.99.

CDNow

www.cdnow.com

Not so much a distinctive homepage as a homage to Amazon, CDNow has a whacking great stock archive, including Japanese imports and the 23-track *Ultimate Collection* by Benny Hill for just £4.02, a price that reflects the built-in currency converter. Delivery charges vary but you are notified before you're asked to place your order. A damn fine site.

CD999

www.CD999.com

Boasting more than 100,000 CDs at £9.99 (not including doubles or sets) or less, you have to remember there is a base £1.49 shipping charge plus 99p per CD. Still, that does make the prices better than high-street.

THE FAQs

How can I post my band's MP3 files?
You could try any of:
www.clickmusic.co.uk,
www.crunch.co.uk, or
www.peoplesound.com

Where can I watch bands online?
You'll find details of RealVideo live shows on *www.virtuetv.com*

Which is the best newsgroup for musicians?
Try *www.themusicians homepage.com*

Where can I find out tour dates?
There's a brilliant search engine/ordering site at *www.aloud.com*

Where is the best place to search for a band site?
Probably *www.ubl.com* but *www.bigmouth.co.uk* is not bad either

CD-WOW

www.cd-wow.com

Not to be confused with CD Now and not to be confused with a really big music shop because many searches of the database suggested that the shop only sells the most recent or most obvious titles for many artists. That said, the prices are very keen (most of the top 75 CDs are around £8.99) and there's a neat guide to how to use the site. Pre-orders also available.

Cheap or What

www.cow.co.uk

This no-fuss site has heaps of stock but you'll have to be familiar with the albums as there is no detail listed. Prices are better for more obscure artists and titles, but competitive for the mainstream. Policies and info are on the homepage. Free shipping in the UK.

Click Music

www.clickmusic.co.uk

You'll think you've been Tangoed from this vibrant orange directory with everything you could ever want to know about the music world. News bulletins every five minutes show who's topping the charts, gigging and generally mincing around. There is useful info about using MP3 sites and the shopping directory lists specialist shops as well as the high-street ones.

Crotchet

www.crotchet.co.uk

Idiosyncratic site which 'specialises', if that's not putting it too narrowly, in classical music, jazz, world

Records, CDs etc

Artists — The stars can't leave home without a homepage

URL	Artist
http://members.tripod.com/~taz4158/beatles.html	The Beatles
www.davidbowie.com	David Bowie
www.catatonia.com	Catatonia
www.bobdylan.com	Bob Dylan
www.bryanferry.com	Bryan Ferry
www.macygray.com	Macy Gray
www.jamiroquai.co.uk	Jamiroquai
www.bbking.com	BB King
www.manics.co.uk	Manic Street Preachers
www.bobmarley.com	Bob Marley
www.videoranch.com	Michael Nesmith
www.oasisinet.com	Oasis
www.des-oconnor.com	Des O'Connor
www.elvis.com	Elvis Presley
www.prince.org	Prince
www.radiohead.com	Radiohead
www.remhq.com	REM
www.stereophonics.co.uk	Stereophonics
www.supergrass.com	Supergrass
www.travisonline.com	Travis
www.robbiewilliams.co.uk	Robbie Williams
www.weirdal.com/home.htm	Weird Al Yankovic

music, film music and soundtracks. The site has a *Which?* Web Trader seal of approval for secure ordering and has a lovely ambience, almost as if you'd popped into your local independent store for a natter with the owner. The added attraction online is that you can search the database which contains, for instance, 93 items on jazz saxophonist Stan Getz.

Disc 'n' Tape

www.disc-n-tape.co.uk
The site comes equipped with a huge but quirky database. The directory is pretty comprehensive and easy to navigate. If you can't find the musical object of your desire you are invited to e-mail the company with your request. While this kind of invitation can often be ranked in the top five lies of modern business (just above 'People are our most important asset'), Disc 'n' Tape says it can find every CD, LP, MC,12in, 7in, DVD and Mini Disc now available in the UK. High-street prices apply but immediate shipping is free in the UK.

Dotmusic

www.dotmusic.com
Originally an online extension of trade mag and all-round industry bible

Music Week, this site is now visited by professionals and punters alike, not primarily to shop but to catch up on the latest news. The shop, which looks like it has been tacked on to the back, helps the site pay its way and is actually far more comprehensive than it might seem at first glance, so it's worth a try. Other mag sites with online stores include www.nme.com and the fast-improving (but still disappointing if you're a devotee of the magazine) www.qonline.co.uk.

Eil/Esprit
www.eil.com

Fancy that Japanese limited edition picture disc by your favourite artist which came out 10 years ago and was only sent to the country's DJs? Well, this is the place to begin your quest. It has thankfully lost the 'world's biggest and best online music store' macho marketing posturing and gets right down to business. It has, for instance, The Farmer's Boys seminal slice of East Anglian rock *Muck It Out* in its pig-shaped picture-disc format. But be warned: you

Coming your way... CDs on order

There's nothing the consumer likes more than a price war, especially when it rams prices down to a third, maybe even a half of what you used to pay in the high street. And, happily, there's still one raging in the Web CD market.

In a shopping test by *The Net* magazine, mystery purchasers had trouble pushing more than a tenner into the hands of many online stores in exchange for a chart CD (they bought Madonna's *Music* and the *Beatles Compilation 1* at 12 stores), Cheapest for both was CD-WOW, selling each for £8.99, though CD Universe did undercut them by 24p on the Fab Four's album.

While both of the aforementioned stores are consistent performers when it comes to low pricing, shoppers should have little loyalty when it comes to buying CDs online and should always shop around or use a shopping bot to survey the price scene (see page 40). Several offer free delivery and one to two days is the average delivery time, based on *The Net*'s test. CD Universe and CD-WOW didn't perform as well on the delivery front, with the former taking 26 days and the latter nearly two weeks for the Beatles' album. However, overall, the Web CD market is a mature and developed one which has now ironed out most of its problems. Buying from the US can bring further reductions but always check delivery charges – it's usually economically unviable to buy just one CD no matter how cheap it seems.

Obviously, for some people, nothing will replace the thrill of running their hands along racks of vinyl and CD covers, but as broadband communications become more widespread and listening to sample tracks from the Internet becomes even easier, even the hardened record shop groupie is now likely to be seen online.

can get addicted to searching this site. If rarity really turns you on, you could also try www.vinyl-tap.co.uk.

HMV

www.hmv.co.uk

Nice-looking and well-organised, this site will get you bopping to the latest releases in no time. It covers all the usual categories, and highlights webcasts and free downloads from the likes of Peter Gabriel. If you're a student you get a 10 per cent discount, as if being young wasn't enough of a reward. Not too friendly towards Macs though.

Music 365

www.music365.com

From the people who brought you Football 365, this is a decent site which offers the visitor the latest news as well as an extensive CD shop and a nice little earner (for Music 365 and Boxman) called 2000 for 2000, where you can find reasonably authoritative reviews of top albums.

Tower Records

http://uk.towerrecords.com
or www.towerrecords.com

If you want to increase your options, you could browse both the American and European sites. As you would expect, both are decently stocked, with a wide range of titles, sound samples and free downloads. Because of the absurd price of CDs in this country you can find bargains on the US site, eg BB King's *Blues on The Bayou* is $16.99 on the US site and £14.49 in Europe. You don't have to find too many CDs you want to buy to pay for the cost of shipping from the US and still save money. (The same technique might also save you money if you're buying your sounds from Amazon.) The only criticism of the European site is that in busy times you might get a "sorry we're unavailable" message – the online version of the local post office shutting in everybody else's lunch hour.

Virgin

www.virgin.com

There is no mistaking the familiar red and white

SLEAZY LISTENING

This top 10 of online music sales, from a random week in the Net's life, shows that surfers have no better taste than offline fans

1 Linkin Park
Hybrid Theory

2 Limp Bizkit
Chocolate Starfish and The Hot Dog Flavored Water

3 Dido
No Angel

4 Eminem
The Marshal Mathers LP

5 U2
All That You Can't Leave Behind

6 Staind
Break The Cycle

7 The Beatles
One

8 Red Hot Chili Peppers
Californication

9 Tool
Lateralus

10 Back Street Boys
Black & Blue

Source: www.cddb.com

World domination
The world music giants

Until you get into the online ordering business you have no idea how much stuff is out there. Impressed by the obscure Latin American beats your mate in the local indie record shop can get his hands on? You just wait till you see what, via the power of the Net, this little lot can come up with...

Amazon
www.amazon.com amazon.co.uk
Awesome search engine which will pull up almost any US or UK release and much besides, often with audio samples, reviews from customers and (soon) Rough Guides' music books, making vast acquisitions dangerously easy.

Borders.com
www.borders.com
Borders is a nice, clean, browsable site very much like its terrestrial stores. There is a reasonably deep catalogue and array of sound samples.

cdnow.com
www.cdnow.com
Pretty good on Latin music and they have keen prices with lots of samples.

CD Universe
www.cduniverse.com
CD Universe's world music section is well laid out, browsable country-by-country, with an excellent search engine and a far-ranging catalogue.

Tower.com
www.towerrecords.com or www.uktowerrecords.com
Tower's US and European sites deliver impressive catalogue returns and they have sound samples for a huge number of discs. If you know what you're looking for, you stand a very good chance of finding it here.

Virgin colours and this comprehensive site lives up to the reputation. The music arm includes its own label (V2) and Net radio station plus the option of either the UK or US megastore sites, though these only offer store locators plus music news. To buy online, click on Virgin.net where you will find all the latest CDs at competitive prices, editor's picks and the chance to pre-order. Only lets you ship to the credit card address, but delivery is free.

Waterloo Records

www.waterloorecords.com

A rare curio amidst all the musical hypermarkets selling music over the Net, Waterloo is based in Austin, Texas, although curiously it uses the sign for the London underground station as its logo (a tribute to The Kinks?). You can find releases by anyone from Aaron Neville to Joe Cocker and Sarah Brightman, but the main attraction is the huge stock of Texan and rootsy music. If Papa Mali & The Instigators' *Thunder Chicken* does it for you, then you'll find it here. If you're not au fait with this kind of stuff, you might have trouble telling the name of the artist from the title of the album.

WHSmith

www.whsmith.co.uk

The music section of WHSmith Online is far more extensive than you might think from the rather mainstream product on display in some of its high-street branches. This site offers keen prices, a vast catalogue and a tickertape of names like Shania Twain and Morcheeba advancing across the screen. Check out also the sister site www.cdparadise.com/hme/hmepge.asp which has a wealth of stock at such unfamiliar (to the high street) prices as £7.99.

Woolworths

www.woolworths.co.uk

Woolies has actually got a pretty good music library and also plenty of news and music-related articles. It's no cheaper than the high-street store, but most offline Woolworths do not stock much beyond the top 40. Here the selection is extensive, though the info on some releases is scanty – you may need to know the tracks on that album that grabs your attention. First order must be sent to the credit card address, anywhere else after that.

No connection to Bridge, Station or Sunset, but a good stopping off place if rootsy, Texan sounds are your thing

The 2look4com site gives you the opportunity to look for all manner of weird nationality/genre mixes. Sadly, in most cases, you're likely to be left empty-handed

MP3 The hottest music format since 8-track cartridges

2look4com

http://en.sonico.com

Fancy downloading a few seconds of Uruguayan grindcore? Or maybe a quick sample of Ecuadorean death-metal? If the answer is yes, you will be sadly disappointed on this occasion, but the beauty of this site is that it allows you to search for any combination of type of music and nationality. Perhaps sadly, you're most likely to succeed with traditional Latin American genres.

Lycos MP3 search

http://music.lycos.com/mp3

This site offers one of the simplest and fastest ways to find out what MP3 files are available for downloading and for which artist. Lycos obviously knows a thing or two about search engines and it fairly zips through your request. Worth bookmarking, especially if you're just starting out in MP3.

MP3.com

www.mp3.com

If you're going to join the hordes downloading music from the Net, you are almost legally obliged to go this site. Apart from the fact that there are over

500,000 songs from 80,000-plus artists (to say nothing of 3,500 classical recordings), you'll also find an excellent FAQ if you're at that stage in your digital education where you don't know your MP3 from your Fun Boy Three. This site can be read in five languages and is much more than just music.

Specialist For connoisseurs, experts and utter posers

BLUES

Midnight Records
www.midnightrecords.com

Midnight is such a great name for a blues label that you warm to this site at once, and if you like the blues, you won't be disappointed. The site looks and reads like a fanzine but the catalogue is exhaustive – spanning blues, rock and rock 'n' roll, and including such obscure acts as The Ferrets, Dwarves, Suburban Nightmare and the Woofing Cookies, some of whom are on Midnight's own label. There's secure ordering and delivery to the UK costs a BB King-sized $7.50 for the first item and $2.75 for each one after that.

CLASSICAL AND JAZZ
Classical 33
www.classical33.co.uk

More than 8,000 CDs and LPs of classical recording to browse through here, though you have to download the regularly updated catalogue (in HTML or Microsoft Excel) to see what's on offer. When we visited, owner Stuart Tomanek was on a buying trip to Russia, so no British LPs were listed. Unusual, independent site, worth a bookmark for checking in with regularly.

Counterpoint Music
www.counterpoint-music.com

Search for all kinds of jazz CDs, from big bands to solo artists, at excellent prices on this US-based site. There's lots of stuff here you won't find on the big commercial sites, and they can even try and hunt down a special order for you if you can't find what you want. International shipping costs start at $5.45.

LP Classics
www.lpclassics.co.uk

This is a basic site offering vintage vinyl recordings of

THAT'S CRAP THAT IS...

It's hard to resist a site called Collecting Crap Records. When you open www.78rpm.sonow.com/ 002/crwhy.htm you see an album sleeve starring a fake Loch Ness monster for a record by The Improvisors called, appropriately enough, *Loch Nessie*.

Nor is that the oddest record alluded to on a site that acts as pop music's dustbin. That closely contested honour probably goes (just) to an EP recorded by *Animal Magic* host Johnny Morris for Winalot.

For more in this line try http://franklarosa.com/ $spindb.query.new.vinyl although the inclusion of the Banana Splits in this site's compilation of the musically disadvantaged does undermine its credibility somewhat.

classical music. You can download the catalogue and order through the site, although the form is not secure so you might prefer to phone. Unusual ordering system in which, rather than selling first-come, first-served, you must bid for an item and the higher your bid or the more records you bid for, the better your chances. Delivery costs vary, and reflect the breakable nature of LPs, so it may be best to buy more than one at a time.

Timewarp

www.tunes.co.uk/timewarp

An online CD store with a strong emphasis on unusual jazz and jazz-based music. Be-bop rubs shoulders with trip-hop, with titles searchable by artist or title. After a base charge of £1, CDs cost 25p each to mail, LPs cost 75p and deliveries take two to three days.

COUNTRY

County Sales

www.countysales.com

From old-time banjo music to modern bluegrass and fiddle, this Virginia-based site is as country as grits. The extensive catalogue includes popular and rare work from Bob Amos and his new bluegrass sounds, to Druha Trave and their blend of country from the Czech Republic. Don't be put off by the fact that this is a US site: most albums cost $8-13 and shipping is a bargain at $6 for six to eight CDs.

The Music Barn

www.themusicbarn.com

Asking you to get all nostalgic and remember your first barn dance in the same ilk as your first car may seem slightly extreme, but the CDs and cassettes on sale here are 'old skool country' if there is such a thing. Vernon Dalhart and Lulu Belle & Scotty feature in the limited onsite database. If they have nothing to suit, you can always print out their complete catalogue.

DANCE MUSIC

Juno Records

www.juno.co.uk

This functional site is extremely easy to use but rather bland. No reviews, just the complete listings of new dance releases in the UK and the chance to hear them, then buy them. There's a secure shopping trolley and you'll know exactly how much your choice costs and how soon it will get to you.

INDEPENDENT

imusic

www.imusic.com

Apart from offering all the usual releases and reviews, this site entices you with a bargain box, the ability to buy and sell secondhand CDs, and the chance to give your view on the latest Travis song. There's a huge news section and an alphabetised board so you can go straight to your favourite band. Your details are kept secure and you'll get your CDs between three and 21 days after they receive your order, depending on your shipping method.

Indie music

www.cdnow.com
An excellent, easy-to-use site, even for online virgins. There's a page on every type of music you could hope for, but the indie/alternative page is tops. It has truthful reviews, new releases, interviews and a really good staff pick if you fancy chancing it. When we visited, their top 20 albums included Staind, Tool, Radiohead and Eva Cassidy. Your details will be safe as houses and they'll ship you the CD of your choice, hopefully in two weeks. To find out how much it'll all cost, just log in to your account.

Unsigned

www.unsigned-indie.com
This site offers "the best unsigned and independent artists you've never heard of". Not a bad site and – and this is where thousands of would-be musicians get really excited – you can even put yourself on the list and hope for fame. You'll enjoy picking out the class tunes from the dirges.

NOSTALGIA

Magpie Direct

www.magpiedirect.com
A bare-bones site that nevertheless will find you that missing LP that would

Read all about it The muzak press online

The Web is also a great place for intelligent comment about music. Here are a few of the best sites to get just that:

www.channel1.com/users/obscure is for the musical obscurantist and trivia champs.
www.gramophone.co.uk is for the serious student of classical music.
www.laritmo.com is for music fans who know they don't speak latin in Latin America.
www.launch.com offers new music with lots of exclamation marks!!!
www.nme.com Nuff said.
www.rollingstone.com is authoritative, occasionally worthy, comprehensive.
www.webnoize.com is for insiders and professionals.

Records, CDs etc

Classics from 50-plus years ago presented on an art deco backdrop. Past Perfect says it all really

complete your Dusty Springfield collection. For music from the '40s through to the '80s, this friendly site is worth a bookmark so you can check back on its growing catalogue.

Past Perfect
www.pastperfect.com
All the good-time tunes you could want, with hits from the 1920s to the 1950s including jazz, swing, and big-band hits. Browse the art deco-inspired pages for CDs and cassettes at high-street prices. Each CD is an original recording but has the clarity of today's sound. Noel, Gertie and Glenn (Miller, that is, not Matlock) are all there, along with Winston Churchill himself.

POP

Abbey Records
www.abbeyrecords.com
Such an original name for a shop based in Liverpool. Abbey Records sells everything from dance to punk, but with an emphasis on pop. This is one of the few places you can pick up vinyl and CDs from such 1990s relics as Martika, Pepsi & Shirlie and Sonia. Discounted prices, many under a fiver, apply, plus shipping charges, and they'll be with you within two days.

ROCK

BURBS
www.burbs.co.uk
BURBS is an acronym for British Underground Rock Bands. Use this suitably patriotic site to read up on these underground luminaries, mark their gig dates in your diary and then browse the online store for a taste of their seminal offerings. It's pointless to list featured artists as they're so far underground, but albums can be bought online at bargain prices and you can download tracks as a taster before you buy.

The Music Index
www.themusicindex.com
The headline 'This Day In Rock' isn't entirely accurate – you're not going to find Stereophonics or Bon Jovi here; Ozric Tentacles and Lawnmower R n B are as famous as it gets – but there is a database of 26,000 artists selected from reviews in Q magazine. Download MP3s or head for the online store. Worryingly, Rick Wakeman is used as to help explain the search facility.

WEIRD STUFF
Lama Gyurme
www.lamagyurme.com
Well you won't find tracks named Chenrezi Pure Land Prayer on the next Spice Girls album. This site looks flashy but sells just one album by Lama Gyurme and Jean-Philippe Rykiel. The hip Buddha-loving Lama sings prayers while Rykiel plays keyboards. Barely. If you're still a little wary after viewing the duo, you can check out the downloadable samples before you buy.

Self-Abuse
www.selfabuserecords.com/home.html
Not for the squeamish music fan or even just the music fan, Self Abuse owns the Abuse Label and releases stuff with titles like *Skin Crimes* or containing the sound of a 1khz test tone. You can buy online – but why would you?

Sleep Machines
www.sleepmachines.com
First there was the Miami Sound Machine, then Tin Machine, now comes Sleep Machines – a Californian company which sells CDs with a single sound and which are guaranteed to help you nod off. The titles are equally stupefying – *Dryer* is a good example – and at $13.49, they're not cheap, but they guarantee there are no subliminal messages involved. Insomniacs might be better advised to buy Michael Nyman's soundtrack to *The Piano*.

WORLD SPECIALIST
Descarga
www.descarga.com
This Brooklyn-based Latin mail-order specialist offers an awesome store with a vast catalogue on its superbly designed website. It has a great search engine (it will direct you to 187 CDs featuring Celia Cruz, for instance), extensive track listings, reliable reviews, and includes the Descarga journal with features and interviews. A must for anyone into Latin music.

Digelius Music
www.digelius.com
Helsinki-based shop, specialising online in Baltic and Nordic music.

Records, CDs etc

Mostly Music
www.jewish-music.com
All aspects of Jewish music from the great cantors to klezmer.

Sterns African Records Centre
www1.sternsmusic.com
London's premier African music store is also pretty strong on Latin music.
The team have years of expertise and also act as the UK distributors for
many African, Latin and world music labels, so there are many highly
desirable items in stock.

Trehantiri Music
www.trehantiri.com
Situated in the heart of north London's Greek and Turkish community,
Trehantiri is a retail nirvana for anyone with more than a passing interest in all
types of Greek, Turkish and Middle Eastern music.

 Only one careful owner. You hope

Bus Stop Records
www.busstop-records.co.uk
Preferring to refer to its collection as pre-loved rather than used, Bus Stop
sells 1970s, 1980s and 1990s disco, soul, hip-hop and house. Disco jives
include Amii Stewart's *Knock On Wood* and *Bumper To Bumper* by the
Avenue B Boogie Band, both for under a tenner. There was no online system
when we visited but they list their entire catalogue in genre order. Click on the
order form, submit a request and you could be jiving in a few working days.

Sugar Bush
www.sugarbush.u-net.com
This honeypot of rare vinyl LPs includes the golden era of rock, progressive,
psychedelic and soundtracks from the 1960s. Scroll through the standard
alphabetical lists to find everything from The Mamas & The Papas to Wilson
Pickett. Prices range from £5 to £25 and the list is comprehensive, but there
is no direct link to the order form and the site didn't have a secure server
when we checked, so it may be best to go for the telephone option.

Vinyl Records
www.vinylrecords.co.uk
Don't scroll down the entire homepage because it will probably give you
vertigo. You can browse lists of the vinyl classics available but there are no
direct links from them to the order form. However, the site does allow you to
copy and paste your selections into the form, making it slightly easier than
some similar sites, and the order form is secure.

Shoes & boots

Sensible or spinally challenging, for the fell-walker or the horse-rider, the range of footwear available online is, er, staggering. And most of the time you can get a decent discount

General From well-heeled to straightlaced

Barratts

www.barratts.co.uk

Barratts have let themselves down on the design stakes with this tacky and amatour looking site. The footwear from Barratts and Saxone is exactly what you'll find in the shops with no discounts and £3 delivery charge. On the plus side they offer a direct link to Tall & Small (www.tall-small.com) where you can buy similar fashionable designs in different sizes and at no extra cost.

Buffalo Boots

www.buffalo-boots.co.uk

The Spice Girls may be has-beens by now, but they leave a legacy of platform boots behind them, which Buffalo Boots have duly cashed in on. The site itself is stylish yet practical with thumbnail images which can be enlarged and viewed from multiple angles. More sophisticated footwear for the ladies is available alongside the classic Buffalo boot and a trendy catalogue of trainers. Prices are standard with a £6 delivery charge. A trendy site to bookmark.

Faith

www.faith.co.uk

If fuchsia kinky boots and baby-blue go-party shoes are the sort of thing you're looking for, Faith stocks all the backache-inducing footwear you could ever want. After revamping its image, Faith now sells some of the best designer replicas on the high street. Prices match those offline but the sale selection holds styles you might actually want rather than stuff it hasn't been able to get rid of. Delivery is free and will take between four and five days, in time for high stepping at the weekend.

Shoes and boots

Faith gets sporty – though probably running for the bus is about as far as you'd want to push any of these

Jones the Bootmaker
www.jonesbootmaker.com
Despite being awkwardly placed at the higher end of the high-street price bracket, you can't help but love Jones and the sophisticated range of men's, women's and children's footwear on this refined site. Delivery is free on orders over £25 (and you'll be hard-pressed to find a pair of shoes for less) and Jones have sensibly embraced the Internet, offering exclusive online discounts on some styles. Better than the high-street equivalent.

Office
www.office.co.uk
High heels, mid heels, low heels, ankle boots, knee boots: Office and its casual sporty partner, Offspring, have a shoe for every occasion. Bright, blazing graphics match polka-dot kitten heels and pink snakeskin boots. Trainer brands include Adidas, Nike and the ultra-trendy Acupuncture. Prices range from £20-60 and ordering is simple and secure.

Nine to Eleven
www.9211.co.uk
Not to be confused with 911 (the swanky designer high-street brand), this rudimentary-looking site offers women's shoes, socks and hosiery in larger sizes. Despite a limited range, each style is up to date in the fashion stakes, making a welcome change to the usual dreary specialist collections, and each item is only slightly more pricey than the average high-street 4-7 size range.

Schuh
www.shoe-shop.com
It doesn't look it, but this is the online store for high-street trendsetter Schuh. With labels DKNY, Duffer, Red Or Dead and Diesel all at reduced prices (£10-£15 off RRP), free delivery and Price Watch (they'll match the price of any of their online competitors), it's a great place to buy your designer kit. They also have perfect shoes for the wider foot, and those that are larger or smaller.

Shaka Sandals
www.shaka.co.uk
Based in Kent, this is actually a shop window for South African sandals. The 4x4 of footwear, there are five styles – Fisherman, Hiker, Outback, Raider and Whitewater – all made from waterproof fabrics and following ethical and environmental guidelines. Up-to-date styles, and all at under £40 including p&p.

Shopeeze

www.shopeeze.com

A bizarre combination of men's and ladies' footwear alongside perfume and electrical goods, with everything at discounted prices. Although not all the styles are up to date, the bargain prices make this site well worth a look.

Tim Little

www.timlittle.com

Get hold of a £200 pair of Tim Little shoes, normally only found at the likes of Harvey Nichols. Shipping is pricey at £9, but if you can afford the stock in the first place an extra £9 probably isn't a problem.

 **Dance yourself dizzy or go veggie**

Cox The Saddler

www.saddler.co.uk

Smarten up for the local gymkhana with smart riding boots galore here. Postage is calculated as you add items; delivery is via Parcelforce.

Danceworld

www.danceworld.demon.co.uk

Salsa, flamenco, tap, ballet, le roc or rock 'n' roll are all catered for. No online ordering but worth a look for the sheer quantity of footwear to choose from.

John Norris of Penrith

www.johnnorris.co.uk

The Rolls Royce of Wellington boots is sold here at a reasonable price. We even found a special offer which lowered the cost of Hunter boots further.

Regalos Country & Western Store

www.linedancing.co.uk

Billy Ray Cyrus et al are back to haunt us. Regalos sells suitably tasselled and fringed boots, generally priced at £30-50, with £4.50 next-day delivery.

Sports Shoes Unlimited

www.sportsshoes.com

Alongside the usual trainers there are useful sub-categories like pool shoes. Postage and packing costs £3 and orders should arrive in five days.

Vegetarian Shoes

www.vegetarian-shoes.co.uk

A large selection of vegetarian footwear ready to be bought and worn with pride. Click on the thumbnail images to view enlarged pictures and get detailed descriptions. Prices are standard with a £4.50 delivery charge.

Snow sports

All the essential gear for the slopes, from the hippest clothing to the coolest equipment. Even beginners can look the part on their way downhill, not to mention keep up with the in crowd back at the ski lodge. Plaster casts not supplied

 For all you piste artistes...

Big Day
www.bigday.co.uk
Speedy online store for men's and women's ski clothing, with a small but attractive range of jackets, trousers, hats and gloves. Shipping costs £5 for any order and your goods are promised within seven days.

Blacks
www.theoutdoorsonline.co.uk
The Blacks online store is just like the high-street version – all the biggest (and a few smaller) brands to help you cope with the great outdoors. The range of categories is impressive but failed to live up to the initial promise with the phrase "We are currently building our new range of product" often popping up when we were hoping to be deluged with sumptious skiwear. No skis or ski boots here though. Blacks presumably prefers you to opt for their personal in-store service for those. Orders are dispatched one working day after you place them, with delivery costing £3.50 for orders under £20, otherwise it's free. And the delivery address can be wherever you choose.

Edge 2 Edge
www.edge2edge.co.uk
You can buy or rent both summer and winter sports equipment from Edge 2

Edge with minimum fuss and at good prices. First decide whether you're with this hobby for the long haul. If not, ski and boot rental packages are available from under £30 for five days.

Ellis Brigham
www.ellis-brigham.com

The ski section of this well-designed and speedy outdoor sports site has an excellent choice of boots, skis and other accessories for secure online purchase. There's sound advice on offer, especially when it comes to buying boots, which it recommends you definitely try on before you buy as the fit varies so much from make to make; the customer service department can help you with enquiries about sizing. Prices are average, but there were some very good savings to be made in the Sale section when we looked. Delivery is via Parcelforce and the reasonable charges are calculated when you reach the checkout. If you're not happy with your purchase, you can return it unused within 14 days for a full refund.

Facewest
www.facewest.co.uk

Hi-tech equipment for back-country skiers and boarders. If you're thinking you're likely to be going off-piste, or anywhere you might encounter an avalanche, then this selection of transceivers, lightweight shovels and other rescue items might just save your life. Their online ordering was offline last time we checked but they insist this is a temporary blip. Delivery is £3 for orders under £100 and £5 thereafter. As long as your request is in stock, it will be dispatched within 24 hours.

JTL Skiwear
www.jtl-skiwear.co.uk

Nicely designed skiwear site with jackets, trousers, all-in-ones and accessories for the whole family. The catalogue is limited to a few items per category, but prices are good – jackets between £50 and £100, and sale items on top of that. Hopefully by the time you visit they will have rectified the flickering order page so you can actually buy something.

Rei
www.rei.com

Despite the hectic homepage, a wade through this American outdoor site will turn up a fabulous selection of ski gear at prices that make you vow never to shop in the UK again. As well as bargains on skis and boots, there are particular savings to be made on hi-tech clothing like Polartec fleeces and thermal underwear. The checkout page gives you a choice of shipping within the US or outside, and all international deliveries are insured and sent via DHL. It's worth bearing in mind that charges start at $13 for surface mail and $19 for air mail, but if you head to this site with the aim of kitting out the entire family you could end up quids in.

TAKE A PAIR OF OLD SKIS...

In this age of looking after our planet and recycling anything and everything, old skis and snowboards have been added to the list, redesigned to emerge as the very latest in dining room and patio furniture chic.

I kid you not. Some bright spark, no doubt currently recovering from a few too many clashes with hard objects while plummeting down a cliffside, has put together this site showcasing his creations.

Chairs, benches, and even kiddie high chairs can be admired online, but sorry to disappoint, Vail isn't yet ready to sell its wondrous designs to the rest of the world.

Vail Ski Art
www.vailskiart.com

Ski Net
www.skinet.com

When you're looking to buy skis or boots for the first time, how do you find out which are best suited to your needs? This vast ski resource site has nothing to sell, but its 'Gear' section is packed with up-to-date product reviews and has a Gear Finder tool which can match your skill level against a database of different skis. There are also plenty of lively message boards where snow dudes argue about the relative merits of Atomic Beta V8.20s versus the Salomon X-Scream Series.

Snow And Rock
www.snowandrock.co.uk

It was high summer when we visited this site, so it wasn't surprising that they had little in the way of winter sports gear on offer. However once the ski season looms there's no shortage of equipment and accessories available online here. There's a Flash version, which stubbornly refused to let us into the online store, but the non-Flash version works just as well. Prices are the same as on the high street and standard delivery costs from £2.50 (orders over £500 are carriage-free), although there is a rush service if you're in a hurry to hit the slopes.

Snow Shack
www.snowshack.com

Search this site by manufacturer or equipment type for good deals on many top-brand skiing products. There are also a few excellent accessories which you probably won't find in the temperate UK – frequent snow-sitters should consider the thermal butt-muff for extra comfort on their next trip. Overseas orders are sent via US parcel post and charges are calculated online before you input your credit card details. All goods come with a 30-day money-back guarantee.

World Ski & Snowboard
www.worldski.com

The seriously committed can register with this US-based site and get discounts on kit and holidays.

YHA Adventure Shops
www.yhaadventure.co.uk/

Its YHA-badge gives this a stamp of authenticity and the limited product range makes it ideal if you're the sort of person who gets phased by a wealth of choice. The categories aren't the clearest – Mountain Extreme, Outdoor Challenge etc – but once you end up in the right place you'll be surrounded by comfortably familiar names including Berghaus, The North Face and Lowe Alpine. It didn't seem possible, however, to get delivery details without actually placing an order.

You can get further technical information on the skis you're considering at the following manufacturers' websites:

Elan	www.elanskis.com
Dynastar	www.dynastar.com
K2	www.k2skis.com
Rossignol	www.skisrossignol.com
Salomon	www.salomonsports.fr
Völkl	www.volkl.com

Snowboarding — Be the dude who says "Eat my snow"

Big Deal
http://bigdeal.com

This American site offers cheaper-than-average costs at $96 for boards (well, it is an expensive hobby) and a matter of a few dollars for accessories. Pick a category and use the scroll-down brand menus to select an item. Each one comes with a full spec sheet and enlarged pictures, and the brands include Airwalk, DC boots, Vans and Gnu. A useful site for overseas bargains.

Boards Online
www.boardsonline.co.uk

Boards, bindings and boots can all be bought online from this smart yet vibrant site. Before you begin, the advice section offers useful tips for novice boarders, such as how to decide what length of board to choose. Product descriptions are brief but pictures are clear – and it is all about image after all. Newcomers to the sport should opt for the special package deals to be had, £250 getting you the whole caboodle, board, boots, bindings and bag. Free delivery within the UK.

Complete Snowboarder
www.complete-snowboarder.com

Peaceful aqua shades fill the screen, putting you more in the mood for a relaxing holiday rather than one that involves flinging yourself down snow-covered mountains. Search for flights, accommodation and last-minute packages to boarding resorts around the world. £300 for a week in Italy isn't bad going, and the site will make a booking when you find a deal that interests you. As for gear, you can search for boards, boots and bindings with the interactive gear-finder but unfortunately you can't buy online. They will, however, find the boards to suit your own level of skill, and rookies can read the gear guide to learn the difference between freestyle and free ride.

Ocean Sports Board Riders

www.boardriders.co.uk

Don't be deceived by the nautical name – these boys know their boards whether your liking is for sea, snow or skateparks. Based in Hove, East Sussex, the shop has been doing mail order since 1990 which is always a comforting sign for the online shopper. All the snowboards had been placed in Latest Deals when we visited so it was difficult to assess their range but if the rest of the stock is anything to go by snow fiends won't be left wanting.

A charge of £3 is slapped on most UK orders but if you're buying something big like a board, expect it to go up. Snowboard delivery is set at £6. Also check out their "no snow" Freeboards.

Slam City

www.slamcity.com

Slam City is a simply designed skate and snowboarding store, with a well-stocked online catalogue of clothing, accessories and boards – but first you need to check to see whether you're eligible to shop as those with older browsers will face numerous problems. Once in, prices are good, with plenty of accessories for you to customise your own board. Descriptions and images are good enough to give you a pretty fair idea what you're buying.

Snowboard Asylum

www.snowboard-asylum.com

Most snowboard enthusiasts are looking for adventure and excitement with a bit of style thrown in and could be put off by the dull black design or the Santa music playing as you enter – but don't be: far more thought has gone into the actual content. All the usual categories are there, ready for you to search for your favourite brand (QuikSilver, Billabong and Airwalk etc), and there are details of each item. For boards, prices start as low as £140 and go all the way up to £500. There's also a handy search section, whereby you input your skill level and what your requirements or interests are (beginner, big feet, tricks and flips etc), and the site suggests a board to match your criteria.

MEANWHILE IN MONTANA

If you measure out your life in ski holidays, you might want to log onto Resort Ski Network (www.rsn.com).

The site has won loads of awards but what really makes it stand out is an idea so simple it's pure genius. RSN has put webcams (little cameras which feed images back to the website) on the slopes of 110 ski resorts (109 in North America and one in Chile).

So if you can't go skiing today, you can at least console yourself with the thought that there's no snow in Big Sky, Montana, not today anyway. But when you do get set to go, you can check the weather, buy gear and even order your holiday (often at low prices) through this site. Roll on the day when they can put their web-cam on the Cairngorms!

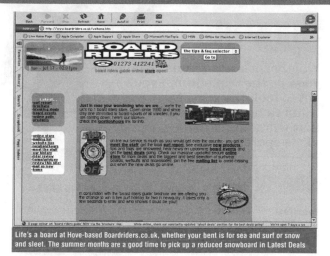

Life's a board at Hove-based Boardriders.co.uk, whether your bent is for sea and surf or snow and sleet. The summer months are a good time to pick up a reduced snowboard in Latest Deals

Snow Traders

www.snowtraders.com

A visit to this site begins promisingly enough. The site is willing to ship to the UK – all you have to do is contact them and they'll search through their shipping partners to find you the best deal. Such service! The shine begins to disappear when you start shopping. They sell boards, boots and every other accessory imaginable, and each item is discounted, but prices are still high compared to their competitors – boards remain around the $400 level. But even if you do find something you want, you can't move any further until you register all your details on the site and, although they say that they ship goods to the UK, no one seems to have told whoever set up their system as it requires you to list a US state. A little more planning – and possibly a geography lesson – is needed, it seems.

The Boarder

www.theboarder.co.uk

Nothing to buy but worth a look for the novelty factor. Read how plans for numerous snow sites across the UK are progressing, find the best dry and snow slopes in the country (Wycombe Summit features highly) and plan your TV viewing from now until next year for boarding programmes. You can even spend Christmas Day watching snowboarding from Austria on Eurosport!

Sports

Whether it's real tennis, astanga yoga or the triple jump, you've got to look the part. No grubby trainers here, just go-faster gear that will at least make you look like a sporting star even if…

General Outdoors, indoors, in the gym, on the pitch

Fitness Peak

www.fitnesspeak.co.uk

Leeds-based company offering an extensive range of gym equipment from exercise bikes and heart monitors to treadmills. Basic but functional interface with useful site links to other manufacturers. Click on the product name and you'll get a comprehensive description with obligatory fit-girlie-in-action and close-up shots. Cost comparisons are given but a few high-street prices may have been inflated for comparison purposes so check in stores to verify your 'bargain'). Orders by e-mail, phone or fax, Monday to Saturday.

JD Sports

www.jdsports.co.uk

The JD site is a class performer. It's easy to navigate – so you can hop easily from the men's to women's section if you decide that lilac rather than navy is your colour – and by simply letting your mouse hover over any item, you can see a bigger image. There are all the usual suspects in terms of brands, with prices across the board. Shipping is added at the checkout and however much we chucked in our basket it appeared to stick at £3.99.

Kitbag

www.kitbag.com

Visit one of the biggest and best known sports shops on the Internet and you'll find a huge range of football, rugby, Formula 1 and cricket kits, with accompanying accessories. A self-proclaimed "sports shop for the sports fan", this site is aimed at people who want to buy replica or retro shirts as worn by their favourite team. This being a male-oriented market, sizes reflect that. It's also excellent for extensive cricket equipment and souvenirs. Everything is clear and upfront. Get your order in before 4pm and you should receive it the next day, and delivery is free of charge for orders over £15.

Newitts

www.newitts.com

The UK's largest mail order supplier of sports equipment offers a vast range of clothes and equipment for boxing to bowls and tennis to trampolining. But due to the sheer volume of goods available, products are initially listed without pictures, which makes shopping slower as you can't view anything at a glance. Special offers exclusive to online shoppers are available. Prices include VAT and there's free next-day delivery for all orders received by noon.

Outlet Direct

http://shops.1shop.org/outletdirect/

This site follows the pile 'em high, sell 'em cheap sales model, and although it can be painfully slow, if you're after a sporting bargain you could do worse than take a look. We found a crew-neck Puma sweatshirt reduced from £30 to £10, and that wasn't even in the 'Special Offers' section. As long as you manage to spend over £10 you don't pay anything for delivery either.

Simply Sports

www.simplysports.co.uk

Navigating your way around the busy homepage can be trying but this lively site offers more than most sports shops, including pretty much every net, hoop or goalpost used in mainstream sport. It also has exercise bikes, a sports bookstore and a new medical section offering heart-rate and blood-pressure monitors. It's one of the best sites for outdoor or indoor games, with backgammon, chess, archery, croquet, table tennis and table football on offer. Prices include VAT, but delivery time and cost varies, depending on stocks and the size of the product. Shipping is mostly free for the UK.

Sportsking Online

www.sportsking.co.uk

This is a bargain basement site and no bones about it. It's quite prepared to admit that the range might consist of "last month's or even last year's products"; its USP is low prices and clearance lines. No-fuss, easy to use, and worth a quick rummage. Allow three working days for delivery at £2.95.

Sweatband.com

www.sweatband.com

When online stores were lining up for names, sweatband.com was clearly at the back. This is, though, a well-designed site divided into tennis, squash, cricket, rugby and football shops. Each section has its own news updates, plus a host of special discounts and competitions. It's especially good for tennis rackets and cricket bats – and you get a free sweatband for registering.

From trainers to spikes

Sportsshoes Unlimited
www.sportsshoes.co.uk

Sportsshoes Unlimited claims to be the largest sports shoe retail outlet in the world, with 4,000 different styles of footwear. To see more, request a catalogue. There's an enormous choice for men, women and kids, including top-brand trainers, specific sport shoes and even a Big Foot collection. Orders should arrive in three to five working days and all deliveries cost £3.

 **Recreation over air, land and sea**

Acme Whistles
www.acmewhistles.co.uk

Acme Whistles is the online trading name for Messrs J Hudson & Co of Birmingham, purveyors of police, hunting, bird-watching, marine and sports whistles for over 130 years. Prices range from £3.25 to £30 – VAT and £1.50 shipping are added at checkout. Mastercard, Visa and Amex are all welcome.

Avalon Guns
www.avalon-guns.com

Green wellies, cleaning equipment, protection togs, camouflage, books, videos, guns and ammo. Unlike some US sites, Avalon does not pander to survivalist sensibilities. No hysterical 'blast 'em up' flashes here, only a sensible military green and brown interface advertising good deals for hunting and shooting enthusiasts. Orders for general equipment are taken by e-mail or phone and are dispatched by Parcelforce. For shotguns and rifles, personal details, gun licence and Police Notification forms must be provided by recorded delivery. Once processed, Avalon will ring to clarify and send completed papers to your nearest 'agent' – who will then only hand over on a face-to-face basis. Licence and Notifications are returned by recorded delivery.

Denney Diving
www.divingdirect.co.uk

If you're going diving, you'll find all you need under one virtual roof at Denney Diving. Excellent for all diving goods, it has an exhaustive range of fins, masks, protective clothing and technical equipment. Delivery is next day by courier; the cost depends on the weight of the goods you buy.

Diving Daisy
www.divingdaisy.freeuk.com

For a full review see the watersports section on page 323 of this guide.

It's a serious business, this kite-flying, and The Kite Shop has everything from beginner's kites to models for 'power kite flyers'. Scary

Encore

www.encoredw.freeserve.co.uk

The Internet is for everyone, as this site proves: it's run by an enterprising 'dance mum' for other dance mums who wish to sell or buy unwanted or outgrown kids' costumes. If you think the grey and pink homepage accompanied by a synthesised version of *Puttin' On The Ritz* is a killer, wait until you get to the catalogue – little girls in tutus appear to the strains of Richard Clayderman's rendition of the theme to *Titanic* (the James Cameron movie, not the Lew Grade one). Click on a photo and shoes, dresses, leotards et al, modelled by aspiring Darcy Bussells, are revealed. Encore does fancy dress, as well. No zoom facility for the pic and you can't actually buy online – but you can phone or e-mail Jan.

The Kite Shop

www.kiteshop.co.uk

Whatever kind of kite you're looking for – sports kites, power kites or kites for beginners – you can't do much better than this. A quick flit round this site reveals a comprehensive selection of the best the kiting world has to offer, including visuals and full individual specifications. There's no postal charge, but special delivery costs £3.50, and UK customers should allow seven days for their chosen product to arrive.

M Steel Cycles

www.msteelcycles.co.uk

Excellent online offshoot of more-than-a-century-old Newcastle company run by former Commonwealth gold medallist Joe Waugh. Less a website, more your friendly neighbourhood corner shop, because that's exactly what it is. There are no whizz-bang graphics here, just lots of proud text and photos of the store, staff and history. M Steel stocks only four pre-manufactured bike ranges – Trek, Specialized, Dawes and Peugeot – as the bulk is built in-house.

Buy what you see or go for a custom-made model (right down to the paint job and company logo). Orders are taken by phone and paid for by credit card, and are then dispatched by recorded delivery or Parcelforce (cycles come boxed and ready to ride). M Steel will also check your bike after six months and a year for free.

Freetown Sports

www.freetownsports.co.uk

Online arm of the Hull-based sports store that focuses mainly on cycles and cycling gear at the moment. However, the soon-to-open clothing section will be offering general sports gear from the likes of Animal and Oakley and it has a huge range of the latter's shades. The standard of their product imagery is excellent and we've high hopes for their customer service since they claim that "even the Queen herself" would be impressed by them on this score. Over to you Ma'am.

MASSEY ATTACK

What's the fastest-growing sport in the UK? No, not Beckham-baiting; tractor pulling.

'Invented' by our US cousins, the agricultural equivalent to F1 has now gone global, Britain has a Tractor Pulling Association (BTPA) and there are several magazines, notably the US's *Full Pull.*

If you fancy a mudfest while dragging a colossal John Deere along a

100 metre track, try the site below. And leave the kitten heels at home.

----

www.powerpulling. co.uk

Rock Run

www.rockrun.com

If hanging off sheer rock faces by your fingernails or striding through the Lakes in torrential rain is your thing, then this is a must. Aside from mountains of outdoor equipment there's info on climbing, safety, weather (including Scottish avalanche forecasts), books, rocktalk forums and related sites. Zoom in on products or mosey round the bargain basement. Shopping basket sums are given in sterling and US dollars. Brilliantly, there's also a currency converter. The site is endorsed by *Which?* and shopping is secure. Major credit cards are accepted and if you place your order before 12 noon, expect to receive it in 24 hours – otherwise it's two to three days.

Roch Valley

www.roch-valley.co.uk

The UK's leading classical dancewear distributor has a strangely secretive site. Each simple and stylish page – intro, garments, dance shoes, ballroom/Latin and information – contains a couple of photographs with very sparse text in English, French and German. Instead of buying online you complete what they call a 'feedback' form which gives you details on how to make a purchase, for a brochure or for details of your nearest stockist. Enquiries will be answered by the following day, by fax, e-mail or post.

Snookernet
www.snookernet.com
Recently awarded five stars by *The Net* magazine, this Lincolnshire-based site is more like an online encyclopedia than shopping mall. The site (decked out in, you guessed it, 'green baize green') has an image gallery – so you can drool over your favourite addled champion – discussion forums, a FAQ section and more. You can also buy everything bar that big, shiny Benson & Hedges Cup. All prices are quoted in both pounds and US dollars and are inclusive of VAT. Buy securely online with your credit card or mail order by fax or phone. If quoted delivery times change, you'll be notified by e-mail before the order is processed.

Sporting Auctions
www.sportingauction.com
You can bid for almost anything here from a 'Stearns Shorty wetsuit medium black and blue' to a Mizuno baseball cap. What's more, as it has been approved by US consumer review site BizRate, it's safer than many auctions. Remember to check with UPS how much they will charge to deliver.

Sporting Irish
www.sportingirish.com
A Dublin outfit dealing solely with Irish sportswear: rugby shirts and Gaelic soccer jerseys, all sourced from Irish manufacturers to really hit an authentic spot. The basic, no-frills interface features product photographs and a brief description of your chosen shirt. Orders can be placed securely via credit card or by mail order via fax or phone. Once you've placed your order you will be given a password for future buys, or you can become a member which guarantees a discount.

Sweatshop
www.sweatshop.co.uk
Online branch of high-street aerobic and cross-training specialists. A bright and colourful interface with a user-friendly navigation button guides you through history, jobs, sports injury advice or straight to a "small selection" of equipment (although if this is anything to go by, their shops must be hangar-sized), of which much is very reasonably priced footwear. There are also heaps of sale items which you can check the availability of by e-mail. Click on your specialist area – track 'n' field, fitness etc – select an item and a photograph accompanied by a decent description and sizes will pop up. Buy either by mail order or online – it's a secure site and all major cards are accepted. Delivery is by recorded snail mail within five to seven working days.

Tennis Nuts
www.tennisnuts.com
A site for tennis enthusiasts by tennis enthusiasts, and designed to mimic a salesman guiding you through your purchase. Having received your pep talk

on choosing a racket that's right for you, you can make the most of the 10 per cent discount available during the launch period. Also on offer are badminton and squash rackets and some sports shoes. Postage is £4 for orders under £100, free above that. Delivery is within three to six working days.

Trail Buzz
www.trailbuzz.com

This new Internet retail outlet of Dorset's Shepherd Cycles (pedalling since the '60s) features a snazzy blue-and-orange interface offering deals on bikes, accessories, components, clothing and 'specials' by every cycle manufacturer in the book. Contact details are repeated on every page, all major credit cards are accepted and it's a secure site. Prices include postage, and delivery is by recorded snail mail within three working days – although, if in stock, they'll try to send goods the next day. Returned goods are refunded but unless they're faulty, postage is not reimbursed.

Sportswear — From fashion brands to active wear

FX99
www.fx99.com

This site claims that its products have adorned the limbs of Denise Van Outen, All Saints and Zoë Ball. The site's message is clear – looking good and feeling good during exercise can be one and the same. The original and good-looking separates are ideal for aerobic workouts, dance classes and gym sessions alike. In some places 'tax to be added' notices misleadingly appear. Delivery charge is £2.50.

If you tend to look more Johnny Ball than Zoë Ball when you're working out, a little something from the FX99 range might help

Hosana

www.hosana.co.uk

A Flash-happy baskets site with a community feel and a nice buzz about it. The visuals are great and Roger Hosannah's hip US college hoops gear, ranging from mesh shorts and tanks to long-sleeve sweats, is the epitome of gotta-have-it cool. Ordering is by e-mail and callback, and shipping costs £2. You'll want some.

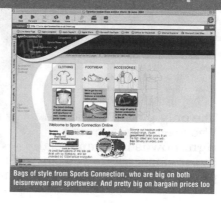

Bags of style from Sports Connection, who are big on both leisurewear and sportswear. And pretty big on bargain prices too

M and M Sports

www.mmsports.co.uk

The Internet arm of the M and M Sports Mail Order Company, this site is like the catalogue in that it offers a wide range of goods, but unlike the catalogue it's quite difficult to find your way around. Even making your way to the specific sections doesn't seem to save much time, as all the products are listed in pages. However, its highly competitive prices make it worth checking out and it has a very good children's range. Delivery costs £3.99 and takes up to 10 days.

Sportackle.com

www.sportackle.com

An online shop of sporting briefs? Sadly not. In fact this has quite a small product range of branded sports clothing, be it shorts, shirts or shoes. But it does have an ever-changing special offers list of items at reduced prices and it's particularly easy to navigate. Products are usually dispatched within 24 hours, and it keeps you updated by e-mail on the expected delivery date of any item you order. VAT is not included.

Sports Connection

www.sportsconnection.co.uk

This Scottish-based company offers a range that's ideal for anyone who is as interested in fashion as they are in sports clothes. Click on past the stylish homepage and take a look at the affordable collection of urban-style leisurewear – and you'll find that the latest gear is considerably cheaper here than elsewhere. Everything on this site has 10 per cent already taken off the price. Delivery takes just one week and costs £2.99 for anywhere in the UK.

Television & video

The only place TV and the Web are really merging right now is in commercial hyperspace, where you can get knockdown prices or spend a fortune on some plasma

 General For those who want to merge with their sofa

Digital Choice

www.digitalchoice.co.uk

A *Which?* Web Trader, Digital Choice makes a lot of promises – secure ordering, a no-hassle returns policy, and a refund of the difference in price if you find the same item cheaper elsewhere. This is all in its favour, but the descriptions of the televisions, videos and DVD players are too brief, and the pictures poor quality. Top brands include Sony, Philips and Aiwa and you can search by model, manufacturer of price point. Not for the window shopper.

Dixons

www.dixons.co.uk

You know where you're at with Dixons. Choose a product category and scroll through the list of high-street priced DVDs, videos etc. Basically, just the virtual equivalent of their bricks and mortar outlets, with similar products, prices and discounts. On the downside, the added info is a bit simplistic.

Empire Direct

www.empiredirect.co.uk

A decent selection of TVs, DVD players and other audio/visual equipment, all claimed to be at least 30 per cent below retail price. Conveniently presented as a product list with minimum details, you can then click on a selection to see a pic and get all the specifications and availability status. Delivery charges are calculated as you add to your basket.

Home Entertainment

www.home-entertainment.co.uk

Before you invest thousands on that big screen, read all about it on this site, which will give you the history, tech specs and their verdict on the performance quality in great detail. Every TV out there may not have a review, but enough do for you to make an educated choice, certainly better than relying on the spotty 18 year-old in your high-street shop.

Hutchisons

www.hutchisons.co.uk

A dull, bargain basement design, without the bargains. The extensive catalogue comprises every TV set, DVD and video player imaginable. Click on the image of the one you like the squint of and make your selection based on the limited info and tiny pictures. This is a shame because the range on offer beats any high-street store and there are prices to suit all. Video recorders range from £99 to £500, although the site doesn't really explain why the prices differ so much.

Link On-line

www.linkonline.co.uk

If you bought one of the first DVD players, don't panic – Link On-line specialises in DVD upgrades. The Paragon kit will allow you to make your existing model even flashier than it already is, although what exactly this entails isn't clear unless you link to a page of minuscule type. If you know why you want an upgrade, click on a kit code and see if your model is compatible. Most buyers pay around £30, unless you opt for the fitted price for double that.

New Era Antiques

http://neweraantiques.com/overview.cgi?
televisions

Hard to believe the TV is now so old that you can buy retro models. And they don't come much more retro than this. For around $200 this American antique company offers portable TV sets from the likes of JVC and Hotpoint to General Electric and Admiral. The *Happy Days* 1950s designs range from two-tone colour models to what look like astronaut helmets. No online

BREAKING DVD'S CODE

Not a DVD expert myself, the guide to what exactly 'code free' refers to was adequate enough to have me hooked to the Code Free DVD site (www.codefreedvd.com), and panicking about any other uninformed purchases I may have made recently.

Basically the DVD world is divided into regions and if you buy a player from one, you won't necessarily be able to play DVDs unless they're from the same region. But this doesn't apply here so you're free to watch movies from anywhere. More expensive than coded models, £500 to £700, you do pay for the viewing freedom but it should be worth it in the long run.

Mail UK (www.mailuk.com) works along the same system with slightly cheaper prices, £300 to £400 in most cases.

TV TOYS

You've seen the show, now you want the toys. But what if the show is a gem from your long-lost youth? Never fear, check out *www.tvtoys.com* and you can find figurines, lunchboxes, videos and cookbooks from your favourite programme.

Shows from *The Bionic Woman* to *The Flying Nun* are featured and, if you're lucky, a full history of the show plus the going rate for memorabilia is discussed, with links to fan clubs and e-commerce sites selling all manner of collectibles. Did you know *The Brady Bunch* recorded five albums? Only available on vinyl, natch. So dig around your loft and see what embarrassing treasures you can dig up – *The Waltons Country Store Playset*, perhaps? Now worth \$75-100.

buying but you can make e-mail enquiries to discover how to buy. If TV memorabilia tickles your fancy, you might also want to drop in on **www.retrostuff.com** which has an *I Love Lucy* toy TV set for sale for less than \$20. It sounds horrendous, looks charming and will probably be sold on eBay for a small fortune 20 years from now.

Plugged In
www.pluggedin.co.uk
Northern Electric's crisp and clear site could be a great site to browse for all your electrical needs. Could be being the operative phrase. Plugged In is, unfortunately, tedious to browse with simple pages taking forever, images of the products are too small to get a real feel for the products and descriptions are limited at best. Prices are, however, competitive so we recommend this site to those who know what they're looking for and are simply searching for the best price.

Remote Controls
www.remotecontrols.co.uk
No prizes for guessing what this site sells. With 30,000 replacement remote control units to choose from, the one you lost down the back of your sofa with the hamster should be there somewhere. Select the manufacturer and model number or code, which they help you to locate, and you're now completely rid of the need to indulge in your last remaining form of physical exercise – stumbling to the set to change channels

Satellite Shop
www.satelliteshop.co.uk
Detailed spec sheets, product guides and star ratings, plus discounted prices to boot. The scroll-down menus for TVs, videos and DVDs makes the site far less cluttered than many of its rivals. Strangely, given the company name, the one button which didn't lead to any more info said 'Satellite'. It's probably worth another look when they get all the gremlins sorted.

Techtronics
www.techtronics.com
You won't find any dinky portable or 21in TV sets here, only your extra widescreen, 50in plasma displays and rear projection monitors. Beyond the hyperactive homepage the site is easy to navigate with page-long spec

sheets and handy customer reviews. The cheapest set you're likely to find will still set you back something just short of a grand, but it'll satisfy the couch potato within you. The perfect site for your ultimate home cinema buys.

Tempo

www.tempo.co.uk

A fairly basic, no-nonsense site. Browse the store, read the standard spec sheets including the information you probably knew already, and buy. Delivery generally takes seven to 10 days, and if you find the same item cheaper elsewhere they pay you the difference. Most items offer savings off RRP, often of around £30.

Unbeatable

www.unbeatable.co.uk

This online-only site is a neat alternative to the high street with competitive prices on top brand names including Panasonic, Sony and Philips. Click on a category and browse the long lists of TVs, video recorders and DVDs. The information is limited to a few features and pictures. Better for buying than browsing in our view.

Value Direct

www.valuedirect.co.uk

Despite spreading themselves to cover a host of electrical goods, Value Direct does offer a catalogue of hundreds of items of audio-visual equipment to suit all budgets. Images are clear and descriptions are listed as spec sheets with a handy jargon guide on hand to explain why two scarts are better than one. They also offer model comparisons, finance options and you can collect Web Rewards as you shop. Prices aren't bad either.

Video Logic

www.videologic.co.uk

Aptly titled, Video Logic offers a cheaper, and therefore definitely more logical, way to turn your old bog-standard television set into a home cinema unit. Systems can be connected to your DVD player or PC, adding that digital edge. Prices start around £150 with a £5 delivery charge. The only downside is the lack of additional information. Help with installation is available, but encouragement that you actually need one of these systems in the first place is lacking.

Limited selection but with buyer's guides and finance plans you can have a home cinema by the weekend

Web Electricals

www.webelectricals.co.uk

Comprehensive yet to the point. Search for TVs, videos and DVD players, or read the buyers' guides with their glossary of all those manual terms that have meant nothing to you thus far. The range is limited to four or five items in each category and if you can't drag yourself away from the home cinema units, there are finance plans to help you stiffen your purchasing resolve.

What TV & Video

http://catalogue.barclaycard.co.uk/cgi-bin/tv.storefront

Not to be confused with the offline magazine of the same name, this site is part of Barclaycard's cybermall Barclay Square. Instead of tips on how to find the system to meet your needs, you just get the usual list of models and the Barclay Square guarantee of safe shopping. Feels homey, though.

 If your roof seems naked without a dish

Satellite UK

www.satelliteuk.com

There's not much to a satellite dish but they have tried to liven things up a bit since we last checked in with better pics and type colours, though essentially you still just get headings to cover what's on sale, reviews and the essential FAQs. Still, at least you know they're not spending money on design that could be knocked off their prices. Pick up digital receivers and accessories from the fill-it-in-yourself online order form and read up on Sky Digital – you could even find out what "free set-top box" actually means.

Wizard Satellite

www.wizardsatellite.co.uk

Wizard Satellite has everything you need for satellite reception and the obligatory graphic of a rotating dish for those people who have trouble with the words 'satellite dish'. You can buy online but you might be put off by the fact that between pages the screen is filled by a blue Artex effect which looks suspiciously as if the site has crashed. It probably hasn't, so just wait.

You might also find these sites of use. Then again you might not.

www.comet.co.uk

Standard site and prices from the high-street king.

www.electrical.coop.co.uk

Limited selection of products at discounted Internet prices.

www.electricalwarehouse.co.uk

A sparse selection and too brief descriptions but keen prices.

www.teleview-direct.co.uk

Buy online or make a renting request and have them call you back to finalise.

Tickets

Not the kind your local bus conductor inspects, but the kind of ticket which earns you a spin in a Ferrari or a seat in a West End theatre which doesn't involve watching Martine McCutcheon

 General happenings and the Orient Express

Aloud

www.aloud.com

The opening homepage may be loud and fiercely busy, but this is a well thought-out concert and theatre ticket site. It offers a comprehensive list of music events in the UK up to six months in advance, and you can search according to artist, venue or town. This site is easy to navigate and they tell you on each page if an event is sold out rather than waiting till you've decided to purchase. Only the selling-fast marker is a let-down, as it seems to be more of a way to panic customers into buying than an accurate account of sales. The cost comprises the usual additional postage fee but you can track your ticket to see what stage of processing your order has reached.

Bigmouth

www.bigmouth.co.uk

A simple, alphabetical directory makes this site easy to search for information about tours, venues and travel. You can't always book online but postage is priced per total buy, not per ticket, so it may work out a lot cheaper than a number of its competitors (some sites charge £4 per ticket). This is more of a one-stop shop than an involving site, but useful nonetheless.

Latest Events

www.latestevents.com

Offering package events rather than simple ticket sales, Latest Events has some fabulous days out to choose from – if you have the money. Select their unusual events category and you'll find such tempting excursions as lunch on the Orient Express for £414 (well, it is a five-course meal), or the Ferrari

WHAT'S ON WHEN

Despite a distinct lack of online selling, What's on When (*www.whats onwhen.com*) deserves a mention as the most comprehensive events directory.

With the option to search continents and countries as well as city and type of event, you're pretty much guaranteed to find at least one event, wherever you are.

Each listing includes details of the event itself alongside the when, where's and how much. From here you can also link to official sites that will often allow you to book online.

Experience, which offers Ferrari-driving plus lunch for £235. Concert and sporting tickets are also on offer, but again only as part of bigger travel packages. Despite the annoyingly slow system, this site is worth investigating if you're after that something extra special.

Scene One
www.sceneone.co.uk

This cheery-looking site is one of the few to offer reviews and additional information about its featured artists and events to encourage you to buy tickets. The site includes music, film, comedy and even television reviews, but you can only buy music tickets online. Ordering is simple but can be expensive with an added booking fee and then postage of £4 on top, but this site certainly offers more of a shopping experience than many of its competitors.

Ticket Master
www.ticketmaster.co.uk

The new look Ticketmaster site is slightly brighter than its predecessor, but it remains simple and well-categorised, offering sports, music, arts and family events. It's particularly useful for sporting events and theatre tickets, as you can specify where in the audience you would like to sit. You can also opt to collect your tickets in person to avoid extortionate postage fees. The only drawback is the lack of any additional information about the events on offer.

Film Book tickets and receive 'personalised' info

Warner Village cinemas
www.warnervillage.co.uk

Warner Bros has moved one step beyond the usual online cinema-booking site, inviting you to register your details on the homepage and receive personalised information. If you live in the Reading area, for example, they'll send you the Reading Warner Village listings each week, along with those for one other cinema. Buying is as simple as it can be. Click on the location, film and time, and then hand over the money without having to pay a booking fee. They'll even tell you how to get there. Nothing could be easier.

Clubs and rock concerts to opera and ballet

First Call

www.firstcalltickets.com

Despite the user-friendly scroll-down menus, and the option of searching by artist, venue or date, First Call has improved the speed for its pages, which makes this site much easier to use. Its coverage of sports, theatre and music events is comprehensive, with a straightforward booking process. This is particularly useful if you're an online novice. Major downside is you not only get charged a £4.25 booking fee, but even if you pick up the tickets from the venue you get charged a dispatch fee – get them mailed for the same charge.

Raymond Gubbay

www.raymondgubbay.co.uk

Gubbay, a leading promoter of classical music, opera and ballet, offers a stylish and uncluttered site which is worth visiting, if only for the thought that has been put into it. Once you've specified the date and show which you want to attend, you can ask them to try again if you're not happy with the first selection of seats they come up with. They also offer additional information about each performance, there are extracts of reviews of the shows on offer, and there's also a mailing list that you can join.

Ticket Web

www.ticketweb.co.uk

Nothing flash in terms of design or contents, Ticket Web is a safe bet for all your UK gig and club tickets. You can search by venue or a particular artist, but booking fees apply despite the promise that the Web is always cheapest. If you're reluctant to pay their high postage charges, you can pick up your tickets at the venue. You can also track your order as it is processed. This is, however, a very functional site which offers no additional information.

 Premiership football and 'the sport of kings'

Aston Villa and other Premiership clubs

www.avfc.co.uk

Aston Villa are one of very few Premiership football clubs to use the Internet to sell match tickets. Although they have yet to set up their own box office, they offer a convenient link to Ticket Master to make your purchase. From here the standard Ticket Master rules apply. Other forward-thinkers include:

www.bradfordcityfc.co.uk	Bradford City
www.ccfc.co.uk	Coventry City
www.sunderland-afc.com	Sunderland

Tickets

Epsom, Sandown and Kempton racecourses all make it dangerously easy to watch the gee-gees

Epsom Derby

www.epsomderby.co.uk

Epsom racecourse, along with Kempton and Sandown Park, offers a simple system from which you can buy tickets for race meets throughout the year. You can search by event or the approximate time that you would like to go, state whether you want to watch from the paddock or the premier area, and that's it. You can pick up your tickets or have them posted out to you, either way it's free. Refreshing.

www.kempton.co.uk — Kempton Park
www.sandown.co.uk — Sandown Park

Newmarket

www.newmarketracecourses.co.uk

After making a good impression by offering an online ticket service in the first place, the Newmarket organisers lose marks for the inept system they use. Before you order you need to consult the price guide and then memorise exactly when you want to go, which tickets you want and how much they are, because once you go to buy they expect you to work out the cost yourself. Oh, and you can't book online more than two weeks before an event.

 Theatre London only – still at the rehearsal stage

What's On Stage

www.whatsonstage.com

This dedicated theatre shop is one of the few to offer extra info about each performance, with news, reviews and regular thespian features. It would be nice to see them branching out of London and improve their range, as they only have half a dozen options under each category, typically the most popular shows. Face-value prices apply and you can specify post or collection. A good start with the potential to improve.

TheatreNet

www.theatrenet.co.uk

You can't buy here but you can join a club through the site which gets you discounts on tickets. Worth considering if you're a regular West Ender.

Toys

With more cuddly toys than the The Generation Game conveyor belt and more models than a Milan catwalk, the Internet means you have absolutely no excuse for buying gift vouchers for your niece

General Save money, time and tantrums

FAO Schwarz
www.faoschwarz.com
America's premier toy store will ship to the UK if you're desperate to get hold of an international Barbie or Furby but they charge 40 per cent of the total of your order as a fee for the privilege, and you must order goods at least to the value of $200. If this hasn't put you off, the site is easy to navigate with brand and character shopping areas, and a number of items as yet unseen in the UK, including Gene, the Hollywood celebrity doll.

Funstore
www.funstore.co.uk
If your usual visit to the toy shop is typified by screaming tantrums and pleas never to have to leave their favourite haven, Funstore will be able to fulfil all your child's toy needs and spare you a headache at the same time. Scroll through boys' and girls' toys, board and computer games, and construction and creative pursuits. Popular brand names include Action Man, Monopoly, Mr Potato Head and K'Nex alongside unusual alternatives including Truth or Dare Jenga. Fast and easy.

Hamleys
www.hamleys.co.uk
Hamleys has generally been ranked on a par with Harrods as one of those stores only found in the capital, and is now regarded as more of a tourist stop rather than an actual business. Now Hamleys has launched itself online,

open to everyone, but doesn't unfortunately carry anywhere near as extensive a catalogue as the offline version. You can narrow your search down by specifying gender, age and price requirements, however we suggest you stick to the category search as more often than not they came up with no suitable toys. Ordering from here is simple, although images and descriptions could be improved. An average effort from such a reputable store.

In 2 Toys

www.In2Toys.com

Despite its bargain basement nature, this site is well laid out with bargains, special offers, and boys' and girls' sections to browse. Alternatively, search by brand or price range if you have something specific in mind. Every item sold is reduced to some extent, many toys by as much as 70 per cent, so you should be able to pick up a Super Soaker for £4.99 and a darts board for £1.

Toy Chest

www.toychest.co.uk

This family-run company sells fun, educational and activity-based toys and games for children 10 years and under. Search according to the age of your child, baby, toddler and so on, then browse through the toys on offer, each with brief descriptions and illustrations. Fun activities include candle-making and mug-painting kits for under £10, and Ocean Zoo Sea Monkey pets for £6.50. A particularly useful site if you happen to be a little late buying presents as delivery takes only two days.

Toys "R" Us

www.Toysrus.co.uk

Just as the shop itself is a lurid assault on the senses, this site isn't easy on

the eye. But there are benefits in shopping at such an outlet, the biggest bonus being that there is a huge range of toys. Customer service is excellent: any problems with orders and you're personally e-mailed with a £10 voucher as an apology. If you have loyalty points from the stores, however, you can't use them here. Prices are the same as in the shops. Delivery takes two to three working days and costs £2.50 per order.

Free delivery marks this site as a winner – do all your Christmas shopping in one stop and wait for the delivery van

Toy Town

www.toytown.co.uk

This site is part of the Shoppers Universe mall. Search through the extensive catalogue of children's items to suit all ages, from cuddly toys and model kits for infants, to roller blades for the older ones, and even a few for that very tall, silver-haired child. Standard prices but delivery is free so it saves you having to carry the pool table back from the shop.

 **Chicken Run to Pokémon**

Aardmarket

http://aardmarket.aardman.com

Specialising in 3D animation models, the Aardmarket sells toys and gifts, predominantly from the Nick Park stable: *Wallace & Gromit*, *Chicken Run*, *Angry Kid*, and coming soon, *Morph* and *Creature Comforts*. It sells the usual array of franchised merchandise, cuddly toys, watches, and back-packs at high-street prices. Worth a look for a gift to complete your child's collection.

Character Warehouse

www.character-warehouse.com

Every child has a favourite toy or cartoon character, so your easiest option when buying a present is to stick to what they know. Yes, their bedroom may turn into some kind of surreal furry shrine but at least they'll be happy. You can search here by character, brand or price. Popular characters include Bagpuss, Miffy, Bob the Builder and of course, Pokémon. Items on sale range from soft toys and games, to bedroom sets and clothing, with a choice of items to suit every price range. For once you should also opt for the Express 48-hour delivery, as at only £1 more than the standard seven to 14 days it's worth it.

Mail Order Express

www.moetoys.co.uk

Christmas can be a nightmare for those parents frantically trying to find the one Pokémon toy their child doesn't own. Happily, Mail Order sells every toy, game, piece of clothing and collector's card associated with such must-have brands as Lego, Scalextric, Barbie and Pokémon. Just click on the brand and then search the entire catalogue or cut directly to the price you're willing to pay. Another good site for late pressies, next-day delivery is charged at the unreasonably reasonable price of £5.99. Worth a look.

LET'S ROCK!

You never really know what's going to become really cool in cyberspace and what ends up with a kind of virtual BO.

Wooden horses are (let's get the pun out of the way) carving a niche online with such stores as Tom Cobley & All on *www.rockinghorses-by-tom-cobley.co.uk*.

Yes, it sounds like a cheesy PR name but the maker of these rocking horses (which retail at anything up to £1,950) really is a distinguished member of the Cobley family who made his first rocking horse in 1984 for his daughter.

Shop 4 Toys
www.shop4toys.co.uk
Yet another site that can sort you out with toys, activities and accessories elegantly branded (not) with all your children's favourite cartoon characters. Furry creatures of the moment include Barney, the Mr Men and the Tweenies. Perfect for die-hard fans. Delivery is just £2.95 but it takes up to 14 days.

Whether you're dippy about Dipsy or mad for Milo, this site will sort you out. Teletubbies, Tweenies and much more

Traditional As the slogan says: 'For kids of all ages!'

Action Man
www.actionman.com
Be warned, if you visit this site at work you'll become horribly conspicuous in a cybersecond as the arrival of the homepage coincides with the kind of alert siren you used to hear on the good old USS Enterprise. When you've chosen the country you're browsing from, you'll be called to action-stations. There's a link to a UK online store where you can buy the figures and the associated accessories. Well worth visiting, especially for thirtysomething men who can't believe the soldier of their youth is still doing the business.

Airfix
www.airfix.com
Another dream site for overgrown kids. All the Airfix models you could ever imagine at cheap-as-you-like prices. Search by model type, classic ships, cars, war heroes and space models, and narrow your selection down to an era or type. Pick up Henry VIII or an Aston Martin DB for a mere £3.99, although the more advanced HMS Belfast and Cutty Sark sell for £7.99. Sizes and skill levels are included in descriptions alongside images. A bit amateur-looking – but, be honest, that's how your models will probably end up anyway.

Dawson and Son
www.dawson-and-son.co.uk
A delightfully old-fashioned specialist in wooden toys and games, this site

offers lots of quaint, romantic toys to dilute the Pokémon collection. Jack-in-the-Boxes, spinning tops and old-fashioned pastry sets are usually still hits with small children, although the knitting sets and flower press kits are perhaps a little optimistic. The toys are quite pricey but they are beautifully made and built to last. Dawsons are a *Which?* Web Trader.

Huggables
www.huggables.com
Gold, red and blue teddy bears, chimney sweep bears, mohair lambs, terriers and even polar bears. Yep, you guessed it, Huggables is a cuddly toy site, with prices ranging from £10 to £200. Not much you can really say, the only niggling feature being the lack of direct link to the order form. Another pen and paper job then.

Letterbox collection
www.l-box.co.uk
Presents, dressing-up clothes and a whole range of personalised items are on sale here, but steel yourself for some spectacularly un-politically correct costumes such as the Blushing Bride and Red Indian Chief outfits. Still, there's a decent range of goods focusing on fun and imagination rather than the practical, including birth announcement pictures and personalised pillows, towels and cutlery. These take 28 days to deliver – the non-personalised items take seven – with prices from £2.35 for goods up to £10 (free over £120).

On Tracks
www.ontracks.co.uk
Boasting 35,000 model and hobby items to buy, it's only a shame the site itself wasn't a little more slick and advanced. In the spirit of old-fashioned items, once you've found that steam locomotive model which will complete your collection, you'll need to jot down the details for the secure, if rudimentary order form. Aside from Hornby model railways, On Tracks also offers a substantial catalogue of slot cars, radio-controlled toys and kit cars and figures. One for experts really as descriptions are poor with few images.

Toy Robots
www.toyrobots.com
Obviously not your run-of-the-mill toy selection, here you'll find a fine range of tin robots, plastic robots, and even a robot clock, as well as space toys. Very reasonable prices, but it does assume you know your robots – the Robbie (from *The Forbidden Planet* and YM-3 (from *Lost in Space*) are not exactly given their pedigrees on the catalogue page. The photos could be of better quality too. Some of these are close to one-offs – like the red Russian robots bought from a now-defunct factory. Ordering is by e-mail but you have to send them a draft in US currency as they don't do plastic.

Up to toddlers — From the pram to the playpen

Babies "R" Us

www.babiesrus.co.uk

The baby version of Toys"R"Us offers baby products such as nappies, a range of gadgets and larger items like prams, car seats and high chairs, as well as a pretty decent selection of baby toys like activity cottages, Mr Potato Head figures and a musical pop-up piano. The rattle-teethers aren't really pure toys but may be a medical necessity.

Early Learning Centre

www.elc.co.uk

A good, reliable site, where you can shop by age, category and type of toy if you're stuck for ideas. Includes some decent discounts in the sale section, plus helpful categories such as Award Winners, Best-Sellers and What's New. The toys are organised into interesting sections such as Imagine, which includes dressing-up clothes, as well as the more self-explanatory Sport and Activity and Discover. Deliveries arrive promptly within three days and cost £2.95 for goods up to £60; after that postage and packing is free.

DIRECT TO YOUR DOOR, IF YOU LIKE TANK ENGINES

This should really be called the *Thomas the Tank Engine* site as they only currently sell Thomas and his friends.

There's a huge catalogue of friendly engines, the Fat Controller, and every station house, tunnel and signalling tower from Thomas's world.

The only shortfall is the customer service section – or lack of. Click to order and you are led to the cashier to fill in your credit card details, but they don't tell you how much or how long shipping will be.

www.directto yourdoor.co.uk

PlayBug

www.playbug.com

A bright and uncluttered homepage lends itself well to this easy-to-navigate site. Search by age, price, product or department, each with a large range of toys suited to babies and infants. And there's no need to worry about safety: every toy has passed the European Toy Safety Directive. If you take advantage of a next-day delivery option, it will cost you £15.

Toy Craft

http://catalog.com/uk/toy

With toys and games on sale for as little as 40p, this is a particularly useful site for children looking for a way to spend their pocket money. Cog puzzles are 60p and gliders 40p. Old-school favourites include Fuzzy Felt sets for £3.99 and I-Spy for £6.95. Pictures of the toys rather than text descriptions would go down well and they'd be advised to replace the amateur order form, simply a long list of toys, with an automatic buying link.

Travel

It doesn't make any difference whether you think it's better to travel or to arrive. The Net offers so much choice that it has been known to induce a state of analysis paralysis in the indecisive or weak-willed

General — Where to go and how to get there

A2B Travel

www.a2btravel.com

A2B contains information on every mode of transport possible. If you're in a buying mood, you can log on to the flight-finder to buy tickets online, or rent a villa in France, Italy or Spain. The site doesn't offer its own package deal section but it does offer hyperlinks to Bargain Holidays (see below) and Escape Routes. Standard search systems apply, so just type in the wheres and whens and see what they come up with. A2B is particularly useful as an information portal for travellers, with insurance quotes, airport and accommodation guides, plus flight, ferry and train timetables.

Bargain Holidays

www.bargainholidays.co.uk

This is one of many sites where you can do everything apart from actually book a holiday online. When we visited it offered only flights for booking, but this site stands out for its resort guides, weather information and brochure request service, not to mention its regular competitions. A useful site to begin with if you're not sure where you want to go, or how much you should pay.

Destination Group

www.destination-group.com

You can't always book online from this crowded, text-laden homepage. In the majority of cases you search through the exotic package holidays, choose a deal, click on it and they ring you back to make the booking. You can book flights online, though on a few occasions you may find yourself linked to a separate site to book. Whatever the option, there are cheap deals to be had.

E Bookers
www.ebookers.com
Despite the automatic connection to the flight bookings section, you can also book accommodation, insurance and car hire online. For flights, type in your destinations, dates and details and it's guaranteed to come up with list upon list of flights. Once you've made your selection, however, the problems begin. You need to register before you can go any further, and this inevitably takes too long while you try to think up a password no one else in the world is already using. If you do have the patience, the step-by-step buying process does make spending hundreds of pounds that little bit easier.

Expedia
www.expedia.msn.co.uk
An easy-to-navigate complete travel resource, with online booking for flights, accommodation, package holidays, car rentals, resort and even airport guides. If you're booking a room you can make as many specifications as you want: non-smoking, wheelchair access etc. Flights generally aren't cheap, but it's worth a look if price isn't your primary concern.

Late Escapes
www.lateescapes.com
If you've read Chapter 4 on auctions you'll know that you really can bid for pretty much anything online. Late Escapes deals in holiday auctions, flights, packages, city breaks and cruises. Aside from the incredibly small type, which can make reading rather difficult, the site is well laid out and easy to navigate. All you have to decide is where you want to go. A good starting point is the Holidays for £1 section, which sounds to good to be true, but isn't.

Tel Me
www.telmeglobaltraveller.com
A useful all-round resource for business travellers, with online flight bookings and hotel reservations, as well as city guides and Tel Me miles to be collected by the frequent traveller. Prices are steeper than those of low-cost airlines. But then, if the company's paying...

The First Resort
www.thefirstresort.com
You should only use First Resort if you're definitely

going to book that day and if you don't intend to travel for another 10 weeks, as you can't book late or semi-late deals online. It takes too long to register – you have to give personal details and spend time choosing your favourite resorts. Otherwise, the site is simple to use and searches the top tour operators for good deals.

Thomas Cook
www.thomascook.co.uk
This high-street chain has created a bright, eye-catching website that's perfect for young and old, new or experienced travellers. Search for package deals or villas, or by age with Club 18-30 and over-50s holidays on offer. Standard brochure stuff, though special requirements vary, with golf, cabaret dancers and bridge for over-50s and nightlife a must for the young ones.

All-in-ones One-stop shops

Club 18-30
www.club18-30.co.uk
A loud fuchsia-and-yellow homepage with a pulsating heartbeat pounding in the background – this could only be the Club 18-30 site. Search through the resort guides to get an idea of where you'll hear the loudest music and book your fun, fun, fun trip. As you generally pay more for specialist holidays, the descriptions and pictures are deliberately made comprehensive and enticing enough to encourage you to buy – as if you really needed any encouragement anyway.

Kuoni
www.kuoni.co.uk
If you're accustomed to passing over the Kuoni brochure at the travel agent for fear of price overload, you'll be surprised to find cheap deals for such dream destinations as Cuba, Grenada, Egypt and Goa to name but a few. Top offers when we visited included a five-night Egyptian stay in a four-star hotel with a Nile view for £400. Stylewise, the destination guides include history and places of interest. You can search by price, destination or date, and Kuoni uses a step-by-step buying guide to put the less confident at ease.

Last Minute
www.lastminute.com
Forget all the media pot-shots against this company. The bright design of this

SO YOU WANT TO GO TO FRISCO?

Many songs have been written and warbled, film stars have been immortalised and you can't beat the *Streets of San Francisco* for TV cheese. If this is the sum of your knowledge on the city by the bay, try one of the multitude of Internet destination guides. Our own online *Rough Guide to San Francisco* (http://travel.roughguides.com) allows you to read content from our books, and Condé Nast's *Concierge* (*www.concierge.com*) provides dining, lodging and events information plus a slide show.

Try American Airlines (*www.aa.com*) for low-cost yet comfortable long-haul tickets. Or you could always opt for one-way, just in case you're hooked.

When you're there you don't want to end up being stuck in your run-of-the-mill five-star Holiday Inn. Anyone can do that. The Lighthouse Society (*www.maine.com/lights/others.htm*) currently rents out 15 lighthouses in the Bay area, including the Pigeon Point Lighthouse & Hostel. Prices range from $60 to $295.

site eggs you on to buy a holiday through its enthusiasm. The boxed captions include all the key information you need to save you wasting time browsing fruitlessly. You do need to register, but this takes about three seconds and they send you regular updates of the best offers as compensation (well, that's the point).

TraveloCity

www.travelocity.co.uk

Huge promises but smaller returns. Supposedly you can book holidays, flights and hire cars from this site, but a recent search for a trip from London to LA, while initially seeming to come up with a dozen or so options at decent prices, on closer inspection was for dates five months away. Earlier dates rapidly doubled or tripled the airfare – a hefty premium to pay for travelling during the summer holidays. So it is possible to book a trip here, but be specific about your dates and check your overdraft facility.

Trrravel

www.trrravel.com

One of the best-designed sites, Trrravel has had the foresight to use scroll-down menus and quick links to avoid over-active homepages which can often put people off. The auction section is a fun way to search. Depending where you want to go, you are linked to different 'agents' where prices are upfront, but there's not much about where you're going or where you'll be staying – and judging by Ann Robinson's mailbag, you're going to want to know. Once again, though, it's a case of making your selection and then waiting for the telephone to ring.

Virgin Holidays

www.virginholidays.co.uk

The suitably sunny homepage clearly maps out all the online offers with late deals, package and flight-only trips to the Mediterranean and Florida, and to more exotic locations. After selecting the part of the world you wish to explore, things get more complicated, with no clear signs pointing to the online booking section. Once resolved, simply fill in the standard requirements. If they can't find exactly what you're looking for, they come up with a list of alternatives, not always suitable. Each resort, hotel and flight is, however, described in detail.

 ## On track to see the sights

Great Western Trains
www.great-western-trains.co.uk
Fancy a trip to Bath Spa, Taunton or even Swindon? Train-operating company Great Western has embraced technology and allows you to book your tickets online. The simple system asks the same questions they would if you rang up, but your boss won't know you're using company time to book some fun.

The Train Line
www.thetrainline.com
Buying with The Train Line turned out to be quite a complicated process. First you need to register before you can do anything and, once in, it's advisable to know exactly where you want to go. Scroll-down destination menus would be helpful. (If you really want to confuse the site, try to book a trip by sleeper.) Search according to the cheapest or fastest journey, whichever you prefer.

Virgin Trains
www.virgintrains.co.uk
Similar system to the Train Line, the only difference being that they don't rashly claim to cover the whole country, just the Bransonised bits.

 ## Wave goodbye

Drive Alive
www.drive-alive.com
Obviously motoring holidays to Europe begin with a ferry or tunnel crossing. The aim here is to take the hassle out of planning your trip by handling all the booking arrangements on your behalf. The system is quite unique. Enter your proposed dates and destinations for ferry crossings and then navigate your way around selecting where you would like to stay. It calculates the price and books for you. All you have to do is the driving.

P&O Ferries
www.poportsmouth.com (Portsmouth); www.posl.com (Stena Line); www.ponsf.com (North Sea); www.poscottishferries.co.uk (Scottish); Ferry crossings to Europe remain the cheapest option. Fill in the form (complete with meal preferences and insurance requirements) and a P&O rep will call you back ASAP to finalise your holiday.

Flights Just get up and go

Buzz

www.buzzaway.com

Buzz is one to note for the future
as the low-cost-flights-to-Europe
company gradually adds more cities
to its destination list. Popular city
breaks include Paris and Milan, along
with such rather more adventurous
destinations as Helsinki and Berlin. On
the downside, keep in mind that Buzz
quotes one-way prices, and is slow to offer
flights from anywhere in the UK besides London
Stansted. Booking is easy and can be done in six
languages – so have fun and try to make your
reservation in the language of your destination.

Deckchair

www.deckchair.com

Pick any departure point and destination in the world and Bob Geldof's
Deckchair (well, not his personal deckchair) will scour the globe and every
flight company for a price to suit. A very annoying feature is the 'Fare Jump',
as the site only applies conditions and extras after you have selected the air-
line (based on price, presumably). This can almost double your fare.
Unfortunately things go a little pear-shaped when you do find a flight as the
process by which you move from selecting your flights to actually buying
them is a bit too much like hard work.

EasyJet

www.easyjet.com

Hurray! Cheap European flights from UK airports other than London Stansted
and Luton. Those in Liverpool can fly to hot spots like Amsterdam, Barcelona
and Nice, to name but a few, for as little as £50 return. Standard booking
system applies and again you receive discounts if you book online.

Go-Fly

www.go-fly.com

Now independent from parent British Airways, Go flies to holiday hot-spots
Tenerife and Alicante. The cheapest flights remain those that are booked last
minute. Easy to navigate with resort guides, insurance, car hire and a hotel
booking service, and a nifty destination guide that lets you know what's
happening at that time of year. Just £35 was quoted for a return to Edinburgh.
From Stansted, naturally.

Korea move
See the Stalinist Las Vegas!

For the seriously independent traveller, there is only one part of the world which now counts as seriously unexplored: North Korea. The People's Democratic Republic (or the weirdest place on earth as it is often described) may seem like the most closed society on this planet but it has not been slow on the uptake when it comes to the Net.

In the capital Pyongyang stands a rare realistic statue of North Korea's great late leader Kim Il Sung. With backache

If you fancy a different type of package holiday you can browse some of the options at *www.stat.ualberta.ca/people/schmu/kito.html*, the official site for the Korea International Travel Company, the brainchild of Kim Il Sung, the late, lamented (in Pyongyang) leader. This site says that 30-40,000 tourists arrive in a republic which calls itself "the eastern country of courtesy". The five packages here all start in the capital Pyongyang, the Stalinist Las Vegas. But you can't order online, only by telex, mail or fax. Inconveniently neither the snail mail nor the telex address (or indeed the fax number) are included here, though it does have a fine shot of the statue of the first Kim with a backache.

You probably won't be going to North Korea for the climate but if you want to check the weather in the capital just log on to *http://as.orientation.com/dispatch/home.html*. Whenever this visitor checked, the weather ran the whole gamut from "partly cloudy" to "cloudy".

If you're still not deterred, you can order package tours of North Korea by e-mail, through a Dutch travel agent VNC on *www.vnc.nl/korea* where you'll also find plenty of essential info like the fact that 'maekchu' is the word for beer. A typical tour costs £707. If you want to order from a UK agent, try *www.bestravel.co.uk/northkorea.htm* where the tours start at £779 with a train journey from Beijing to Pyongyang.

Want to check the news before you go? There's nowhere better than *www.kcna.co.jp*, the official site for the official Korean news agency to catch up on which ambassador is presenting his credentials. You've probably heard about all the fuss about North Korea and its nuclear missiles. They're often in trouble for pointing them at the wrong people (ie everybody) and for peace of mind you might want to check out the country's nuclear arsenal on *www.fas.org/nuke/guide/dprk/nuke/index.html*. If that puts you off, don't worry, you can virtually travel to North Korea by reading David and Bill's travel diary on *www.ozemail.com.au/~davidf/homepage/nk_1994.htm*.

Ryanair
www.ryanair.ie
Another low-cost flight site, Ryanair flies to more unusual destinations, such as Aarhus in Denmark and Perpignan in France, along with the more run-of-the-mill Genoa and Dublin. Don't get too excited by the £5 one-way flights blurb on the homepage: this covers a very limited range but they're always worth checking out. Flights are still cheap, but most flights from UK locations outside London Stansted fly via Dublin.

Travel Select
www.travelselect.com
As basic as it can get, this site uses plain pages from which you select your route and see what they can come up with. Not for those looking for the cheapest options – £120 for a ticket to Barcelona from London is a typical offering, though again there is a fare jump once they apply restrictions. A useful site for those after a no-nonsense approach.

You can also try:
British Airways
www.british-airways.com

British Midland
www.iflybritishmidland.com

Resting places A room with a view

B&B In London
www.londonhometohome.com
Looking for somewhere to stay while you're on that shopping-and-theatre trip to the Big Smoke? This excellent site is a real find. Home To Home is a west London B&B agency that will find you a classy and comfortable home from home at rates much cheaper than hotels. Booking is by fax or e-mail.

Bed & Breakfast
www.beduk.co.uk
Grim-looking homepage hiding a good selection of B&Bs complete with full descriptions, images and room rates. You can't book online, but send your requests to the company and they'll make the arrangements.

Book That
www.bookthat.com
A database of villas, country houses and apartments covering the

> Just imagine drifting down the canals of England, sipping a brewski on the deck, sun shining...

UK, France, Spain, Portugal and Italy. Prices range from £500 to £1,000 depending on the season. The really good thing here is that it only puts in what's available. You can book online too.

Easy Stay

www.easystay.co.uk

Easy Stay is easy to search and easy on the eye. Select a region and browse through lists of B&Bs and swanky hotels. You can't book direct online but you can make reservation enquiries.

Hotels Online

www.hol.co.uk

The best advice here is to look at as many hotels in your chosen area as possible, since some provide extensive information and others barely leave their postal details. Simply select a destination, browse and you will get linked to the hotel's own website to book.

Hoseasons Holidays

www.hoseasons.co.uk

A subdued homepage hides a comprehensive site that will have you boating down the canals of Cambridgeshire in no time, You can choose from boating and holiday park holidays in the UK and Europe. Though some sections have a disappointing "online brochure to come" notice, the parts that are up and running are chock-full of relevant information, enticing photos and descriptions. Prices vary considerably, but this could be the ideal site for large groups looking for a cheap getaway, or for two wanting a romantic waterways break.

Travel Web

www.travelweb.com

You can book flights as well as hotel rooms from this US site, but they list prices in dollars only which is a hassle. Although the accommodation section again sticks to the native currency of the hotels, it makes up for this with a comprehensive directory of worldwide hotels with descriptions and pictures. Make your search as nit-picky as you like, down to whether you want an alarm clock, and you'll be offered a wide choice every time. Mostly large hotel chains represented.

Worldwide Apartments

www.nothotels.com

This sophisticated site looks more like an advertisement for interior design than accommodation, but the serviced apartments here aren't your average

Useful info Need a helping hand?

Travel Xtras

www.travelxtras.com

It's the week before your holiday and you've forgotten to buy your mosquito repellent. Travel Xtras can sort you out no problem at all but you'll inevitably be sucked into buying many more of their miniature gadgets. The Wonder towel caught my eye, only 70cm x 25cm yet it does the job of a bath towel due to the amazing capillary action. Alternatively pick up a pegless clothesline for £2, and a handy waterproof pouch so you need never hide your valuables in the sand never to be found again.

The Foreign Office

www.fco.gov.uk/travel

Official travel and visa advice and contact details for the respective British embassies.

Oanda.Com

www.oanda.com

Lists the exchange rates for 164 countries.

VISA

www.visa.com/cgi-bin/vee/main.html

The location of every cash machine in the world.

World Meteorological Association

www.wmo.ch

Weather news and updates from around the globe.

Have your calculator to hand to do the currency conversion, but the choice – and detail – is impressive

B&Bs. Select anywhere in the world and the Foxton's database should be able to find something to suit your taste, if not necessarily your bank balance. Prices are in the country's currency, so a converter would be a useful addition to the site. There's no online booking, but you can make online information requests or use their call-back service. Good alternative for well-to-do families that are staying for more than a week.

Independents — **For something completely different**

Bales Worldwide

www.balesworldwide.com
You won't find Ayia Napa or the Costa del Sol here, only luxury holidays at luxury prices. Explore Thailand, China, South America or even Iceland. Each itinerary includes details of what you get for your thousands of pounds, including insurance, meals and guides, along with a brief run-down of the delights ahead. The descriptions are a bit short and could do with more pictures. You can book online if this doesn't bother you, or order the brochure from the site to get a better picture. For the experienced traveller only.

Caravanserai Tours

www.caravanserai-tours.com
Clearly Caravanserai Tours has no pretensions to being the next Thomas Cook as it specialises in tours to Iran and Libya, two destinations which have yet to have their own *Exposed* series on Sky One. This is a nice, uncluttered site that never takes its eye off the fact that it's the destinations that you're interested in. You can e-mail them your requirements for tours to either country.

Magic of Bolivia
www.bolivia.co.uk
For many, Bolivian magic is defined by Lake Titicaca but Che Guevara's bones were found there recently and a 'Che is God' concert is being organised (obviously Eric Clapton won't be playing). It's part of this site's unique charm that it seems as keen to share such snippets as it is to get you to click on a button for a Bolivian holiday. Online ordering was planned when the site was inspected. Meantime, you can download an itinerary.

Pack Your Bags
www.packyourbags.co.uk
Pack Your Bags is both a useful late-deals site where you can find your bargain break and e-mail your request, and a source for holidays of a more adventurous nature. Be as one with the wolves and bears in Transylvania for a week at £718, or search for the hidden secrets of Zeus on an archaeological dig in Turkey for around £900. Or just go to Greece tomorrow for £109, for a week's self-catering accommodation.

The Russian Experience
www.trans-siberian.co.uk
Not in fact the full Russian experience: you don't get to be the victim of rampant hyperinflation or wait for months for your wages to turn up. But this company does offer you the chance to stay with a typical Russian family as well as do the more predictable stuff like travel on the Trans-Siberian Express (which is as basic as the Orient Express is luxurious). Order by e-mail from a site which also allows you to download the brochures, but this site takes its time.

Sherpa Expeditions
www.sherpa-walking-holidays.co.uk
The title of this site is slightly misleading: not every holiday here involves a duel with the world's highest mountain and a close encounter with someone called Tensing. You can go walking or trekking across Corsica or even the Cotswolds. Just book by e-mail and phone over your credit card details.

STA Travel
www.statravel.co.uk
If you're a student or under 26, this offers you (not so) cheap flights and insurance to destinations all over the world. If you have problems connecting to STA's server to search its database, you can always ring its service line for bookings. If this is your first foray into serious travelling, the site also contains useful healthcare and resort information.

Wild Dog
www.wild-dog.com
There's a lot of information to plough through so you'll need to take your time

using this online directory, but it'll be worth it in the long run. Aside from the online flight and hotel-booking service which scans more than 100 operators for the best deals, Wild Dog is particularly useful if you're looking for such adventures as gorilla-tracking in Uganda and the like. The site now allows you to book online.

Wildlife Worldwide

www.wildlife-ww.co.uk

Walruses in the Arctic, jaguars in Ecuador and rhinos in Namibia are just a few of the beasts eager to be observed. If you're not sure what's happening in the wildlife kingdom, you can look at their wildlife calendar and request brochures to cover your next trip. If you're satisfied with the day-by-day itinerary which maps out each trip you can e-mail them details of your chosen holidays and they'll reply. Not for the budget traveller but it could be money well spent.

 **Car hire** Open road, here you go

Hertz

www.hertz.com

If you're looking for that little bit of adventure but aren't yet willing to trek the Himalayas, renting a car and exploring the countrysides of Cyprus or Morocco or Costa Rica is a more tentative step. Hertz can accommodate you in all these locations. Choose your destination, dates of travel and not so swanky Escort or Mondeo, all the Ford classics, and make your reservation. If you are renting for use abroad they include a handy currency converter, most prices seem to work out at around £15 per day.

Car Hire 4 Less

www.carhire4less.co.uk

Specialise in searching reputable vendors including Budget and Hertz and coming up with discounted prices. This said they failed to beat Hertz themselves on matching deals.

Chariots Motorhome Hire

www.chariotsmotorhomehire.co.uk

Motorhomes have (almost) all the comforts of home. Now available to Australian and South African citizens. Printable booking form.

Easy RentaCar

www.easyrentacar.com

Yet another Easy venture, letting you pick up a Mercedes A class to tour London, Barcelona or beautiful Paris. Unfortunately this is all the information I could access as my connection didn't match their requirements.

Winter Vacations to chill you out

1 Ski

www.1ski.com

This site takes information to the extreme. You can read up on any ski resort in the world, down to the tiniest detail: difficulty ratings, snow reports, events diary and techniques. If this whets your appetite, you should also be able to find a skiing holiday, although the usual enquiry and call-back service does apply. If interested in flights alone, the site will redirect you to Bargainholidays.com, where you can buy online. The Top Ten deals section can be a source of great savings if you can plan well in advance. Worth browsing.

Center Parcs

www.centerparcs.com

A viable alternative if your bank balance won't stretch to a week in the Canaries, the Center Parcs website teems with greenery, much like the forest villages themselves. Here you can read about and view the villas (that house two to eight persons), the restaurants, bars, heated outdoor pools and pamper palaces. You can also make specifications for adjoining villas, en-suite facilities and even Turkish baths. Center Parcs now allows booking online for straightforward visits of a week or less – but if you want to stay for longer or have any special requirements, call the service line.

IGLU

www.iglu.com

This site looks fantastic with lots of snow pics and everything you need to know to book a skiing holiday or a summer sunshine vacation depending on when you are browsing. Resort and hotel guides, snow reports, even webcams and 3D maps are all there to browse. The accommodation photos are excellent, and the FAQ section has info about everything from cancellation charges to visa requirements. Because of availability, you have to e-mail your enquiry and they will get back to you.

Inghams

www.inghams.co.uk

This would be a comprehensive site to book from if Inghams could just organise the navigation a bit better. The site is elegantly designed and there are photos and good descriptions of accommodation. You can choose from ski resorts, lakes and mountain villas, and city breaks. You can book online, but it is a confusing process.

Watersports

Offline surfing is now so mega that someone will soon decide it's the new rock 'n' roll. Meantime, feast your browsers on this little lot...

Diving Daisy

www.divingdaisy.freeuk.com
Strictly for the Newquay set. Busy blue and pink interface in the style of Miss Teenage fanzine reveals that it in fact sells only après scuba diving T-shirts. Buy direct by credit card, and if you order over four items you'll get a freebie. Less expensive than most surf shops at £25 and under, including delivery.

Jag Wet Suits

www.jagwetsuits.co.uk
Jag, one of the UK's biggest suppliers of all things neoprene, has outfits and accessories for every occasion. No cavorting babes here – just neat product illustrations with brief descriptions. Jag will ring/e-mail you for free (whether you live in Aruba, Ivory Coast or Zimbabwe) to answer any queries and take orders – or you can just go ahead and use your credit card.

Marine Products

www.marine-products.com
This Salt Lake City-based store ships international orders in five to 10 days. Shipping costs are calculated once you've ordered but nothing is charged to you unless you agree. More unusual items include water trampolines for $700.

Robin Hood Watersports

www.roho.co.uk
Despite the envy-inducing images of expert water babies, Robin Hood starts at the bottom of the ladder with Kayak Starter Packs for £299, and moves on to the radical wave boards with flashy designs and flashy prices, some over £1,000. If you're really keen, everything is delivered the next day for £7.50.

Simply Scuba

www.simplyscuba.co.uk
With dive equipment and courses to buy, news and reviews, Simply Scuba is as comprehensive as it gets. If you're new to the sport the review sections will tell you the difference between your Aqua-Lung and your Typhoon dry suit.

Weddings & Bar Mitzvahs

Big day approaching? Why not let the Web ease the strain of planning. There are loads of sites with plenty of cool goods from tiaras to furry handcuffs to make it a truly special event

 From stag/hen nights to rotating dresses

Alternative Gowns
www.alt-gowns.co.uk
An unusual venture selling alternative wedding dresses, evening gowns and bridal accessories from a variety of stores. You won't necessarily have heard of many of the makers but you'll get the basic idea of the gowns on offer with styles like Celtic, medieval and speciality couture from Yorkshire. Prices range from £100 to £1,000 so you won't break the bank. Not likely to suit every taste (PVC undies?) but useful if price and making a statement are your priorities.

Celtic Bride
www.celticbride.com
Items similar to that worn by Posh Spice herself on her wedding day with handcrafted Celtic style tiaras, crowns and jewellery items to add an extra slice of chic. Prices are £100 and £200, and orders can be confidently made online, with clear images and helpful descriptions so you know exactly what you're paying for. Bear in mind delivery can take up to three weeks.

Confetti
www.confetti.co.uk
Alongside the usual guff about etiquette, there's some cracking stuff here to calm a harassed bride. Our favourite is the rotating dresses section where you can see what a selection of gowns looks like from all angles before you try them on. There's also a selection of pretty and reasonably priced tiaras for those who are not fortunate to have a diamond one in the family, and jewellery thank-you gifts for bridesmaids. Truly a one-stop shop.

Hens and Stags
www.clickandbuild.com/cnb/shop/hensandstags
Online shop for party supplies aimed at hen parties and stag nights. Fake breasts, furry handcuffs, inflatable men and women – you get the drift. Delivery is £4 but be prepared to wait up to 14 days for your order to arrive.

Martha Stewart
www.marthastewart.com
Martha is the uncrowned US queen of the stylish wedding. Her website has a whole section devoted to wedding ideas (think discreet luxury rather than raucous knees-up). They ship internationally, but you have to phone the details of your order to the US to find out shipping costs.

Ultimate Wedding
www.ultimatewedding.com
Another online wedding mall from the US, with loads of fun products such as printed matchbooks or personalised champagne bottles filled with jellybeans. Overseas shipping is calculated separately on your order, depending on size.

Web Wedding
www.webwedding.co.uk
The gifts section is handily broken down into categories – mother of the bride, best man (lovely waistcoats) etc – with presents for everyone which can be gift-wrapped and delivered anywhere in the UK. But carriage charges are only calculated once you start ordering and can be hefty (£6.50 on a £40 order).

Wed Guide
www.wedguide.com
Fantastic prices on American wedding accessories such as bubble-blowers or car decorations. There are lots of things here that you won't find in the UK so it's worth the extra effort of calling in your order to check shipping details.

 **"Just one more for the album"**

Guild of Wedding Photographers
www.gwp-uk.co.uk
Advice on what to look for in a good photographer, plus contact details and links to Guild members.

Studio Images
www.studioimages.co.uk
Representing photographers all over the UK who specialise in modern wedding photography. There are loads of pictures to look through to help you choose, and an online request form for more information or contact details.

PIC Productions

www.pic.clara.net

These wedding videographers provide plenty of stills from actual wedding videos so that you can get a real idea of the coverage and service they offer.

 **Something different for your invitations**

ABC Publishers

www.shadicards.com

Suppliers of invitations and cards for Indian and Pakistani weddings, including Muslim, Hindu, and Sikh ceremonies, although many designs are suitable for non-Asian weddings too. There are lots of different designs, and insert paper is included in the price for you to print on your own printer (they even offer clip-art to download) or they can print the inserts for you at an extra cost.

ARTeMISS Design

www.artemissdesign.fsnet.co.uk

Easy to use with lots of photos of the designs, this is a great site for brides looking for something a bit different for their invitations. Cards are handmade using high-quality paper and fabrics, and a range of art techniques such as collage or watercolour. Fill in the order form and send it along with a deposit, and all you need to do is buy the stamps.

Big Leap Designs

www.bigleapdesigns.com

This is an impressive, bright and modern wedding invitation and thank-you card site. There are plenty of designs to choose from and they also do orders of service, candles, place cards, evening invitations and reply cards. The order form is comprehensive right down to the wording (don't worry – you will be sent a proof before they print) and the customer service is exemplary.

Wedding locations **And other unusual ideas**

County Marquees

www.countymarquee.co.uk

Home counties marquee hire for celebrations of all sizes. The site can be a bit slow but there are letters from satisfied clients and plenty of pictures on show.

Federation of Professional Toastmasters

www.federationtoastmasters.fsnet.co.uk

If you're planning a big do, consider hiring a toastmaster (generally a man with a moustache, red jacket and a loud voice) to keep things running smoothly.

For Better For Worse

www.forbetterforworse.co.uk

Directory for a wide variety of sites for UK civil weddings. There are stately homes, country house hotels and unusual venues such as football grounds.

The Occasional Poet

www.theoccasionalpoet.com

Commission a poem which is tailored to you and your intended's lives. Forty lines costs you $100 and will save anyone struggling to write personal vows.

Polhawn Fort

www.polhawn-fort.co.uk

For something extra special, why not hire a real-life fortress on the stunning Cornish coast? Available for weddings and receptions most of the year.

The Printed Candle Company

www.printedcandle.com

Candles of various shapes and sizes which can be printed with your names and wedding images, plus lots of gift ideas for bridesmaids. This US company will ship internationally, but allow at least six weeks for your order to arrive.

Bar & Bat Mitzvahs Make it a kosher event

Jewish.co.uk

www.jewish.co.uk

General site with a useful directory of specialist firms who supply invitations, photographers and kosher catering for a Bar or Bat Mitzvah celebration.

The Cake Company

www.thecakecompany.co.uk

This cake order service can design a kosher cake for any occasion. View the very elaborate examples to get your mouth watering. E-mail with inquiries.

Rosenblums World of Judaica

www.alljudaica.com

Original Bar and Bat Mitzvah gifts as well as supplies for the ceremony and books on Judaism can all be found on this US-based site. The site is secure, but for international orders you have to phone your order; delivery is via UPS.

Talit.com

www.jewishart.com

Online mall of Jewish products directly from Israel. Many items are handmade and holy products such as Talis are certified kosher. Prices are in US dollars but they ship anywhere; deliveries to the UK cost $12 and take eight days.

Weird stuff

Fear not, not every
Internet novelty has
to do with flatulence
or Bill and Monica.
Surf and ye shall
find – from a redneck
doll to a combined
telephone and blender…

Cattle Mutilation Shirts
www.ufoshirts.com
Tasteful T-shirts featuring a drawing of a cow with a bullet hole where part of
its midriff should be are just one of the highlights on this site. The designs
may be naff but at $15 a throw, these T-shirts are pretty cheap. If you need
extra protection from "government truth beams and cosmic rays", the
manufacturers advise you to line the shirts with aluminium foil. The aliens
have apparently made away with the 'add to basket' technology, instead you
have to fill in all the fields yourself and then send payment in US funds.

Demotivational calendars
www.despair.com/index2.html
For those who, like that supreme loafer Philip Larkin, don't want to let the
toad called work squat on their life and are proud of it, this is the ultimate site.
The online catalogue contains an amazing array of demotivational posters and
calendars, containing such perversely inspiring slogans as "If at first you don't
succeed, failure may be your style." Despair.com does ship outside the US for
a charge of $20 an order – almost worth it to buy the Pessimist's Mug which
comes complete with the recommendation: "This mug really makes everything taste bitter." Not to be missed.

Diving maps for the Red Sea
www.venus.co.uk/diveplan/intro.htm
Fancy diving in the Red Sea but scared that your lack of local knowledge will
let you down? Well, shed those fears and get ready to scuba because for £30
you can buy a dive plan pack which includes a 16-page guide describing
each site and incredibly detailed maps packed with such useful information
as "much small life".

E-mail the rest of the universe

www.messagetospace.com/index2.html

Sending a message into space could, the people at the Message to Space company politely suggest, release your inner self and enhance your creativity. Whether it does either, both or none of the above probably depends on the sender, but one thing's for certain: it will cost you $10.95 for a one-page message and $4.95 for each subsequent page.

Flightless fruit flies

http://drosophila.herpetology.com

Inspecting the shipping and returns policies of a site is usually the dullest part of online shopping but not here. To the FAQ "what is our liability?", the Drosophila Company (snappy motto: 'Flightless fruitflies for reptiles and amphibians') replies, "We only guarantee live delivery and you must notify us within 24 hours of any DOA vials." A vial contains 25 to 50 adult fruitflies, so if they are dead that's the fruitly equivalent of genocide. The company does deliver overseas but only if you order at least 100 cultures. Inviting 5,000 genetically impaired, biologically grounded fruitflies into your home doesn't sound that drastic. After all, they only live for 25 to 30 days (not good news if they get sent by surface mail by mistake). But they do spend most of that time breeding. So if you fancy having your pad taken over by thousands of sex-crazed, rotten-fruit gorging fruitflies which can't fly, this is for you.

Food-blender and telephone

www.cycoactive.com/blender/

It's a telephone and a food-blender all in one! This astonishing device comes complete with a testimonial from Bill Jenkins who bought it for a friend's wedding in Boulder, Colorado, and says: "It was incredible… the groom kept ringing it on his mobile all night… it was the only gift they carried home with them." If you think it's a tasteless wedding present, recall the Blendmaster's wise words: "It's their fault for getting married." This site is so well done that it's only when you e-mail for info that you're convinced it isn't a spoof.

Humorous underwear

www.cautionunderwear.com

Not even Kenny Everett's character Cupid Stunt would describe this site as "in the best possible taste". If men's boxer shorts decorated with a road sign which says "Slippery when wet" tickles your funny bone, this is for you.

A GOTTLE OF GEER!

If you harbour a secret desire to be Keith Harris (and your doctor, despite your increasingly desperate pleas, cannot suggest a cure) log on to www.axtell.com/vent.html.

- - - - - - - - - - - - - - - - -

All you really need is a Net-friendly computer, a cuddly toy to stick your hand up and a willingness to ignore your workmates as you mutter "Gottle of geer! Gottle of geer!" incoherently into your screen.

- - - - - - - - - - - - - - - - -

And remember, to slightly misquote an old cliché, on the Internet, no one can see your lips move.

Weird stuff

John Wayne Porcelain Doll
www.franklinmint.com
The John Wayne 'Little Duke' Baby Porcelain Collector Doll, created from a "rare treasured photograph of John Wayne as a baby" and wearing clothes inspired by his movies, is yours for just $135 here. At least you can't order online from the UK and the time expended in ringing up the London sales office should bring most people to their senses.

Nancy Sinatra fridge magnets
www.fridgedoor.com
Quite frankly your fridge isn't pulling its weight. Why should it be allowed to just sit there, big, white and blank, just keeping things cool when it could be contributing to the ambience of your palatial abode by wearing, for example, a tasteful Nancy Sinatra fridge magnet complete with red boots? These people "gladly accept international orders" which sounds a tad desperate.

Noble Title
www.elitetitles.co.uk
This site should probably be rechristened Fantasists 'R' Us. "C'mon ladies – for 200 smackers you can call yourself a marchioness!" It's the kind of offer even a certain sitcom market-trader might find a bit fishy but as the site says, a proper title would cost you £8,000 so by clicking the order form here, the aspiring noble can save £7,800! Of course, your reign as baron(ess) will not entitle you to the usual privileges: the right to pass this honour on to your offspring, or be thrown out of the House of Lords by New Labour. An off-the-shelf title could be yours in just 14 days, though a title with its own bit of land costs £995 and could take up to eight weeks for all the formal guff to go through. A small price to pay for ersatz nobility.

Robopup
http://store.yahoo.com/faoschwarz/493825.html
Dr Who fans still mourning the demise of the allegedly loveable robodog K9 may or may not find solace in this interactive puppy with the less-than-appealing name of Poo-Chi. This virtual pet thinks you were born to make him happy: the more you play with him the happier he gets. He's now developed into Super Poo-Chi, but will still play with regular Poo-Chis and other Robo-Chi pets. Just $49.95 and he promises not to soil the carpet.

Snowthrowers
www.cleanairgardening.com/
Snow-clearing is not a problem most of us have to grapple with on a regular basis, but if you're a sucker for the kind of American movie where Ma and Pa spend much of the screen time clearing away snow from their extravagantly proportioned house, then the Toro electric power curve 1200 snowthrower is yours for $270 (without shipping) – it's a cheaper way of getting in the mood than moving to Nebraska.

Redneck doll

www.spumco.com

From those terribly amusing people who brought you Ren and Stimpy comes the subversively named site, Spumco, probably the Web's finest cartoon show. Buy a George Liquor doll for just $34.95 plus $20 shipping and, the blurb promises: "He'll teach you to be a God-fearing American, no matter what foreign country you're from. Girls! Give one of these to your boyfriend. George will make a man out of him for you!" But

For that totally tasteless gift idea, check in to Spumco and be overwhelmed – or is that underwhelmed?

don't order in July because everyone in the studio store goes on holiday. All month.

Samurai-style helmet

www.majestic-n.com/

The place to go if you're willing to spend $235 on "an authentic style samurai helmet". (Note the careful interjection of the word "style" in that description.) If that doesn't tempt you, why not buy a fairy, gargoyle or a skull-shaped piggy-bank? The generous people from Majestic Novelties has also been known to give away stuff like a miniature barbarian axe, which is promoted with the slogan "Get them while they're hot!" Thankfully you need an ID and password to visit sister site SwordsRUs. No, we're not making this up.

Virtual makeover

www.compucloz.com

Digital makeovers sound deeply superficial but The Digital Looking Glass takes this subject very seriously indeed – it's the company's avowed aim to become the "dressing room of the digerati", courtesy of some clever software. Ignore all the corporate guff (this site is really aimed at retailers) and get a total head-to-toe makeover online today (for more on this and how you can create a 3D model of yourself, see page 103).

Woolly mammoth hair

www.twoguysfossils.com

Elton John need look no further for his next hair transplant. For $60 he can buy some two-million-year-old hair with one careless owner: a Siberian woolly mammoth. But hurry, Elton – there are only four samples left! Among the other prehistoric artefacts on this site are 1/10 scale models of tyrannosaurus rex, a sabre-toothed tiger's skull and what's left of a 36-million-year-old wolf spider. Two Guys Fossils does deliver overseas, although charges vary from $9-50.

White goods

Whether you've got a fridge that keeps the milk nicely lukewarm or you just blew up the oven, there are plenty of websites that can rescue you from any domestic crisis. There's even a site that will go comparison shopping for you

General | Because electrical shops are so dreary

Argos
www.argos.co.uk
Microwaves might be the largest household appliances on offer, but Argos' refreshingly vibrant design at least offers relief from the samey, white goods sites. Vacuum cleaners, microwaves and heaters online, along with smaller electrical accessories. Discounts are generally just a few pounds.

Benfleet Electronic Services
www.bes-direct.co.uk
BES sells everything from cookers and microwaves to fridges and freezers. The site is easy to navigate, but it is below par when it comes to providing additional info on each model. We had to try and guess what a Cannon Cambridge cooker with double slot oven looked like. Brands range from luxury Neff and Smeg items to high-street regulars Zanussi and Hotpoint.

Best Buy Appliances
www.best-buy-appliances.co.uk
This family-run business guarantees a 110 per cent refund of the difference if you find a purchased item cheaper elsewhere within seven days. There are all the top brands in kitchen and home appliances and everything is delivered free. The catalogue contains more items than you'll generally find on the high street, with the American section with walk-in fridges a real winner.

Comet

www.comet.co.uk

Cookers, fridges, washer-dryers – all the usual wares.
Delivery for these is charged at £11.95 and there's a
handy Sunday delivery for only £3 more. The best
prices are not the best on the Net but Comet is a
name that won't disappear overnight and you can
complain in person if things go wrong.

Co-op

www.electrical.coop.co.uk

This site has a stylish design with fast connection to
the sub-categories and a search facility for cooking,
cooling and washing appliances. The e-Co-op
undercuts the bricks-and-mortar stores by around £50
in most cases and has all the big names like Dyson.
Delivery is set at £11.95.

Electrical Direct

www.electricaldirect.co.uk

Hundreds of pounds worth of discounts across the
board here. What's more, if you take a few minutes to
join their Privilege Club you can benefit from even
cheaper prices. The search categories offer the neat
advantage of listing their findings by brand or price.

Empire Direct

www.empiredirect.co.uk

Still one of the most comprehensive electrical stores on the Net, Empire
completes its catalogue with as many lily-white home appliances as you
could possibly want but if you're looking for the best deal we suggest you
set time aside for some serious browsing. Descriptions are brief, but every
item is listed at a discount price, with hundreds of pounds off in many cases.

Farthing and Short

www.farthingandshort.com

This site has a phenomenal selection of goods – 143 dryers when we visited.
Even better, the designers have made it idiot-proof – just about every
question is addressed and contact details are prominently displayed, along
with info on energy ratings and how to be environmentally friendly. A jargon
buster section helps with the specs. Delivery is included in the price.

Freenet

www.freenet.ltd.uk

You may well be thinking "bargain basement" as the shocking-yellow
homepage hits you in the face, but discounts are few. The sub-categories get

as detailed as slimline dryers and electric slot-in ovens, so you don't need to waste time browsing, but you still have to make your choice based on brief descriptions and small images. Good if you know what you want.

Home Electrical Direct

www.hed.co.uk

Free delivery and a buy-now, pay-nine-months-later option from this friendly site. The spec sheets are brief but adequate, including images of each item with its own individual order form. The price listings aren't backed up by high-street comparisons but you'll already know these if you've shopped around.

Miller Bros

www.millerbros.co.uk

Nothing special, but worth a look for discounts on many top-name brands including Zanussi, Belling, AEG and Ariston. If you have time to spare then browse the catalogue sub-sections; if you know what you want search by brand or product. Delivery, which should take four days, is a flat-rate £10.

Buy, buy, buy White goods put to the test

Traipsing around an electrical superstore does not equal a quality Saturday afternoon in most people's book. However, even though the Internet offers massive savings on electrical goods, people are still nervous of buying a brown or white good over the value of £10 without actually seeing it. In a perfect world, of course, you eye up your goods in a normal shop and then order online – easy and the best of both worlds. However, what if you see a bargain online – and we're talking £300-plus reduction – and need to act then and there to secure the deal? Can you satisfy yourself of the product's suitability by looking at a screen?

Despite technology being able to do wonderful things with 3-D graphics, most brown and white goods sites rely on a piece of specification and a 2D photo, often of dubious quality, to show off their wares. It helps if you're buying from a manufacturer whose product line you know and like since there will be inevitable similarities in styling and finish. One of our online shoppers wanted to complete their Baumatic kitchen by shopping online and saved over £500 on the collective RRPs of a washing machine and an extractor fan at www.qed-uk.com. There were no nasty surprises when the goods arrived because they had the same distinctive styling as the rest of the range.

If you've any doubts about the spec, call the site. We nearly bought a Siemens washing machine, which the QED site implied was stainless steel all over. We found it was the porthole door that was stainless steel not the casing and a kitchen design disaster was averted. QED's Customer service was knowledgeable and guided us to another machine.

Plugged In
www.pluggedin.co.uk
If this online version of Northern Electric wasn't so slow, they could be on to a winner but product guides and shopping tips are on hand to help you make an informed choice. They don't always knock the socks off their competitors in terms of price, but the additional information is alone worth a look.

QED
www.qed-uk.com
A web designer out there is having a laugh. Exactly the same site design as Miller Bros, same products and same layout, but with different prices. QED, however, should be your first port of call as the site offers hundreds of pounds in discounts and free delivery.

SLB
www.slb.co.uk
Not the most appealing of sites to look at or search, just keep telling yourself everything listed is at trade price or less, so you're bound to be able to find a bargain or two. Descriptions are brief, if not non-existent, but it's worth a look if you're looking for an unbeatable price on a specific model.

Value Direct
www.value-direct.co.uk
The clear navigation lets you make your search as simple or as detailed as you like, but it's best to use the step-by-step approach as it took this reviewer several attempts at narrowing down the criteria enough to find any results. The price comparison tool is also helpful when checking off what each model can do. Buying is simple and you can spread your payments over two years.

We Sell It
www.we-sell-it.co.uk
Wordy and jumbled, We Sell It is nevertheless recommended for its range of ever-trendy Smeg appliances. Fridges, freezers and cookers are all available: read the specs and place your order. Delivery is free if it's more than £200 – and you're not likely to get a Smeg for much less.

These sites are also worth checking out:
www.tempo.co.uk
Tempo
www.bedirect.co.uk
Be Direct
www.easybuyappliances.co.uk
Easy Buy Appliances

Small appliances

Americana From The Heart

http://shop.store.yahoo.com/americanafromtheheart

This site deserves an honorary mention even though it sells ironing boards not irons. Americana makes the kind of schmaltzy all-American kind of products which are designed to leave a hole in the wallet and a lump in the throat of any right-thinking American. Their ironing board is described as "America with birdhouses" but you have to see it on screen to gauge the full scale of the atrocity. Americana From The Heart does deliver to the UK and there's also a lighthouse themed board. It says supply is limited. Right. As in "limited to the number we can sell".

KITCHEN SINKS

That ultimate kitchen item, the much-thrown sink, is the house speciality at In-Sinks. Browse through luscious stainless steel, granite and ceramic designs you won't find at MFI. The designer brands, including Kohler, Luisina and Blanco, may not mean anything to those who aren't fanatical about doing the dishes but they are luxury additions to any kitchen.

Prices range from £200 to £800 including delivery, which should take three to five days.

----

www.kitchen-sinks.co.uk

Global Power

www.globalpower.co.uk

It isn't immediately obvious what Global Power sells. You need to focus on the image bar surrounding the picture of the helpful sales assistant to enter the shop. Once in, you'll find a limited range of white goods and a comprehensive store of smaller appliances including coffee-makers, toasters and kettles. Standard £20 white models are included alongside such luxurious items as a Delonghi espresso and cappuccino-maker for £90 and the ultimate toaster for £165. Buying is simple.

Ifex

www.ifexonline.com

You have to scroll through the list of items at this online department store until you reach Kitchen Appliances. Everything looks the same so far, but Ifex sells some of the more unusual white goods around. Do you have a burning need for a crumb vacuum? There's a Guzzini model for £16.95. Or, you could buy the ultimate American appliance, the waffle iron, selling at a slightly pricier £280, and well-heeled margarita drinkers will be thrilled with a £428 Dualit ice crusher.

Priceright

www.priceright.co.uk

The yellow and mint-green design of this site co-ordinates well with the appliances sold within. According to the site's sales spiel, their limited catalogue of stock means that selling is based on a first-come, first-served basis, but this seems less than convincing and most shoppers will be able to cope by searching elsewhere. Toasters, kettles etc can work out as much as £20 to £30 cheaper than the high street and, if you become a member, you can benefit from an extra five per cent discount off your online purchases.

Vacuum cleaners Dust bunnies beware

Dyson

www.dyson.co.uk

Dyson is the must-have fashion accessory and when you're through with this stylish site you'll know everything there is to know about vacuum cleaners. You can read all the specs to learn what the funny nozzles do, and buy, or not. The shopping cart symbol is there but it's not clear how to add to it.

Hoover

www.hoover.co.uk

You can't buy Hoovers from here but the riveting explanation of its Triple Vortex cleaning system with "continuous triple section power 300 G-force" is a must read. You need to have Flash to be treated to the fastest moving animation this side of *The Simpsons* only without the humour or the content.

Unbeatable

www.unbeatable.co.uk

Another one of those sites to aim for if you know exactly what you're looking for down to the model number, and are simply searching for the best price. Descriptions and images are close to non-existent but a large selection means prices range from under £50 to in excess of £200.

Vacuum Cleaners Direct

www.vacuumcleanersdirect.co.uk

Using the product-search wizard you can make your search as simple or as comprehensive as you like, down to your upright or canister preferences, attachments and price limit. This site is good for specialist models, wet-and-dry, three-in-one, four-in-one and so on.

Vacuum World

www.vacuumworld.co.uk

Find tools, bags, belts and rollers to fit your machine from the biggest range of vacuum-cleaner accessories online. Just select the brand and scroll away.

Wines and Spirits

Fed up with carting all those clinking bottles back from the supermarket? Get someone else to do it for you with these wine and spirits delivery sites that offer everything from an amusing little Pinot Noir to a hardman-humbling tequila. Now we just need someone to take care of all the empties...

Wines Far too good to drink out of a bag

Alexander Dunn

www.alexanderdunn.uk.com

Celebrating an anniversary or looking for a present for your fussy uncle? Here's your answer: personalised wine gift sets, port or champagne. A calligrapher will hand-inscribe the name and message on the label. The wines and spirits are good to vintage quality, and shipping is included in the price.

Allez Vins

www.allezvins.co.uk

Blissfully easy-to-use site from this French regional wine specialist with clear instructions and no having to search around for information on products and services. Allez Vins imports wine directly, mostly from smaller vineyards, so it's a very good place to look for something you may not be able to find at the usual high-street outlet. They try to use their own vans, so delivery might take four weeks, although urgent orders can be dealt with, and it's free within many postcodes. If you live outside those areas though, it will cost you £6.50.

Berry Bros & Rudd

www.bbr.co.uk

Can you serve red wine with salmon? Well, yes, as long as it's dry and fruity like the selection recommended here in the hugely useful food and wine matching section. This is a top class wine merchant where you can find delicious vintages or simply outstanding everyday wines, as well as learn more about your choices and the site's own recommendations before you buy. A great place for people who would like to drink better. Delivery costs £7.50 for orders under £100, free over that, and your order should be with you in six working days.

Buy Wine Online

www.buywineonline.co.uk

Outstanding prices on good wine delivered right to your door. Plenty of choice to make up your own case or you can follow the experts and buy a ready-made selection. The wine advice section is a good overview of the mysteries of wine appreciation and should help you understand which wines you may prefer. There's secure credit card ordering or send a cheque if you can wait the seven days for it to clear. Delivery is within five days and will cost you just £4.95.

Champagne Bubbles

www.champagne-bubbles.com

Champagne can often be a tricky thing to buy as only those in the more exclusive wealth category, and the celeb It girl of the moment, know whether a bottle of Bolly is still the drink to be seen with. This site won't provide you with a chic tutorial but you can at least select from the top brands at reasonable prices.

Discount Champagne

www.discount-champagne.com

Good champagne, including a number of vintages, sold in cases at knock-down prices. The site is basic, as is the customer service set-up, but all this means is that their overheads are low and the savings are passed on to the customer. Case prices include delivery to the UK mainland.

True joy can be experienced with the right bubbly. Here you'll find the big-name brands at decent prices

Wines & spirits

Drink Finder

www.drinkfinder.co.uk

If your chosen tipple is whisky or wine you'll love this site, with hundreds of bottles from around the world to choose from. Whatever your drink however, you'll be hard-pressed to find better-stocked shelves, with a price to suit every budget. Delivery is charged at £6.50 no matter how full your shopping basket is.

Grapeland UK

www.grapeland.uk.com

This Hertfordshire-based venture offers a great range of wines from around the globe. Select a region, Chile, South Africa and France included, to view simple yet effective descriptions that won't make you think you're about to buy a bottle of perfume or furniture polish rather than the finest Chardonnay. Prices start at around £5 a bottle, but you do need to purchase by the case, which you can mix yourself. Handy wine guides are also promised for the future. A good simple site.

Hot Wines

www.hotwines.co.uk

An amusing cartoon opens this site, which claims to have all the wines featured in stock. That meant 161 reds when we visited, ranging in price from £7.49 all the way to a level probably best-described as budget-blowing. Bottles are clearly illustrated for you label fans, and brief but relevant info like best serving temperature and top flavour are noted. Free delivery when you order a case or more.

Laithwaites

www.laithwaites.co.uk

Formerly Bordeaux Direct, this site actually sells wines from all over the world. Savings of more than £20 are offered on their mixed cases and there's an intriguing magical mystery section where you can buy random mixed cases for £30 off the original price. If you don't like the wine, for whatever reason, they will replace it or give you a refund. A user-friendly site that aims to take the fear out of buying wine.

Mad About Wine

www.madaboutwine.com

Good selection of worldwide wines with a range of prices from a Cuvée de Vignerons Blanc at £3.69 to a bottle of 1905 Sauternes for £5,351.59. Their mixed cases, like Party Solutions, are good value and make it easy for those in a hurry and you can e-mail the site's experts for advice. They also sell a limited range of beers and spirits. There's a useful freight calculator for you to check delivery charges before you put anything in your basket (it's one of the few sites that can send wine overseas) but UK delivery seems to come out at £4.99 no matter what the number of bottles.

Rouge & Blanc
www.rouge-blanc.com
This French-based site sells wine from all over the world and offers plenty of advice and special offers for the unsure. The bargains section has some excellent everyday drinking tips on offer, or you could consult their wedding service if you need advice on what to serve on your big day. Try ordering in French to get into the mood. All orders cost £3.99 for delivery and will be with you in three working days.

Stanley Ball
www.stanley-ball.co.uk
Independent wine merchant selling a range of wines which can be labelled to suit the customer. There's an online form for further enquiries.

Sunday Times Wine Club
www.sundaytimeswineclub.co.uk
Considering a) their status, and b) their popularity, *The Sunday Times* wine club website couldn't have been more of a disappointment – it was last year and doesn't seem to have improved. The technical hitches may yet improve, but still having blank or flickering pages where luscious wines should be is

And for the morning after "Aaarghhh!"

Ever since man first woke up with a mouth that felt like it had been cleaned with a toilet brush, he's been searching for the ultimate answer to the morning after. Here's what the online gurus recommend:

Estronaut
www.estronaut.com/a/hangovers.htm
Prevention intervention and cures – alcohol advice for women who can't remember how they got home.

Sob'r – K
www.hangoverstopper.com
Miracle pills said to cure even the hairiest of hangovers. Only drawback is that you have to remember to take them while you're still drinking…

Wrecked
www.wrecked.co.uk
Prevention being better than cure, one look at this drinking information site will put you off the sauce for life. Go on, have a peek, you owe it to your liver.

not a good start, and on catching a glimpse of what they do have on offer the disappointment continues. The word 'Club' implies a vast selection of wines but the best buys section limited the buys to around three case choices at the most. Prices are good going on their newspaper supplements, but definite attention is needed here.

Vinceremos

www.vinceremos.co.uk

Specialising in organic wines and spirits, Vinceremos offers a large selection of vintages, with everything from Hungarian to Portuguese. Sold by the case, prices are good for specialised choices and such a vast selection ensures every palate is catered for, unless you're feeling patriotic – the English section was empty on our last visit. The owners have got their act together and all information pages seem complete. You buy by the case and UK mainland is £5.95. Order more than five cases and they'll refund your card.

Wine Today

www.winetoday.com

News, reviews and advice on building a cellar or becoming a wine connoisseur from this comprehensive appreciation site. There's no online shop here, but plenty of links to individual vineyards around the world as well as merchants selling wine and wine accessories online.

Wychwood Wines

www.wychwoodwines.co.uk

The homepage tells you everything you need to know about this importer who concentrates on wines from small vineyards all over the world. Argentina, Chile and South Africa are represented along with the more traditional wine countries, and most bottles are reasonably priced between £4 and £10. They encourage feedback and offer a case of wine every quarter to the most constructive comment. Deliveries cost £6 but are free on orders over £150.

Vegans will be delighted with this site which offers a good selection that will meet their requirements

 **Make mine a double**

Black Mountain Liqueur
www.celticspirit.co.uk
And people say there isn't anything to do in Wales.
Black Mountain Liqueur is a traditional cordial that is
brewed in the Wye valley from local apples and
blackcurrants and packs a comforting punch served
after meals or over ice. Bottles cost £12 each and
delivery is free within the UK.

Drinx
www.drinx.com
If it's got alcohol in it, you'll probably find it here. The
wine choice is limited and prices are not much
cheaper than those you will find on the high street,
but there are some reasonable bargains to be had in
the house wines section. The spirits section is more
comprehensive, with even a section devoted to fruit
schnapps for the very brave. Delivery costs £5.50 for
an order of any size and your goods will be with you
in two to three days.

Drinks Express
www.drinks.co.uk
Aiming to be to drinks what Interflora is to flowers,
this is a convenient site from which to order alcoholic
gifts. Choose from a decent selection of spirits and
wines, add a personal message and the grateful
recipient will be sipping contendedly within 24 hours.

Marchents
www.marchents.com
General fine foods site, also offering a fine, if limited,
selection of liqueurs. You won't find any of your average supermarket variety
aperitifs here, with vintage cider brandy, and fruit liqueurs only. Prices are
fortunately on the friendlier side of exclusive, items delivered within 48 hours.

Whisky Shop
www.whiskyshop.com
From familiar blends to rare single malts (how about a bottle of 40-year-old
Bowmore for £4,000?), this site will keep any whisk(e)y drinker more than
happy. It's well-designed with lots of info on the products and how to shop.
Delivery is calculated when you order and starts at £6.50.

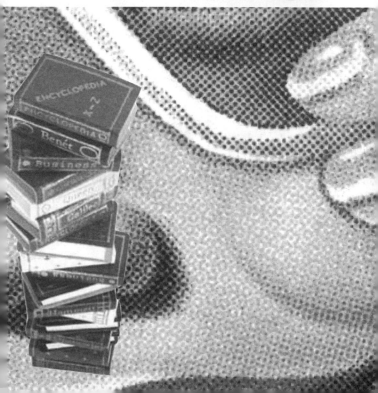

Part Three

Stuff that doesn't fit anywhere else, like the glossary and index

REFERENCE

What (most of) the boring technical words really mean

GLOSSARY

Access Provider

Company which sells Internet connections, more usually known as an Internet Service Provider (hence the initials ISP)

Acrobat Reader

Stand-alone program or web browser plug-in from Adobe that lets you view a PDF file in its original format and appearance. The Acrobat Reader is free and some online stores will let you download their catalogues as PDF files.

Address

The identifier to access a site: http://www.roughguides.com (see URL).

AltaVista

Search engine at www.altavista.com

Applet

Small (Java) program embedded in an HTML page. When you open that web page, the browser downloads the applet and runs it on your computer. Don't worry – applets cannot read or write data on to your computer. Applets only work if the browser you're using supports Java.

AUP – Acceptable Use Policy

AUP is a policy for the use of the Internet laid down by an organisation. Some companies (including your own) may use a AUP filter to exclude some Internet services for staff. Parents can also set AUP limits to block certain sites.

Attachment

A file included with e-mail. If, for example, you bought insurance online you would probably get a file confirming the policy attached to the return e-mail.

Autoresponder

A software program running on a computer server. If someone sends an e-mail to an autoresponder's e-mail address, the autoresponder automatically e-mails this person an answer (for example: "Thank you for your message. I will reply shortly"), and sends the incoming message on.

Banner

An advertisement, in the form of a graphic image on the Web, usually found at the top of a web page. Most banner ads are animated GIFs.

Bookmark

Netscape browser feature which lets you save a link to a web page in a list so you can revisit it easily. In Explorer, the same feature is called a Favourite.

Bot

Virtual robots which behave like search engines, only instead of finding the best web pages they find products you have told them you want to buy.

Bps – Bits Per Second

A measure of how fast data is moved from one place to another, normally in thousands of bits per second (Kbps) or millions of bits per second (Mbps). A 56K modem can transport 56,600 bits per second.

Broadband

Rapid Internet access.

Browser – Web Browser

The software program which allows you to surf the Web. At this moment in cyberhistory, almost everyone uses Internet Explorer or Netscape Navigator.

Browsing

What you do when you visit the Internet, aka surfing.

Cache

Computer memory or directory on your hard disk where your browser stores the web pages you have most recently visited.

Clicks 'n' mortar, aka clicks 'n' bricks

Any store which sells products online and offline.

Client/Server

A client is a computer system that requests a service of another computer system (a server) on a network.

Compression

Technology that reduces the size of a file in order to transfer it rapidly.

Cookie

The small text file that a web server sends to your computer hard disk via your browser. Cookies contain information such as log-in and registration information, shopping cart information and preferences etc.

Cyberspace

The term first coined by the science-fiction writer William Gibson to describe the virtual world which exists within the marriage of computers, telecommunication networks and digital media.

Data encryption key

String of characters used to encode a message. This encoded message can only be read by someone with another related key.

DNS – Domain Name Server or Domain Name System

A Domain Name Server maps IP numbers to a more easily remembered name. When you type http://www.roughguides.com into your browser, the DNS searches for a matching IP address. If the DNS doesn't find an entry in its database, it will ask other DNSes until the entry is found, and you will see the Rough Guides site. Otherwise, you'll get an error message.

Domain name

A unique name which identifies an Internet site. A domain name points to one specific server, while this server may host many domain names. If you look at the URL for the page you called up above, you'll see www.roughguides. com at the beginning – "roughguides.com" is our domain name.

Download

What happens when a web page comes up on your screen. You can use your browser or File Transfer Protocol program to download files to your computer.

E-commerce

Selling goods or services over the Internet. Customers choose what they want to buy (often using a virtual shopping cart) and then type their credit card details into a secure payment form on the site.

E-mail

Electronic mail which is sent and received via the Internet.

Encryption

Technology which scrambles the contents of a file before sending it over the Internet. The recipient must have software to decrypt this file. If you want to transmit 'hot stuff' like credit card information, you have to use some form of encryption. PGP (Pretty Good Privacy) is one such encryption program.

Enonymous

Download for the PC which reads a site's request for personal information and sends an immediate enquiry to its database to check the site's privacy policy rating. Information is then sent back to your terminal in real time.

Excite

Search engine at www.excite.com

FAQ – Frequently Asked Questions

You will find one of these on most shopping websites you visit. A FAQ is simply a file which is supposed to contain answers to the most commonly asked questions on a particular subject.

Favourite

The Explorer equivalent to a Netscape Communicator Bookmark.

File

Anything stored on a computer, like an image, text or a program.

Firewall

Internet security which defends a Local Area Network against hackers.
Hardware and software combine to act as a firewall to divide the LAN into two
parts. Normal data is available outside the firewall, while secret squirrel stuff is
kept inside the firewall. A firewall can also be designed by a company to make
sure that, for example, you cannot buy products from your computer at work.

Flash

Software plug-in which adds interactivity and brings animation to web pages.

Frame

Technology which allows web designers to break the browser window into
several smaller windows, each of which can load different HTML pages.

GIF – Graphics Interchange Format

A compressed graphic format used widely on the Net. Mostly used to show
clip-art images (photographic images are usually in a format called JPEG).
The GIF 89a standard permits the use of multiple images in a single file, and
many online shops will use a GIF file to show some animation on their website.

Hacker

Someone who breaks through computer security strictly for the fun of doing
so. If someone does it with criminal intent they are called a cracker.

Hit

A single request from a browser to a server. Some servers also count each
graphic on that page as a hit. This is why the boast that X site has Y million
hits a month is now a devalued way of measuring a website's popularity.

Homepage

The main page of a website. The term is also applied to any website,
typically created by a private individual, which only has one page.

Host

The server on which a website is stored. Hosting companies store websites of
their customers on powerful web servers (with fast, permanent connections to
the Internet) so, theoretically, you should always be able to access the page
you want, providing the owner has not taken it down (off the Web).

HTML

Hyper Text Mark-Up Language. In simple terms, this is the language used
to create web documents.

Hyperlink

A highlighted word (or graphic) within a web page (technically, these pages are described as hypertext documents). When you click a hyperlink, it will take you to another place within that page, or to another page on the Net.

Hypermedia

Pictures, videos, and audio on a web page that act as hyperlinks.

Hyperspace

Less commonly used variant of cyberspace.

Hypertext

Text that includes links to other web pages. By clicking on a link, the reader can jump straight from one web page to another related page.

Internet Explorer

Web browser from Microsoft.

IP – Internet Protocol

The rules that provide basic Internet functions. Without IP, computers would not be able to find each other.

IP address

A unique 32-bit Internet address consisting of four numbers, separated by dots and sometimes called a 'dotted quad'. Every server – connected to the Internet – has an IP number. The Domain Name Server converts this number into the domain name.

iPrivacy

Software download which brings anonymity to online shoppers. Personal information is stored, allowing you to surf privately. When buying it generates unique information for each purchase, keeping your actual details hidden.

ISP – Internet Service Provider

Most common usage is the same as Access Provider. But it also means any company that provides Internet services such as website development.

Java

A platform-independent programming language invented by Sun Microsystems, used by web developers to create applets. Java-enabled web pages can include animations, calculators, scrolling text, sound effects and even games. Although many web designers like Java, many people using the Web surf with a Java-disabled browser because they don't want to wait until some applet is entirely loaded into their browser. It's not uncommon when accessing a website to get a pop-up box full of numbers and code headlined "Java error messages". Don't worry – this doesn't mean your terminal is crashing. Just click on the box to shut it and keep on browsing.

JPEG – Joint Photographic Experts Group

Image compression standard, optimized for full-colour (millions of colours) digital images. You can choose the amount of compression, but the higher the compression rate, the lower quality the image. Virtually every full-colour photograph you see on the Web is a JPEG file.

Link

Marked text (usually underlined) or picture within a web page. With one click of your mouse, a link takes you to another web page (or to another place on the same page). Depending on the type of file, when you click on a link it will be retrieved and displayed, played or downloaded.

Log in

Entering into a computer system. Also the account name (or user ID) you must enter before you can access some computer systems. Many websites ask you to log in before viewing their pages. Before you do, it's worth checking what the site's policy on privacy is. You don't want to give your e-mail address to a company which is going to pass it on.

MBNA Wallet

Shopping service from the MBNA Bank designed to ease shopping online by taking care of form filling, password management and privacy protection.

Mirror or mirror site

More or less an exact copy of another site. Mirror sites are created when too many people want to access the original site. If buying goods from a global company you may be pointed to the mirror site nearest to you to make it quicker for you to access the pages.

Modem

Abbreviation of MOdulator-DEModulator. A modem allows computers to send information to each other on ordinary telephone lines.

MP3 or MPEG 3

A compressed musical format (see www.mp3.com) which enables you to download music to your computer from the Internet.

My Points

Online shopping incentive program which allows you to collect cyber points while you shop which can used to buy goods from participating stores. Others include Beenz (www.beenz.com) and Netflip (www.netflip.com).

Navigator

Netscape's web browser.

Page

One single document on the Internet.

Patch

A temporary or interim add-on which fixes or upgrades software. Often available from the suppliers for free. For example, iMac users can download a free patch designed to manage modem communications somewhat better.

PDF – Portable Document Format

A file format created by Adobe (see Acrobat Reader) designed to make sure the file can be read on different computer platforms. Created for offline reading of brochures, reports and documents with complex graphic design. When you download a PDF file, you get the whole document in a single file.

PGP – Pretty Good Privacy

Program, developed by Phil Zimmerman, which protects files from being read by others. You can also use PGP to attach a digital signature to a file to prove you are the sender.

Plug-in

Small piece of software, usually from a third-party developer, which adds new features to another (larger) software application. When visiting sites, you may often be asked to plug in programs like Flash or RealAudioPlayer. Downloading these packages can be time-consuming so decide whether it's worth it. There is also a risk that a plug-in may carry a virus.

Portal

A website which attracts visitors by offering free information, or free services. When you are on a portal site, you can use this site as a base from which to explore the Web. The most famous portals are the major search engines.

Protocol

A set of rules and conventions that describes the behaviour which computers must follow in order to understand each other.

Search engine

Website which allows you to search for keywords to find relevant web pages. rather than having to know the specific web address. Every search engine has its own strategy for collecting data, which is why one particular search produces different results on different search engines.

Secure-It-e

Credit card protection service which, for a base price of $4.99, will handle all disputes with online merchants, banks and legal authorities to recover money after any fraudulent online purchases.

Server

A (powerful) computer that has a permanent connection to the Internet. Websites are stored on a web server.

Site
A place on the Web. Refers to a homepage or to a collection of web pages.

Snail mail
Mail delivered to your door by the mailman instead of being delivered to your computer by a network.

Spam
Junk e-mail, considered a serious breach of netiquette.

SSL – Secure Sockets Layer
Protocol that allows encrypted messages to pass across the Internet. SSL uses public key encryption to pass data between your browser and a given server (for example, to submit credit card information). A URL that begins with 'https' indicates that an SSL connection will be used. In Netscape, you can also check if a site you are using is secure – look for a gold padlock at the bottom of your window of the site to which you are sending your details.

Surfer
Slightly passé version of browser.

Time out
When you request a web page and the server that hosts the web page doesn't respond within a certain amount of time, you may get the message "connection timed out". Try again immediately if it's urgent. If not, leave it five minutes. If it persists, the site may be down temporarily or permanently.

URL – Uniform Resource Locator
Web address. Our homepage's URL is: http://www.roughguides.com

User ID
Unique identifier that you must enter every time you want to access a particular service on the Internet. The user ID is always accompanied by a password.

Webmaster
The person responsible for the web server (usually the system administrator).

World Wide Web
Hence the WWW bit. Graphic and and text documents published on the Internet interconnected through clickable 'hypertext' links.

XML
eXtensible Mark-up Language, to give its its full name, is a new language for writing web pages. It's more flexible than HTML, is already running alongside it and may eventually replace it.

Yahoo!
Search engine at www.yahoo.com

INDEX

Absinthe 343
All the Web 39
Alta Vista 39
Alternative Therapies 200
Amazon 10
Antiques 46-48
Art 49-54
    Artists 51
    Auctions 30-32
    Museum shops 235-236
    Posters & prints 53-54
    Virtual galleries 52
Ask Jeeves 39
Auctions 25-32
    Auctions (specialist) 32

Baby 55-59
Bar Mitzvahs 327
Bathrooms 226-227
Beauty 61-64
Beer 65-66
Bikes 67-68
Boats 69
Books 70-77
    E-books 73
    General 70-72
    Poetry 77
    Specialist 74-76

    Used 76-77
Boots and shoes 277-279
Browsers 10
Buying 9-18
Buying from abroad 33-37

Cameras 78-81
Cards 159
Cars 82-85
Catalogues (Clothing) 92-95
CDs 263-276
Celebrities 86-87
Charity 187
Chocolates and sweets 88-89
Clothing 90-107
    Accessories 91
    Catalogues 92-95
    Children's 95-97
    Designer 98-99
    General 90
    High Street 100-101
    Labels 101-104
    Menswear 104-105
    Ties 91
    Underwear 105-107
Coffee 108-109
Collectibles 110-115
    General 110-111

Index

Coins 111-112
Memorabilia 113, 115
Prince Charles 114
Comics 116-117
Competitions 44
Computer games 118-127
Games without guns 119
General 118-119
High Street 120-122
Online retailers 122-126
Specialist 126-127
Computers 128-135
Accessories 133
Apple 130
General 128-129
Novelties 130
PCs 131-134
PDAs 134-135
Price comparisons 134
Reviews 135
Software 242
Condoms 207
Consumer advice 18, 21-24
Cosmetics 63
Crafts 136-137
Credit card advice 18, 23
Custom charges 34

Decorating 222-223
Delivery 14-17
Department stores 140-141
Diabetic foods 177-179
Directories 39-40
DIY 222-223
Dot.com 20
Drugs 142-146
General 142-144
Brands 145-146

Medical advice 146
Online prescriptions 145
DVDs 154

eBay 30
Eco products 147-148
Educational 149-151

Fashion 90-107
Film 152-156
General 152-155
Specialist 155-156
Firewalls 20
Fishing 157-158
Fitness 200-207
Flowers 160
Food 165-180
Britgrub 174
Eating out 165
Hampers 168
General 165
Organic 166-169
Special diets 169-171
Specialty 171-176
Supermarkets 176-179
Sweet things 179-180
Takeaway 180
Fragrances 64
Fraud 18, 29
Free stuff 185-187
Furniture 223-225
Future of online shopping 8

Gadgets 188-191
Games, computer 118-127
Games, traditional 192-193
Gardens 194-197
Getting started 9-11

Gifts 161-164
Golf 198-199
Google 39
Group buying 41-42

Hangover cures 341
Health 200-207
  Alternative therapies 200-201
  Fitness 201-202
  Health stores 202-207
  Quacks 207
Help 13
Hi-fi 208-211
  General 208-210
  In-car 210-211
  MP3 players 211
  Radios 211
Hobbies 212-213
Home 214 227
  Accessories 214-218
  Bathrooms 226-227
  Catalogues 219-220
  Contemporary design 220-221
  Decoration and DIY 222-223
  Furniture 223-225
  General 214
  Inspiration 225
  Kitchen 226-227
How to find what you want 38-44

Islands 6, 259-260

Jewellery 228-230

Kelkoo 41
Kitsch gadgets 191

Magazines 231-232

Maternity 60
Menswear 91, 104-105
Motorbikes 233-234
Museum shops 235-236
Music 237-239
  Instruments 237-238
  Sheet music 239

Net stuff 240-241
  E-greetings 240
  Screen 240-241
  Software 241
North Korea 315

Office supplies 242-243
Organic food 166-169
Outdoor 244-247
  Climbing 245

Parties 248-250
  General 248-249
  Hired help 249-250
  Themes 250
Payments 13-14
Pets and pet supplies 251-252
Pharmacies 142-144
Phones 253-256
  Brands 253
  Networks 253-254
  Novelties 254
  Re-sellers 254, 256
  WAP 255
Poetry 77
Posters & Prints 53-54
Precautions 22-24
Presley, Elvis 86, 265, 359
Price comparison 18, 39-41
Privacy policy 12-13

Index

Property 257-262
  Buying & Selling 257-259
  Finance 259-261
  Unusual 261-262
Pros & Cons of online shopping 7

Radios 211
Rail travel 313
Records 263-276
  General 263-269
  MP3 270-271
  Specialist 271-276
  Used 276
Reviews 42-44

Saving money 7-8
Searches 38-39
Secure server 13
Security 13-15, 19-24
Selling 27-28
Shoes 277-279
Shopping bots 40-41
Snow sports 280-285
  Skiing 280-283
  Snowboarding 283-285
Spirits 343
Sports goods 204, 286-293
  Footwear 288
  General 286-287
  Specialist 288-292
  Sportswear 292-293
Stamps 111-112
Stars 161

Tea 108-109
Television 294-298
  General 294-298
  Satellite 298

Tickets 299-302
Toys 303-308
  General 303-305
  Modern 305-306
  Traditional 306-308
  Up to toddlers 308
Travel 309-322
  Accommodation 316-319
  Advice 318
  All-in-ones 311-312
  Car hire 321
  Flights 314, 316
  General 309-311
  Independents 319-321
  Insurance 310
  Rail 313
  Sea 313
  Winter 322

Underwear 105-107

Vacuum cleaners 337
VAT and tax 33-37
Video machines 294-298
Videotape 153

Watches 230
Watersports 323
Weddings 324-327
  General 324-325
  Photos and video 325-326
  Stationery 326
  Wedding locations 326-327
Weird stuff 164, 328-331
White goods 332-337
Wine 338-342

Yahoo 38-39

From cool K Ban shades for dogs to a hands-free bra

57 THINGS TO BUY ONLINE

Okay, you want to buy something. And by "something" we don't mean anything as dull as groceries. Here are 57 varieties of stuff you can buy at the click of your mouse. The goods listed on auction may have been sold but if you follow the web address you should find other equally ludicrous bargains

1 Framed fragment of bedsheet slept on by Elvis, £20
www.ebay.com

2 K Ban sunglasses for dogs, 99 per cent UVA protection, £3
www.ebay.com

3 Muzfaar 1995 Russian/Spanish chestnut stallion, approx £8,000
www.arabianauction.com

4 The definitive guide to African Malawi-Chichlids (Mbunas only), £31
www.aquariumsite.org

5 Autographed photo of Kevin Bacon in *Footloose*, $29.99
www.autografs.com

6 The domain name 'www.sellnothing.com', no reserve price
www.afternic.com/~sellnothing.com

7 Amusing 19th-century etching: "My gun went off quite by accident; and if your nose is spoilt can't you have a wax one?", £10
www.antiqueprints.com/Prints/humorous.html

8 A book of Johnny Carson's most hilarious fan mail, $2.40
www.half.com

9 Collection of funny-shaped Chinese coins, £16
http://shop.auctionwatch.com

10 Coors Lite neon sign, £30
www.propertyroom.com

11 Wooden Turkish gulet, 27.5 metres, £593,750
www.boathunter.com

12 Your own pub, Bar One, in Preston, Lancashire, £170,000
www.roypugh.co.uk

13 An archipelago of eight islands in the Bahamas, $11,800,000
www.vladi-private-islands.de

14 Electronic slot machine, £470
www.3dhospitality.com

15 An hour of conceptual artist Michael Mandiberg's time, $20
www.mandiberg.com

16 Shot glasses made of ice, £12
www.twistedgifts.com

17 Tokugawa samurai katana sword, £112
www.ubid.com

18 Alluna herbal supplement to relieve sleeplessness, £9.50
www.drugstore.com

19 Shou Wu Chinese traditional medicine for baldness and kidney problems, £25
http://members.fortunecity.com/davidpilling/html/body_sosw.htm

20 An ex-Russian Navy 'Whiskey Class' submarine, $497,000
www.projectboats.com/surplus.htm

21 Seventies hippie polyester blouse with loud swirls, £6.25
www.nancysniftynook.com

22 Casio wrist camera, £125
www.camborg.com/casiocam.htm

23 Blair's Original Death Sauce, £5
www.hothothot.com

24 A double happiness feng shui ring, £1,375
www.lilliantoojewellery.com

25 Gold, frankincense, and myrrh: 9ct gold bracelet, £60; 100 grammes of finest Hojary frankincense, £16; 100 grammes of myrrh, £5.50
www.adventurearabia.com/frankincensenf.htm

The Web's not just for books and CDs, you know. Complete Dr Brandy's online hairloss evaluation and you'll be halfway to a full head of hair

26 Pig ears, price on application
www.aginfo.aust.com/amtf/arkmsgs/March19/1267.html

27 A mermaid costume, £220 (tail only for £125)
www.slinkyskin.com/mermaidvideo.htm

29 A noble title, £4,000
www.surprise.com

30 A full head of hair, £1,250 - £5,000
www.brandymd.com

31 A zoot suit like the yellow one in *The Mask*, $329.99
www.zootsuitstore.

32 Diamond-studded false eyelashes, £750
www.icecool.com

33 A vampire, £10
www.internettrash.com/users/jl/000001.html

34 A Russian bride, $5 (for women over 35)
www.east-women.com

35 Standard divorce pack, £55
www.divorce-online.co.uk

36 Homer Simpson bottle opener, £24
www.drinkstuff.com

37 Remote-controlled helium-filled flying saucer, £59.95
www.premierdirect.co.uk/start.htm

38 Pooh's balloony sort of game, £29
www.poshgifts.com

57 varieties...

39 A bottle of 1973 Krug champagne, £1,250
www.cellarexchange.com
40 An inflatable dragon castle, £1,113
www.boing.co.uk
41 Xenadrine RFA-1 rapid fat loss catalyst, £39.95
www.shoppersempire.com
42 500g Djimmah Coffee from Ethiopia, £6.48
www.ibrax.com
43 Nozovent anti-snoring device, £12.50
www.ptspublishing.com/nozovent.html
44 Go weightless at a space academy, £3,250
www.redletterdays.co.uk
45 Bag a Bambi, price on application
www.scothunt.co.uk
46 Someone to run your life for you, £425
www.liberate365.com
47 Salvador Dali face pot, £30
www.limitededitionsshop.co.uk
48 Roman oil lamp (clrca 100AD), £89
www.qxl.com
49 Will for a married or single person, £19.99
www.desktoplawyer.net
50 Roses dipped in pure gold, from £22
www.goldroses.com
51 A giant spider Hallowe'en cake, £125
www.jane-asher.co.uk
52 Dino-raptor costume, £24
www.charliecrow.uk.com
53 Pikachu-shaped pinata (paper shapes you fill with sweets and hit with sticks), £9.99
www.happyparty.co.uk
54 Hands-free bra, with five pockets, £21
www.splendour.com
55 Drive a tank, shoot a gun, be in the SAS, £199
www.exhilaration.co.uk
56 Hand-held lie detector, £35
www.911.co.kr
57 A walk-on part in *Frasier*, $2-3,000
www.sothebys.com

Don't bury your head in the sand!

Take cover!
with Rough Guide Travel Insurance

100

Essential

CDs

*Eight titles,
one name*

ROUGH
GUIDES

Will you have enough stories to tell your grandchildren?

2000 Yahoo! Inc.

Yahoo! Travel

Do You YAHOO!?